Periodic Table of the Elements

D1536729

						0
IIIA	IVA	VA	VIA	VIIA		2 4.00260 **He** ◯ 1s² HELIUM 0.93
5 10.81 2.01 **B** ● [He] 2s²2p¹ BORON 0.80	6 12.011 2.50 **C** ● [He] 2s²2p² CARBON 0.77	7 14.0067 3.07 **N** ● [He] 2s²2p³ NITROGEN 0.74	8 15.9994 3.50 **O** ◯ [He] 2s²2p⁴ OXYGEN 0.74	9 18.9984 4.10 **F** ◯ [He] 2s²2p⁵ FLUORINE 0.72	10 20.179 **Ne** ◯ [He] 2s²2p⁶ NEON 1.12	
13 26.9815 1.47 **Al** ● [Ne] 3s²3p¹ ALUMINUM 1.25	14 28.086 1.74 **Si** ● [Ne] 3s²3p² SILICON 1.17	15 30.9738 2.06 **P** ● [Ne] 3s²3p³ PHOSPHORUS 1.10	16 32.06 2.44 **S** ● [Ne] 3s²3p⁴ SULFUR 1.04	17 35.453 2.83 **Cl** ● [Ne] 3s²3p⁵ CHLORINE 0.99	18 39.948 **Ar** ◯ [Ne] 3s²3p⁶ ARGON 1.54	

	IB	IIB						
58.71 1.75 ● 4s²	29 63.546 1.75 **Cu** ● [Ar] 3d¹⁰4s¹ COPPER 1.17	30 65.37 1.66 **Zn** ● [Ar] 3d¹⁰4s² ZINC 1.25	31 69.72 1.82 **Ga** ● [Ar] 3d¹⁰4s²4p¹ GALLIUM 1.25	32 72.59 2.02 **Ge** ● [Ar] 3d¹⁰4s²4p² GERMANIUM 1.22	33 74.9216 2.20 **As** ● [Ar] 3d¹⁰4s²4p³ ARSENIC 1.21	34 78.96 2.48 **Se** ● [Ar] 3d¹⁰4s²4p⁴ SELENIUM 1.17	35 79.904 2.74 **Br** ● [Ar] 3d¹⁰4s²4p⁵ BROMINE 1.14	36 83.80 — **Kr** ◯ [Ar] 3d¹⁰4s²4p⁶ KRYPTON 1.69
106.4 1.35 ● ⁰5s⁰ DIUM	47 107.868 1.42 **Ag** ● [Kr] 4d¹⁰5s¹ SILVER 1.34	48 112.40 1.46 **Cd** ● [Kr] 4d¹⁰5s² CADMIUM 1.41	49 114.82 1.49 **In** ● [Kr] 4d¹⁰5s²5p¹ INDIUM 1.50	50 118.69 1.72 **Sn** ● [Kr] 4d¹⁰5s²5p² TIN 1.41	51 121.75 1.82 **Sb** ● [Kr] 4d¹⁰5s²5p³ ANTIMONY 1.41	52 127.60 2.01 **Te** ● [Kr] 4d¹⁰5s²5p⁴ TELLURIUM 1.37	53 126.9045 2.21 **I** ● [Kr] 4d¹⁰5s²5p⁵ IODINE 1.33	54 131.30 **Xe** ◯ [Kr] 4d¹⁰5s²5p⁶ XENON 1.90
195.09 1.44 — ⁵d⁹6s¹ IUM	79 196.9665 1.42 **Au** ● [Xe] 4f¹⁴5d¹⁰6s¹ GOLD 1.34	80 200.59 1.44 **Hg** ● [Xe] 4f¹⁴5d¹⁰6s² MERCURY 1.44	81 204.37 1.44 **Tl** ● [Xe] 4f¹⁴5d¹⁰6s²6p¹ THALLIUM 1.55	82 207.2 1.55 **Pb** ● [Xe] 4f¹⁴5d¹⁰6s²6p² LEAD 1.54	83 208.9806 1.67 **Bi** ● [Xe] 4f¹⁴5d¹⁰6s²6p³ BISMUTH 1.52	84 (210) 1.76 **Po** ◯ [Xe] 4f¹⁴5d¹⁰6s²6p⁴ POLONIUM 1.53	85 (210) 1.90 ◯ **At** [Xe] 4f¹⁴5d¹⁰6s²6p⁵ ASTATINE —	86 (222) **Rn** ◯ [Xe] 4f¹⁴5d¹⁰6s²6p⁶ RADON —

| 151.96 1.01 ● 5d⁰6s² IUM | 64 157.25 1.11 **Gd** ● [Xe] 4f⁷5d¹6s² GADOLINIUM 1.61 | 65 158.9254 1.10 **Tb** ● [Xe] 4f⁹5d⁰6s² TERBIUM 1.59 | 66 162.50 1.10 **Dy** ● [Xe] 4f¹⁰5d⁰6s² DYSPROSIUM 1.59 | 67 164.9303 1.10 **Ho** ● [Xe] 4f¹¹5d⁰6s² HOLMIUM 1.58 | 68 167.26 1.11 **Er** ● [Xe] 4f¹²5d⁰6s² ERBIUM 1.57 | 69 168.9342 1.11 **Tm** ● [Xe] 4f¹³5d⁰6s² THULIUM 1.56 | 70 173.04 1.06 **Yb** ● [Xe] 4f¹⁴5d⁰6s² YTTERBIUM 1.70 | 71 174.97 1.14 **Lu** ● [Xe] 4f¹⁴5d¹6s² LUTETIUM 1.56 |
| (243) (1.2) ◯ ⁶d⁰7s² CIUM | 96 (247) (1.2) **Cm** ◯ [Rn] 5f⁷6d¹7s² CURIUM — | 97 (247) (1.2) **Bk** ◯ [Rn] 5f⁸6d¹7s² BERKELIUM — | 98 (249) (1.2) **Cf** ◯ [Rn] 5f¹⁰6d⁰7s² CALIFORNIUM — | 99 (254) (1.2) **Es** ◯ [Rn] 5f¹¹6d⁰7s² EINSTEINIUM — | 100 (253) (1.2) **Fm** ◯ [Rn] 5f¹²6d⁰7s² FERMIUM — | 101 (256) (1.2) **Md** ◯ [Rn] 5f¹³6d⁰7s² MENDELEVIUM — | 102 (253) (1.2) **No** ◯ — NOBELIUM — | 103 (257) — **Lw** ◯ — LAWRENCIUM — |

The Chemical Elements

Keith J. Laidler
University of Ottawa

Michael H. Ford-Smith
University of Sussex

Bogden & Quigley, Inc., Publishers

Tarrytown-on-Hudson
New York

L. C. Cat. Card No.: 75-119877

Printed in the United States of America

1 2 3 4 5 6 7 8 9 10—74 73 72 71 70

Preface

This book is intended to complement first-year chemistry text-books that emphasize principles by applying these fundamentals to the main experimental results met in an elementary study of inorganic chemistry, organic chemistry, and biochemistry. As such, we cover the chemical elements and their compounds in a somewhat descriptive way; however, the material is related to theory at all times.

Relevance is stressed when practical by relating chemistry research and results to the everyday experiences of the nonscientist. For example, digestion and metabolism in the body are related to a knowledge of the structures of enzyme molecules and the processes that occur when enzymes bring about catalysis. Another example, which gives the student an idea of the pertinency of current research, is the discussion of X-ray crystallography and its importance to the knowledge of the structures of biological substances.

A concerted effort to keep the subject matter up-to-date has been made by including brief discussions of such topics as the compounds of the noble gases and the three-dimensional structures of proteins.

We wish to acknowledge indebtedness to our many colleagues who gave generously of their time, suggestions, and encouragement throughout the writing of this book.

Contents

Chapter 1   Introduction

The subject of chemistry is conveniently subdivided into *inorganic*, *organic*, and *physical* chemistry. The distinction between these sub-divisions is by no means sharp, and the work of many research chemists embraces two and even three of them. By and large, the physical chemist can be described as an applied physicist who is interested in basic physical principles and particularly in the application of these principles to chemical problems. The examples that he chooses for testing these principles may come from either organic or inorganic chemistry. Historically, organic chemistry was mostly concerned with the chemistry of the *kinds* of substances found in living systems; and inorganic chemistry was concerned with substances not found in living systems. It so happens that the main substances that function in living systems contain carbon, so that perhaps the best modern definition of organic chemistry is that it is the chemistry of compounds containing carbon. Inorganic chemistry, on the other hand, comprises the study of compounds that do not contain carbon. Since inorganic chemistry includes the chemistry of all of the elements except carbon—and there are over a hundred known elements—one might think that inorganic chemistry is a much vaster subject than organic chemistry. In fact, however, this is not necessarily the case. The carbon atom is unique in its ability to form an unlimited number of compounds. As a result, during recent years considerable research effort has gone into the study of organic compounds.

Apart from inorganic and organic chemistry, there is the increasingly important subject known as *biochemistry*. There is no firm distinction between biochemistry and organic chemistry—indeed many aspects of inorganic chemistry are of importance to the biochemist. Biochemistry is concerned not so much with the chemistry of the carbon compounds as with the chemistry of substances that play a role in living systems; it is concerned more with the structures of living systems and the reactions that occur in them. Needless to say, biochemistry has a close connection with the science of physiology, and with other biological sciences. The overlapping of these various fields is so great that it is often hard to classify individual research workers in a completely satisfactory way. Many biochemists, for example, were actually trained as organic chemists; and many carry out research in organic chemistry as well as in biochemistry. Indeed, in recent years many physicists and physical chemists have devoted themselves to the study of biological processes, and their work has certainly overlapped that of the biochemists.

The plan of this book is to consider some of the most important experimental results in inorganic chemistry, organic chemistry, and biochemistry. In order to provide a link between the principles of chemistry and the study of these three subjects, the remainder of the chapter discusses selected topics which are particularly relevant to the study of experimental chemistry. Much of the material in this chapter will serve as a review, but some may be new. The main topics covered are: chemical bonding, thermochemical cycles, and some aspects of chemical reactivity.

Chemical Bonding

There are two main kinds of chemical bonds: ionic bonds and covalent bonds. Ionic bonds hold charged species together. Since the electrostatic forces between ions depend only on the distances between them, a given positive ion will attract all the negative ions close to it regardless of their number and orientation; in other words, ionic bonds are nondirectional. The covalent bond is entirely different, being formed as a result of the sharing of electrons between atoms. A given atom can only form a fixed number of bonds of this type, and since the bonds are directional, the other atoms are forced to line up in a definite directional pattern. For example, the carbon atoms in diamond, which form a covalent crystal, are arranged so that each carbon atom is surrounded tetrahedrally by four others.

Neither classical mechanics nor the old quantum theory could explain the existence of covalent bonds. The new quantum mechanics, on the other hand, has scored an enormous success in explaining the nature of the covalent bond. The covalent bond has been explained in terms of a quantum-mechanical concept involving the overlapping of atomic orbitals: the strongest covalent bonds are formed when there is maximum overlapping of the atomic orbitals. We can also look at the problem from a slightly different point of view, in terms of *molecular orbitals*. These are orbitals that apply to the molecule as a whole, rather than to the individual atoms; and they are built up from the atomic orbitals. This molecular-orbital method does not really differ in principle from the method of overlapping atomic orbitals. It is a useful alternative way of dealing with the problem, and it often helps us see why some bonds are formed and others are not.

Orbitals are described in terms of functions known as *wave functions* or *eigenfunctions*. The square of a wave function at a particular region of space is a measure of the probability that the electron is present in that region. These functions are called wave functions because they represent patterns of standing waves. Overlap between two such waves leads to interference between them, just as interference occurs between the two parts of a light beam emerging from a pair of parallel slits (Figure 1-1). Suppose that two hydrogen atoms,

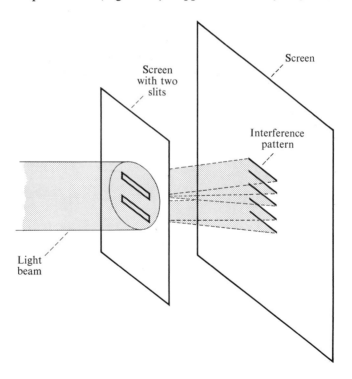

Fig. 1-1 The pattern produced by interference between light beams emerging from a pair of parallel slits.

whose eigenfunctions are represented by ψ_1 and ψ_2, are so close together that their orbitals overlap. The interference between the two waves of eigenfunctions ψ_1 and ψ_2 can be represented mathematically by saying that the eigenfunction ψ of the resulting wave motion is the sum of ψ_1 and ψ_2:

$$\psi = \psi_1 + \psi_2$$

If ψ_1 and ψ_2 have the same sign, ψ is bigger numerically than ψ_1 or ψ_2, and there is said to be *constructive interference*. If ψ_1 and ψ_2 have opposite signs, ψ is smaller numerically, and there is said to be *destructive interference*. In general, the signs of ψ_1 and ψ_2 vary with the position, so that the relative signs of ψ_1 and ψ_2 will be different in different places.

In the case of the two hydrogen atoms, the interfering wave functions, which may now be referred to as *atomic orbitals*, may have the same sign when the orbitals overlap; this case is represented in Figure 1-2a, and there is constructive interference. The resulting wave function ψ, now known as a *molecular orbital*, is larger in the region between the nuclei than either of the component orbitals. This situation leads to bonding between the atoms. Alternatively, as in Figure 1-2b, the atomic orbitals may be of opposite sign, in which case there is destructive interference. A node now divides the molecular orbital into two parts of opposite sign.

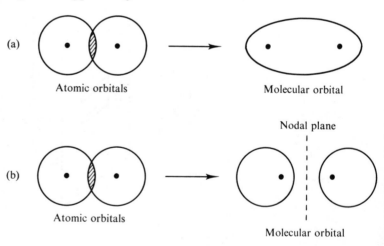

Fig. 1-2   Interference between the atomic orbitals on two neighboring hydrogen atoms. Diagram (a) shows constructive interference, leading to bonding, while (b) shows destructive interference, leading to antibonding.

The electrostatic field caused by the nuclei of two hydrogen atoms is greatest in the region between the nuclei. The molecular orbital found by constructive interference (Figure 1-2a) has a high value in that region, which indicates a high probability that an electron is present there. An electron occupying that molecular orbital is more tightly bound, and so has a lower potential energy, than one occupying an atomic orbital of hydrogen. When the two hydrogen atoms are fairly close together, with their two electrons occupying this molecular orbital, the energy of the system is less than when the atoms are far apart with their electrons in isolated atomic orbitals. The hydrogen molecule is, therefore, more stable than two isolated hydrogen atoms; energy is required to split a hydrogen molecule into the atoms. This molecular orbital picture provides a simple explanation of the covalent bond, as well as an explanation of the concept of overlapping electron clouds. The molecular orbital produced in this case (Figure 1-2a) is known as a *bonding* orbital.

In the case of destructive interference, on the other hand, the electron density between the nuclei is low (Figure 1-2b), so that there is no tendency for the nuclei to be held together; indeed this type of molecular orbital leads to a certain amount of *antibonding*, the net effect being to push the nuclei apart rather than to hold them together. This type of molecular orbital is known as an *antibonding orbital*. The normal hydrogen molecule contains no electrons in the antibonding orbital.

Figure 1-3 shows the electronic energy levels corresponding to these two cases. On the left and right of the diagram are shown the levels corresponding to the atomic orbitals (AO's) when the hydrogen atoms are separate. In the center are the molecular orbitals (MO's), the lower level being for bonding, the higher for antibonding. In the normal hydrogen molecule the two electrons occupy the lower MO; they have opposite spins, as shown by the symbols ↑ and ↓.

It is now of interest to compare this system of two hydrogen atoms with that of two helium atoms. The energy diagram for this case, which is very similar to that for H_2, is shown in Figure 1-4. Again, this combination of atomic orbitals gives rise to two molecular orbitals; the one in which there is constructive interference corresponds to the lower energy, that where there is destructive interference to the higher energy. This time, however, there are four electrons to be accommodated, and the Pauli Principle allows only two electrons to go into each orbital, each with a different spin. Only two electrons can therefore go into the low-energy molecular orbital; the other two have to go into the second MO, in which the electron density between the nuclei is low. The energy here is greater than in the simple AO (Figure 1-4), and the orbital is referred to as an *antibonding* one. Calculation shows that the antibonding effect of these two electrons is greater than the bonding effect of the two in the lowest MO.

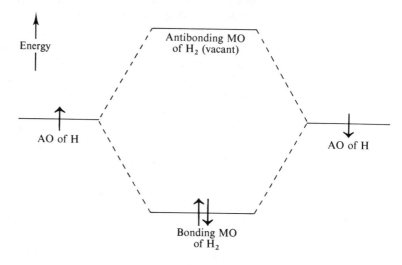

Fig. 1-3   Electron energies for the atomic orbitals of two hydrogen atoms (left and right) compared with those for the molecular orbitals of the hydrogen molecule.

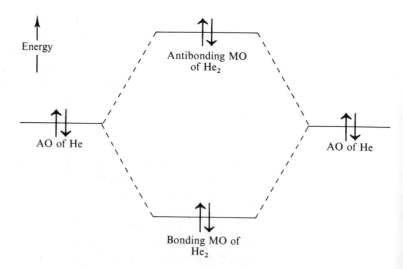

Fig. 1-4   Electronic energies for the atomic orbitals of two helium atoms and for the hypothetical molecule He_2.

Helium therefore forms no He_2 molecule, since the two isolated He atoms are more stable. It is of interest to note that in the ion He_2^+ bonding occurs between the nuclei. This happens because there are now only three electrons in all, two of which go into the bonding orbital and one into antibonding; the net result is equivalent to half a bond. This example illustrates an advantage of the MO method; the stability of He_2^+ cannot be explained on the basis of the electron-pair bond.

The most favorable situation for bonding occurs when there are just two electrons available to form the bond, as in the hydrogen molecule. When the MO's are formed from the pair of AO's, these two electrons can go into the MO of lower energy, as in hydrogen (cf. Figure 1-3), and a stable molecule generally results. In an ordinary covalent bond, each atom contributes one electron, and so each atom must have a singly occupied AO for each covalent bond it forms.

The Dative or Coordinate Bond

There is no reason, however, why a covalent bond should not be formed from two electrons that come from one atom. Such a bond would be formed by the interaction of two AO's, one doubly occupied and one empty. This situation is represented by the energy diagram in Figure 1-5. The atom that provides the two electrons to the bond is known as the *donor*; the one that provides no electrons is the *acceptor*. The resulting covalent bond is known as a *dative bond*, or a *coordinate bond* or link.

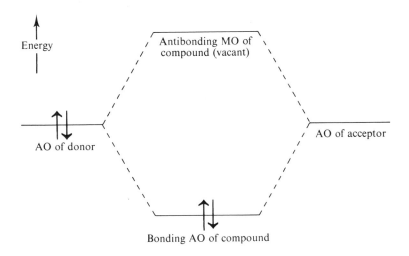

Fig. 1-5 Electron energies, showing the case of the formation of a dative bond in which both electrons come from one atom.

An example of a dative bond is the molecule formed by addition of ammonia, NH_3, to boron trifluoride, BF_3. The electronic structures of these molecules, with only valence electrons shown, can be represented as

$$
\begin{array}{cc}
\text{H} & \text{F} \\
\text{H} \overset{\times\times}{\underset{\times\times}{\times}}\text{N}{\times} & \overset{\text{oo}}{\underset{\text{oo}}{\text{B}}}\overset{\text{oo}}{\text{o}}\text{F} \\
\text{H} & \text{F}
\end{array}
$$

and

The ammonia molecule has a pair of nonbonding electrons, often known as a "lone pair," while the boron trifluoride has a vacant orbital. An additive compound can therefore be formed.

$$
\begin{array}{ccc}
\text{H} & \text{F} & \text{H F} \\
\text{H} \times\text{N}\times + & \text{B} \text{o} \text{F} \longrightarrow & \text{H} \times\text{N}\times\text{B} \text{o} \text{F} \\
\text{H} & \text{F} & \text{H F}
\end{array}
\qquad (1)
$$

By writing the ammonia electrons as crosses and the BF_3 electrons as circles, we have shown that in the addition complex, the bond between the N and B atoms is formed from electrons that originally belonged to the N atom. Of course, there is no distinction between electrons, and once the molecule is formed, the dative bond is of the same character as any other covalent bond.

A molecule such as H_3NBF_3 is known as a *coordination complex*; the ammonia molecule is the *donor* molecule (the N atom is the *donor* atom) and the BF_3 is the *acceptor* molecule.* This complex is *isoelectronic* with H_3CCF_3; that is to say, it has exactly the same number of electrons, and the electrons are arranged in equivalent orbitals. A complex molecule formed by the addition of two molecules to one another, with the formation of a dative bond, is often known as an *adduct*.

It is of interest to look at the formation of this complex from a different point of view, one that emphasizes the resemblance to H_3CCF_3. Suppose that an electron were first transferred from NH_3 to BF_3, with the formation of NH_3^+ and BF_3^-.

$$
\begin{array}{ccc}
\text{H} & \text{F} & \left[\begin{array}{c}\text{H}\\ \text{H}\times\text{N}\times \\ \text{H}\end{array}\right]^{+} + \left[\begin{array}{c}\text{F}\\ \times\text{B} \text{o} \text{F} \\ \text{F}\end{array}\right]^{-}
\end{array}
\qquad (2)
$$

---

* Acceptor molecules are often known as *Lewis acids*, and donors as *Lewis bases*. These names are given in honor of the American chemist Gilbert Newton Lewis (1875–1946), who played an important part in the development of theories of chemical bonds and was responsible for a general definition of acids and bases in terms of their ability to accept or donate electrons.

Each of these resultant ions has a singly occupied AO, and the ions can combine to form an ordinary covalent bond.

$$
\begin{bmatrix} H \\ H \overset{xx}{\underset{xx}{x}} N \overset{x}{x} \\ H \end{bmatrix}^{+} \;+\; \begin{bmatrix} F \\ \overset{oo}{x} B \overset{o}{\underset{oo}{o}} F \\ F \end{bmatrix}^{-} \;\longrightarrow\; \begin{bmatrix} \overset{+}{} \quad \overset{-}{} \\ H \;\vdots\; F \\ H \overset{xx}{\underset{xx}{x}} N \overset{x}{x} \vdots B \overset{o}{\underset{oo}{o}} F \\ H \;\vdots\; F \end{bmatrix} \tag{3}
$$

This last equation emphasizes the fact that in the adduct the N atom has an effective positive charge and the B atom has an effective negative charge. This can be seen equally well from equation (1) where a pair of electrons, initially attached only to the nitrogen atom, end up being shared between the nitrogen and boron atoms; in a dative bond the donor atom always loses to the acceptor atom a part share in two of its electrons. It is convenient to represent a dative bond either by an arrow pointing from the donor atom to the acceptor atom,

$$H_3N \rightarrow BF_3$$

or as a covalent bond between ions,

$$H_3N^+ - B^- F_3$$

It is a general property of the dative bond that it has a high dipole moment, in the direction indicated by the arrow.

Since a dative bond can be regarded as a covalent bond between ions, the energy of a dative bond can be treated as the difference between two quantities; it is the energy E_1, released in the formation of the covalent bond between the ions, minus the energy E_2, required to transfer an electron from donor to acceptor. Thus

$$
\begin{aligned}
E_2 + NH_3 + BF_3 &\rightarrow NH_3^+ + BF_3^- &\qquad(4)\\
NH_3^+ + BF_3^- &\rightarrow H_3N \rightarrow BF_3 + E_1 &\qquad(5)\\
\hline
NH_3 + BF_3 &\rightarrow H_3N \rightarrow BF_3 + E_1 - E_2 &\qquad(6)
\end{aligned}
$$

The lower the ionization potential, I (also known as the ionization energy), of the donor and the greater the electron affinity, E, of the acceptor, the less will be the energy E_2 required to transfer an electron. Thus

$$
\begin{aligned}
NH_3 &\rightarrow NH_3^+ + e - I &\qquad(7)\\
e + BF_3 &\rightarrow BF_3^- + E &\qquad(8)\\
\hline
NH_3 + BF_3 &\rightarrow NH_3^+ + BF_3^- + E - I &\qquad(9)
\end{aligned}
$$

so that the energy required, E_2, is equal to $I - E$. It follows that the best donor atoms are atoms of low ionization potential and the best acceptor atoms are atoms of high electron affinities.

There are three kinds of orbitals in an atom: *inner* orbitals, belonging to inner filled shells; *valence* orbitals, belonging to partly filled shells; and *outer* orbitals, which are empty. The electrons in the inner orbitals could, in principle, act as donors, but their ionization potentials are much too high for them to do so. The empty outer orbitals could act as acceptors, but the binding energy for electrons in them is usually much too low. It follows that dative bonds tend to be formed only with valence-shell orbitals. The maximum number of covalent and dative bonds that an atom can form is, therefore, limited to the number of orbitals in its valence shell. This point is considered in more detail later (p. 11).

Among the elements in the first short period, the order of increasing ionization energy is

$$Li < B < Be < C < O < N < F < Ne$$

This is, therefore, the order of *decreasing* ability of these elements to act as donors. Neon is incapable of acting as a donor, and, since it has a very low electron affinity, it cannot act as an acceptor; therefore it cannot form dative bonds. The same situation exists in all of the inert gases; none can form dative bonds.

Metal *ions* necessarily have high electron affinities and thus frequently enter into dative bond formation as *acceptors*. Beryllium presents an interesting situation; in spite of the fact that a considerable amount of energy is needed to remove the two valence electrons from the Be atom, with the formation of the Be^{2+} ion, salts containing the Be^{2+} ion are known to exist in aqueous solution. This is because the Be^{2+} ion readily forms dative bonds with water molecules, in which the oxygen atoms act as donors and the Be^{2+} ion acts as the acceptor. Aqueous solutions of beryllium salts, in fact, contain the ion $Be^{2+}4H_2O$; the structure of this can be represented as

The four water molecules are arranged tetrahedrally about the beryllium atom. The energy liberated in forming these four dative bonds compensates for the large amount of energy required to form Be^{2+}. Solvation of this kind is found with the ions of nearly all metals.

Dative-bond formation is also important with certain salts in the absence of water. Thus anhydrous beryllium chloride contains giant molecules of structure

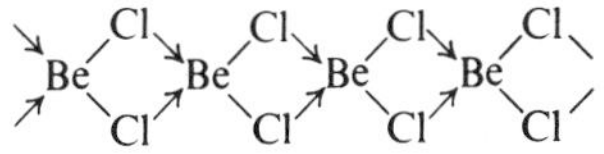

Maximum Coordination Number

Oxygen, with the electron configuration $1s^2 2s^2 2p^4$, has two singly occupied orbitals, the arrangement being

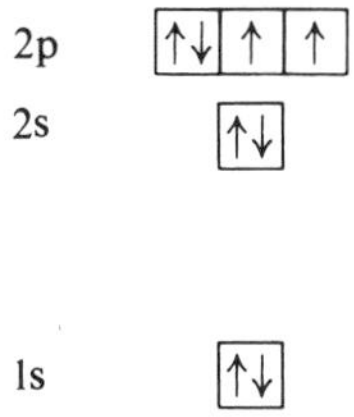

It can therefore show a covalency of 2, as in water H—O—H. Nitrogen, $1s^1 2s^2 2p^3$, has three singly occupied orbitals

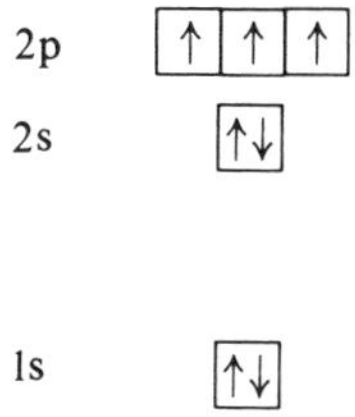

and is therefore trivalent, as in NH_3.

The next energy level above the 2p is the 3s, but the energy gap between the 2p and 3s levels is so great that the higher 3s level cannot be utilized for bond formation. It is, therefore, a general rule that in the elements of the first short period the number of covalent bonds is limited by the number of 2s and 2p orbitals. The covalency maximum for the nitrogen atom is, in fact, 4, since this atom can form three ordinary covalent bonds, as in NH_3, and can form an additional dative bond by utilizing its "lone-pair" electrons. An example is NH_4^+, which can be regarded as being formed from NH_3 and H^+ by the formation of a dative bond:

$$[H]^+ \quad + \quad \overset{\text{H}}{\underset{\text{H}}{\,\,\overset{\times\times}{\underset{\times\times}{\text{N}}}\,\,}}\text{H} \quad \longrightarrow \quad \left[\text{H}\,\overset{\text{H}}{\underset{\text{H}}{\,\,\overset{\times\times}{\underset{\times\times}{\text{N}}}\,\,}}\text{H} \right]^+ \tag{10}$$

No higher covalency is possible, since there are no further available orbitals, the 3s orbitals being of too high energy.

Similarly, oxygen can have a covalency of 3, as in H_3O^+:

$$\left[\text{H}\,\overset{\times\times}{\underset{\times\times}{\text{O}}}\,\text{H} \right]^+$$

A covalency of 4 is possible in principle, as in the hypothetical ion

$$\left[\underset{\text{H}}{\text{H}\,\overset{\times\times}{\underset{\times\times}{\text{O}}}\,\text{H}} \right]^{2+}$$

However, it would require far too much energy to make such an ion; a proton would have to be brought up to the H_3O^+ ion, and the repulsive energy would be very great.

Carbon forms compounds with covalencies of 4, as in CH_4, and this is the maximum covalency possible. Beryllium is limited to a covalency of 4, as in the structure on p. 10, in which each beryllium atom forms two ordinary covalent bonds and two dative bonds.

It follows from what has been said that it is a general rule that the elements of the first short period are limited to a *coordination number* of 4; that is, they can form four covalent bonds.

When we consider elements in the later periods of the periodic table, the situation is different, because there are d orbitals available, and these are not much higher in energy than the valence orbitals. For example, the electronic configuration in the phosphorus atom is

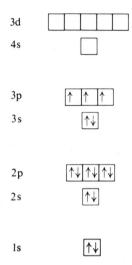

The empty 4s and 3d orbitals are shown, and, since these are not much higher in energy than the 3p level, it does not require much energy to promote a 3s electron into one of these levels. For example, the $1s^2 2s^2 2p^6 3s 3p^3 3d$ state of the phosphorus atom can be produced by promotion, and this is a pentavalent state. It is therefore possible for a compound like PF_5, phosphorus pentafluoride, to be formed; in this compound there are ten valence electrons. The nitrogen analog of this compound does not exist, because of the inaccessibility of the higher levels.

Similarly, the sulfur atom, normally in the $1s^2 2s^2 2p^6 3s^2 3p^4$ state, can be excited to the $1s^2 2s^2 2p^6 3s^2 3p^3 3d$ state, which is tetravalent. Compounds like SCl_4 can, therefore, be formed, whereas no such compound (OCl_4) is possible with oxygen. The sulfur atom can also be excited to the hexacovalent state, $1s^2 2s^2 2p^6 3s 3p^3 3d^2$, so that compounds like SF_6 are possible. Iodine even forms a heptafluoride, IF_7, from the excited state of I in which a 5s electron and two 5p electrons are promoted into d orbitals; the electronic configuration of this excited state is $1s^2 2s^2 2p^6 3s^2 3p^6 3d^{10} 4s^2 4p^6 4d^{10} 5s 5p^3 5d^3$.

It will be seen from the above discussion that the elements in the second short period, and in later periods, are not restricted to a coordination number of 4. Many examples are given in the next chapter.

The Inert Pair of Electrons

Bond strengths of analogous bonds decrease as the atomic weights of the bonded atoms become greater. An important consequence of this is a growing tendency for s electrons not to be promoted as the atoms become larger. The quadrivalency of carbon is due to the fact that the 2s → 2p promotion energy is more than compensated for by the bond energy of the two additional bonds that are formed. Therefore, as the atomic size increases, and the bond energies become smaller there is less compensation for promotion, which therefore occurs to a lesser extent. Consider the Group-IV series carbon, silicon, germanium, tin, and lead. Whereas carbon and silicon are almost exclusively quadrivalent, forming only rather unstable compounds in which they are divalent, there do exist some stable divalent compounds of germanium. In tin the divalent and quadrivalent states are of comparable stability, while in lead the divalent state is much more stable than the tetravalent.

In all of these compounds in which the covalency is two units below that of the lighter analogs, there are two 2s electrons which are not involved in bonding. Such pairs of electrons are known as *lone pairs* or *inert pairs*.

Multicenter Bonds   Boron and hydrogen form a number of compounds whose structures cannot be explained in terms of elementary valency principles. The simplest of these is diborane, B_2H_6. Since this compound is a gas of very low boiling point ($-88°C$), it cannot be an ionic compound. However, the atoms in it cannot be linked by normal covalent bonds, because there are not enough electrons. Since the boron atom has three valence electrons, simple valence theory would allow the structure

$$\begin{array}{ccc} H & & H \\ \diagdown & & \diagup \\ & B - B & \\ \diagup & & \diagdown \\ H & & H \end{array}$$

but there are no electrons available to make bonds with two additional hydrogen atoms. To form B_2H_6 by ordinary covalent bonds, seven bonds are needed, one to link the two boron atoms and one to link each hydrogen atom; thus, 14 electrons are needed, and B_2H_6 contains only 12 valence electrons, three from each boron atom and one from each hydrogen atom.

One might think that 1s electrons could be involved, but this is impossible for energetic reasons. The 1s electrons are held much too tightly for promotion to 2s or 2p states to be possible.

Physical determinations of the structure of B_2H_6 reveal that the atoms are arranged in an unusual manner, as represented in Figure 1-6.

Each B atom is surrounded approximately tetrahedrally by four H atoms, and two of these H atoms are equidistant from the two B atoms, suggesting that these hydrogens are linked equally to both B atoms.

Obviously there is some unusual feature to the structure, since the hydrogen atom has only one valence orbital and can, therefore, form covalent bonds with only one other atom. However, if each of the boron atoms has tetrahedral sp^3 hybridization and uses two of its sp^3 orbitals to form normal covalent bonds to the end pairs of hydrogen atoms, then the remaining sp^3 hybrid orbitals of the boron atoms will overlap each other at an angle and will simultaneously overlap with the 1s orbital of the two central hydrogen atoms. The arrangement is shown in Figure 1-6b.

In terms of molecular-orbital ideas, the situation can be described as follows. On p. 4 we considered the interference effects produced when a pair of atomic orbitals overlap; this corresponds to the simple interference effects produced when light passes through a pair of parallel slits (cf. Figure 1 on p. 3). Of course, there can also be interference involving more than two waves; indeed, in a diffraction grating there is interference of the many waves passing through the slits of the grating. When several atomic orbitals overlap, they blend together into complex molecular orbitals, each a combination of the whole set of contributing atomic orbitals (cf. Figure 1-6c). When the mathematics of this is worked out for B_2H_6, one discovers that when several orbitals all overlap with each other, only one of the resulting MO's is a bonding MO of low energy. Consequently, two electrons can occur in the set of MO's. This is exactly what is needed in B_2H_6. Four pairs of electrons are needed to form the normal covalent bonds with the terminal hydrogen atoms; this leaves two pairs over, just enough to fill the bonding MO's formed by overlap of the boron sp^3 orbitals with the 1s orbitals of the central hydrogen atoms.

Molecular orbitals formed from the overlapping of three atomic orbitals are known as *three-center* MO's, and the resulting bonds as *three-center* bonds. The term *multicenter* is also used when overlapping of three or more atomic orbitals occurs. Molecules involving such bonds, in which there are too few electrons to form ordinary covalent bonds, are known as *electron-deficient* molecules.

A number of electron-deficient molecules, containing multicenter bonds, are now known. Another example is aluminum trimethyl, which exists as $Al_2(CH_3)_6$. In the aluminum atom, there are three

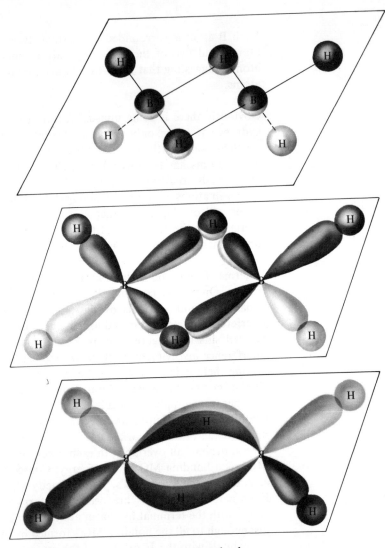

Fig. 1-6 (a) The shape of the diborane molecule.
(b) The overlap of atomic orbitals in diborane.
(c) The resulting three-center molecular orbitals in diborane.

valence electrons and in the methyl group, CH_3, there is one electron available for additional bonding (as in the hydrogen atom); therefore only 12 electrons are available to hold the two aluminum atoms and six methyl groups together; seven bonds would be necessary if the structure were an ordinary one. The situation is, therefore, very similar to that in B_2H_6, and the structures are analogous. It is seen from Figure 1-7 that two CH_3 groups occupy bridging positions in which they are held simultaneously to both aluminum atoms by three-center bonds.

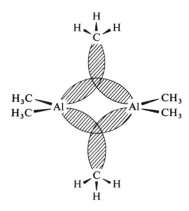

Fig. 1-7   The structure of $Al_2(CH_3)_6$. Each of the two central CH_3 groups is linked simultaneously to both aluminum atoms by three-center bonds.

The concept of the multicenter bond has been used to explain several other types of bonds, including the hydrogen bond and the bonds between metal atoms in the solid state.

Oxidation Numbers   *Oxidation* is said to occur when electrons are removed from a substance, and *reduction* occurs when electrons are added. Thus in the process

$$Na \rightarrow Na^+ + e \tag{11}$$

the sodium atom is oxidized when converted into Na^+, and Na^+ can be said to exist in a higher oxidation state than Na. Since one electron has been removed, we can say that the *oxidation state* or *oxidation number* of Na^+ is one greater than that of Na. Similarly in the process

$$\tfrac{1}{2}Cl_2 + e \rightarrow Cl^- \tag{12}$$

the chlorine is reduced when converted into Cl^-. We can say that the oxidation state or oxidation number of Cl^- is one *less* than that of elementary chlorine.

There are many reactions that we recognize as oxidations and reductions, but in which the interpretations in terms of the gain or loss of electrons is not so obvious. For example, the addition of oxygen to carbon monoxide, with the formation of carbon dioxide

$$2CO + O_2 \rightarrow 2CO_2$$

is certainly an oxidation, but one cannot see at once which atom has lost electrons and which has gained them.

In order to give a uniform treatment for reactions of this kind, the *oxidation number* or *oxidation state* of an atom is defined according to a set of rules that are quite arbitrary but provide a self-consistent scheme. The sign and magnitude of the oxidation number represents, in units of electron charge, the effective electric charge on the atom according to a set of conventional rules which define how shared electron pairs are distributed between the atoms concerned. Since the procedure used is arbitrary, although definite, the oxidation number does not have any particular structural significance. Its use is to be regarded as a kind of bookkeeping of the electrons that are involved in oxidation-reduction reactions. The rules may be stated as follows:

1. *The atoms in each element have an oxidation number of zero, irrespective of the state in which the element exists.* Thus the oxidation numbers of He, Cl_2, S_8, and P_4 and of the atoms of which they are composed, are zero.

2. *The oxidation number of a monatomic ion is equal to the charge on the ion.* Thus the compound $ZnCl_2$ consists of Zn^{2+} and Cl^- ions, of which the oxidation numbers are $+2$ and -1, respectively.

3. *The algebraic sum of the oxidation numbers for all of the atoms combined in a molecule or ion is equal to the net charge on the particle.* This rule enables us to compute the oxidation number by difference when it is in combination with elements having oxidation numbers assigned by the following rules.

4. *In covalently bonded molecules or ions, the shared pairs of electrons are arbitrarily assigned to the more electronegative of each pair of bonded atoms, and the net charge remaining on each atom after this is done is the oxidation number of the element.* In H_2S, for example, the two electrons in each bond are assigned to the sulfur atom, which therefore has an oxidation number of -2 (since there are two bonds). The oxidation number of each hydrogen atom is $+1$. In CCl_4 the oxidation numbers are -1 for the chlorine atoms and $+4$ for the carbon atom.

5. *In combination with other elements hydrogen usually has an oxidation number of $+1$.* The only exceptions are the metallic hydrides, which are regarded as ionic compounds of the hydride ion H^-; this, according to rule 2, has an oxidation number of -1. Thus in CaH_2, the hydrogen atoms have oxidation numbers of -1, the calcium atoms of $+2$.

6. *In combination with other elements oxygen usually has an oxidation number of -2.* One exception is in OF_2; oxygen is less electronegative than fluorine, so that by virtue of rule 4, oxygen has the oxidation number of $+2$ in this compound, and the fluorine atoms have oxidation numbers of -1 each. Another group of exceptional atoms comprises the peroxides, such as H_2O_2 and Na_2O_2. These compounds contain O–O bonds, and the shared electron pair is assigned by dividing it equally between the two oxygen atoms. In these molecules the oxidation number of each oxygen atom is -1. In H_2O_2, therefore, the hydrogen atoms each have an oxidation number of $+1$, as usual.

Some examples of the application of these rules are as follows. In the dichromate ion, $Cr_2O_7^{2-}$, the sum of the oxidation numbers must be -2. That of each oxygen atom is -2, so that the number for each Cr atom must be $+6$. In the permanganate ion, MnO_4^-, the total must be -1, and each oxygen atom is -2; the oxidation number of Mn is, therefore, $+7$.

In formaldehyde, CH_2O, the H atoms are $+1$ and the O atom -2, so that the oxidation number of the carbon atom is zero. In methane, CH_4, the oxidation number of the carbon atom is -4. In carbon tetrachloride, CCl_4, since the chlorine atom is more electronegative than the carbon atom, its oxidation number is -1; the oxidation number of the carbon atom in this compound is, therefore, $+4$. These last two examples show how the oxidation number can vary markedly from one molecule to another. Fractional oxidation numbers can exist. For example, in propane, C_3H_8, the oxidation number of each hydrogen atom is $+1$, so that the oxidation number of each carbon atom is $-8/3$.

According to rule 2, the oxidation number and the valency of an element in an ionic compound are identical. There is no such relationship, however, between oxidation number and covalency, as is evident from the above examples.

The definitions of oxidation and reduction may be expressed in terms of oxidation numbers. *Oxidation means increase in oxidation number, and reduction means decrease in oxidation number.* Thus, consider the reaction

$$2CO + O_2 \;\rightarrow\; CO_2 \tag{13}$$

The oxidation number of the oxygen atom in both CO and CO_2 is -2, so that the oxidation numbers of carbon in the two compounds are $+2$ and $+4$, respectively. The carbon atom, therefore, has been oxidized when CO is converted into CO_2. Moreover, the oxidation number of each oxygen atom in O_2 is zero, whereas its oxidation number in CO_2 is -2; the oxygen itself, therefore, is reduced when it oxidizes CO to CO_2.

Thermochemical Cycles

Many trends in the behavior of chemical compounds are best understood in terms of energy changes. Equilibrium constants are related to *free energy* changes, the relationship being

$$K = e^{-\Delta G/RT} \tag{14}$$

Here K is the equilibrium constant and ΔG the increase in free energy when the reaction occurs under certain standard conditions. The free energy change, ΔG, is related to the heat or enthalpy change, ΔH, and the entropy change, ΔS, by the equation

$$\Delta G = \Delta H - T\Delta S \tag{15}$$

It is obviously important to know the values of ΔG, ΔH, and ΔS for chemical processes, because they give one some understanding of the equilibrium constant, which indicates the tendency of the reaction to occur in one direction or the other.

These changes in G, H, and S are often determined by indirect means. It is sometimes impossible to determine directly the heat of formation of a compound (that is, the heat absorbed when a mole of substance is formed from the elements in their standard states); it is sometimes not possible to cause the compound to be formed from the elements. In such cases, we frequently make use of Hess's law, which allows us to calculate the heat of formation from various other heat changes, such as the heat of combustion.

The same kind of reasoning employed in the use of Hess's law is valuable in many other situations. We can generalize the procedure as follows. Consider any chemical process

$$A \rightarrow P \tag{16}$$

Suppose that the substance A can be converted into P not only in one stage, as implied by the equation above, but also in a number of stages, such as

$$A \rightarrow B \rightarrow C \rightarrow P \tag{17}$$

It then follows that if we consider a quantity such as free energy, enthalpy, or entropy, the change in this quantity in going from A to P must be the same whether we go directly or in stages. Thus if the enthalpy changes are

$$A \xrightarrow{\Delta H} P \tag{18}$$

$$A \xrightarrow{\Delta H_1} B \xrightarrow{\Delta H_2} C \xrightarrow{\Delta H_3} P \tag{19}$$

it is necessary that

$$\Delta H = \Delta H_1 + \Delta H_2 + \Delta H_3 \tag{20}$$

The proof is exactly the same as for Hess's law. If this relationship were not true, it would be possible to go from A to P by one route, return by the other, and have some energy left over. One could, therefore, get energy or work for nothing, and this is contrary to our experience.

This argument applies to ΔG, ΔH, and ΔS and to certain other properties. It is most common to make use of these relationships for changes in enthalpy, ΔH, since we are often ignorant of entropy changes. However, certain trends in behavior (for example, solubility of alkali halide salts) can often be interpreted satisfactorily in terms of changes in ΔH values, even though it is really the ΔG change that is important. We now consider an application of this type of argument. We usually use the term *thermochemical cycle*, since we are considering the system

$$A \underset{\longleftarrow}{\overset{\longrightarrow B \longrightarrow C}{}} P \tag{21}$$

Such a cycle is often useful in analyzing the energetics of chemical processes of many different types, where the single process can be considered as taking place in a series of simpler (and more easily understandable) processes.

The Born–Haber Cycle

Consider the process of forming a solid salt $MX(s)$ from the solid element $M(s)$ and the element X, which is supposed to exist in the gaseous state as $X_2(g)$; the symbols s and g represent solid and gas, respectively. The stoichiometric equation is

$$M(s) + \tfrac{1}{2}X_2(g) \quad \rightarrow \quad MX(s) \tag{22}$$

and an example is the formation of solid sodium chloride from solid sodium and gaseous chlorine.

$$Na(s) + \tfrac{1}{2}Cl_2(g) \quad \rightarrow \quad NaCl(s) \tag{23}$$

Associated with this change is a ΔH value, which, in fact, is the standard heat of formation and will be written as $\Delta H_f(MX)$. The magnitude of this quantity is of some importance as far as the stability of the compound is concerned. If $\Delta H_f(MX)$ were large and positive, for example, the compound MX could decompose into $M + \tfrac{1}{2}X_2$ with the liberation of heat, and therefore might well be somewhat unstable. A compound with a negative ΔH_f, on the other hand, exists at a lower energy level than the elements and will not, therefore, show much tendency to decompose into the elements.

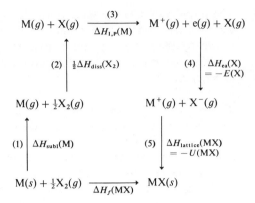

$$M(g) + X(g) \xrightarrow[\Delta H_{1,P}(M)]{(3)} M^+(g) + e(g) + X(g)$$

(2) $\frac{1}{2}\Delta H_{\mathrm{diss}}(X_2)$ (4) $\begin{aligned}&\Delta H_{\mathrm{ea}}(X)\\&= -E(X)\end{aligned}$

$$M(g) + \tfrac{1}{2}X_2(g) \qquad\qquad M^+(g) + X^-(g)$$

(1) $\Delta H_{\mathrm{subl}}(M)$ (5) $\begin{aligned}&\Delta H_{\mathrm{lattice}}(MX)\\&= -U(MX)\end{aligned}$

$$M(s) + \tfrac{1}{2}X_2(g) \xrightarrow[\Delta H_f(MX)]{} MX(s)$$

Fig. 1-8 The Born–Haber cycle for a solid salt, MX(s).

Here, we have written the process in one stage, but it is convenient to consider it as occurring in several stages, as represented in Figure 1-8. The individual stages are listed below.

1. The conversion of a mole of solid M into gaseous M, which is considered to exist in the form of monatomic species. The enthalpy increase in this process, $\Delta H_{\mathrm{subl}}(M)$, is the molar heat of sublimation. This enthalpy increase is always positive.

2. The conversion of half a mole of X_2, in the gaseous state, into a mole of X atoms. The enthalpy increase when one mole of X_2 is converted into two moles of X is known as the heat of dissociation of X_2:

$$X_2(g) \rightarrow 2X(g) \qquad \Delta H_{\mathrm{diss}} \qquad (24)$$

It therefore takes $\frac{1}{2}\Delta H_{\mathrm{diss}}$ of heat to dissociate half a mole of X_2. ΔH_{diss} is always positive for a stable molecule X_2.

3. The conversion of a mole of M in the gaseous state into the ion $M^+(g)$ and an electron. This enthalpy increase, $\Delta H_{\mathrm{IP}}(M)$, is known as the ionization energy, or potential; it is always positive.

4. The addition of an electron to $X(g)$ to give $X^-(g)$. The energy *released* when the process occurs is the electron affinity, E, some values for which are given in Table 1-1. The values of the electron affinity are usually, but by no means always, positive. The ΔH value for the addition of the electron to X, written as $\Delta H_{\mathrm{ea}}(X_2)$ in Figure 1-8, is the negative of the conventional electron affinity:

$$\Delta H_{\mathrm{ea}}(X) = -E(X) \qquad (25)$$

5. The conversion of a mole of $M^+(g)$ and a mole of $X^-(g)$ into the crystal, represented by MX(s). This process is always accompanied by the *evolution* of an amount of heat which can be written as U and is known as the *lattice energy* or *lattice enthalpy*. The ΔH value for this process, written as $\Delta H_{\mathrm{lattice}}(MX)$, is the negative of the lattice energy U.

$$\Delta H_{\mathrm{lattice}}(MX) = -U(MX) \qquad (26)$$

Table 1-1   Ionization Energies and Electron Affinities (kcal/mole).[a]

H							He
313.3							566.5
17.2							
Li	Be	B	C	N	O	F	Ne
124.2	214.8	191.2	259.6	335.1	313.7	401.5	496.9
12.4	−13.8	4.6	28.8	−2.3	33.9	79.5	—
Na	Mg	Al	Si	P	S	Cl	Ar
118.4	176.2	138.8	187.8	253.4	238.7	299.8	363.2
17.0	−6.9	—	—	16.1	47.7	83.2	—
K						Br	Kr
100.0						272.9	322.6
—						77.4	—
Rb						I	Xe
96.2						240.8	279.5
—						70.5	—
Cs							
89.6							
—							

[a] The upper figure is the ionization energy (or ionization potential); the lower is the electron affinity.

A cycle of the kind shown in Figure 1-8 was first considered by the German physicist Max Born (1882–1969; Nobel prize for physics, 1954) and the German chemist Fritz Haber (1868–1934; Nobel prize for chemistry, 1918). It is seen from the figure that the ΔH for the direct conversion of $M(s) + \frac{1}{2}X_2(g)$ into the solid is equal to the sum of the values for the processes (1) to (5).

$$\Delta H_f(MX) = \Delta H_{subl}(M) + \frac{1}{2}\Delta H_{diss}(X_2)$$
$$+ \Delta H_{IP}(M) + \Delta H_{ea}(X) + \Delta H_{lattice}(MX) \quad (27)$$

Using (25) and (26) this can be written as

$$\Delta H_f(MX) = \Delta H_{subl}(M) + \frac{1}{2}\Delta H_{diss}(X_2) + \Delta H_{IP}(M) - E(X) - U(MX)$$
$$(28)$$

The usefulness of these equations stems from the fact that frequently we know all of the quantities except one, so that the remaining one can easily be calculated. Heats of sublimation and dissociation are usually obtained fairly easily, and heats of formation of solids can sometimes be determined without too much difficulty. The ionization energies of most atoms have been determined, in many cases by calculation, but electron affinities present more of a problem. Lattice energies also cannot always be determined in too straightforward a manner. The following types of calculations, based on the Born–Haber cycle, are frequently made.

1. *Calculation of electron affinities.* Sometimes, especially for the simpler solid lattice structures, lattice energies can be calculated in a reliable manner. If $\Delta H_{subl}(M)$, $\Delta H_{diss}(X_2)$, $\Delta H_{IP}(M)$, and $\Delta H_f(MX)$ are also known for the particular case, it is possible to calculate, from equation (28), the electron affinity E of the atom X.

2. *Calculation of lattice energies.* Alternatively, if $E(X)$ is known but not $U(MX)$, the latter can be calculated if all the other terms are known. This type of calculation serves as an important check on the correctness of lattice energy calculations made on the basis of theories of the crystal lattice.

3. *Calculation of heats of formation.* It is often of interest to calculate the heat of formation of a hypothetical ionic solid, in order to see whether it might be stable. Some of the quantities in the Born–Haber equation will be known, and others, such as the lattice energy, can be estimated in a reliable fashion. If the heat of formation of a hypothetical compound, ΔH_f, is calculated to be positive, it is somewhat unlikely that the compound could be prepared, since it would tend to decompose into the elements. For example, calculations of the heat of formation of the hypothetical salt xenon fluoride, Xe^+F^-, would yield a fairly high value, mainly as a result of the very large ionization energy for the xenon atom.

Example

Calculate the lattice energy of the potassium chloride crystal from the following data.

$$\begin{aligned}
&\text{Heat of sublimation of K, } \Delta H_{subl}(K) &&= 21.5 \text{ kcal/mole} \\
&\text{Heat of dissociation of } Cl_2, \Delta H_{diss}(Cl_2) &&= 58.0 \text{ kcal/mole} \\
&\text{Ionization energy of K, } \Delta H_{IP}(K) &&= 100.0 \text{ kcal/mole} \\
&\text{Electron affinity of Cl, } E(Cl) &&= 83.2 \text{ kcal/mole} \\
&\text{Heat of formation of KCl, } \Delta H_f(KCl) &&= -104.2 \text{ kcal/mole}
\end{aligned}$$

Solution

Insertion of the quantities into equation (28) gives

$$-104.2 = 21.5 + \frac{58.0}{2} + 100.0 - 83.2 - U(KCl)$$

whence

$$U(KCl) = 171.5 \text{ kcal/mole}$$

Chemical Stability   The question of the factors that determine the stability of a chemical compound is not easy to consider. The two most important aspects of the problem relate to energetics (thermodynamics) and to the rates of possible decomposition reactions.

If a substance is formed endothermally from its elements, it is in a state of relatively high energy. This means that there probably is a tendency for the substance to decompose, with the liberation of energy, either into the elements or (more likely) into other products. Under these circumstances, we say that a substance is *thermodynamically* unstable.

Another important factor relating to the stability of compounds is the *kinetic* one. A substance that is unstable from the thermodynamic point of view may still survive for long periods of time. That is to say, the equilibrium constant for the decomposition of a compound into its elements may be very high, but the rate of its decomposition may be low. An example is provided by nitric oxide, which is formed endothermally from the elements. The equilibrium constant for the decomposition of nitric oxide into nitrogen and oxygen

$$2NO \rightleftharpoons N_2 + O_2 \tag{29}$$

is high. However, at ordinary temperatures the rate of decomposition of nitric oxide into nitrogen and oxygen is quite low, so that the compound is reasonably stable.

There are no simple rules for predicting the rates of chemical reactions. The rate constant, k, of a chemical reaction can be expressed as

$$k = Ae^{-E/RT} \tag{30}$$

where A is the frequency factor, E the activation energy, R the gas constant, and T the absolute temperature. In order to have a complete theory of a rate constant, therefore, one must be able to predict both the frequency factor and the activation energy. The frequency factor does not present too formidable a problem, but the activation energy still cannot be estimated in a reliable way. Since the rate constant depends exponentially, and therefore very strongly, on the magnitude of the activation energy, it is impossible to have much idea of the rate of a reaction without actually measuring it. As a result, those aspects of stability which depend on kinetic factors must be dealt with in a purely empirical fashion.

Problems

1-1. Basing your reasoning on the molecular orbital energy levels of H_2 shown in Figure 1-3, what predictions can you make about (a) the bond strengths and (b) the bond lengths of the species H_2^+, H_2^-, H_2^{2-} compared with H_2?

1-2. The figure ⬡ represents the electronic energies for
AO MO AO

the atomic orbitals of two *identical* atoms, and for the molecular orbitals of a molecule formed by combination of these atoms. How will the diagram be altered when two *nonidentical* atoms form a molecule?

1-3. State which of the following species are expected to be (a) electron donors; (b) electron acceptors; (c) neither electron donors nor acceptors, or (d) both electron donors and acceptors:

$$BeCl_2 \; ; \; BCl_3 \, , \; BCl_4^- , \; CH_4 \, , \; H_3N \cdot BF_3 \, , \; PCl_3 \, , \; PCl_5 \, , \; H_2O, \; F^-.$$

1-4. What are the oxidation numbers of the underlined atoms in the following species?

$$\underline{Na}Cl \, ; \; \underline{Al}Cl_3 \; ; \; \underline{B}F_4^- \; ; \; \underline{C}_2F_4 \; ; \; Na_2\underline{C}O_3 \; ; \; \underline{P}Cl_5 \; ; \; \underline{P}Cl_3 \; ; \; \underline{P}O_4^{3-} \; ; \; \underline{P}_4O_6 \; ; \; \underline{Xe}F_2 \; ;$$

$$\underline{Xe}F_4 \; ; \; \underline{Xe}F_6 \; ; \; \underline{Xe}O_3 \; ; \; \underline{Xe}OCl_4 \; ; \; \underline{Ni}(CO)_4 \; ; \; \underline{Co}(CO)_4^- \; ; \; K\underline{Mn}O_4 \; ; \; \underline{Mn}^{2+} \; ;$$

$$\underline{Cr}_2O_7^{2-}.$$

1-5. Calculate the molar enthalpy (ΔH) of the reaction in which gaseous atoms of the least electronegative element (cesium) react with gaseous atoms of the most electronegative element (fluorine) to give $Cs^+(g)$ and $F^-(g)$ ions separated by large distances.

(i) $Cs(g) \cdots + F(g) \quad \rightarrow \quad Cs^+(g) \cdots + F^-(g)$

(ii) What is the molar enthalpy of the reaction

$$Cs^+(g) \cdots + F^-(g) \quad \rightarrow \quad Cs^+F^-(s)?$$

(iii) Calculate the molar enthalpy of the process

$$Cs(g) + F(g) \quad \rightarrow \quad Cs^+F^-(s)$$

(iv) Now calculate the heat of formation of a mole of $CsF(s)$ from the elements in their standard states—that is, the enthalpy of the reaction

$$\tfrac{1}{2}F_2(g) + Cs(s) \quad \rightarrow \quad CsF(s)$$

Ionization energy of cesium: 90 kcal/mole,
Electron affinity of fluorine: 80 kcal/mole,
Lattice energy of cesium fluoride: 174 kcal/mole,
Heat of sublimation of cesium: 19 kcal/mole,
Heat of dissociation of fluorine: 38 kcal/mole of F_2.

1-6. Calculate the electron affinity of iodine using a Born–Haber cycle together with the following data:

Ionization energy of rubidium: 96 kcal/mole,
Lattice energy of RbI: 146.5 kcal/mole,
Heat of sublimation of rubidium: 21 kcal/mole,
Heat of dissociation of iodine: 36 kcal/mole of I_2,
Heat of vaporization of iodine: 15 kcal/mole of I_2,
Heat of formation of RbI (from the elements in their standard states):
    -79 kcal/mole.

1-7. Construct a Born–Haber cycle for CaF_2 and use this cycle to calculate the lattice energy of CaF_2 using the following data:

Ionization energies of Ca (kcal/mole): 1st $= 140$; 2nd $= 273$,
Electron affinity of F: 80 kcal/mole,
Heat of sublimation of calcium: 46 kcal/mole,
Heat of dissociation of fluorine: 38 kcal/mole of F_2,
Heat of formation of CaF_2 (from the elements in their standard states):
    -290 kcal/mole of CaF_2.

1-8. Calculate the heat of formation of $CsF_2(s)$ from the elements in their standard states using the following data:

Ionization energies of cesium (kcal/mole): 1st $= 90$; 2nd $= 540$,
Electron affinity of fluorine: 80 kcal/mole,
Calculated lattice energy of CsF_2: 553 kcal/mole,
Heat of sublimation of cesium: 19 kcal/mole,
Heat of dissociation of fluorine: 38 kcal/mole of F_2.
What would probably happen to CsF_2 if it were prepared by some method?

Suggested Reading

Dasent, W. E. "Non-Existent Compounds," *J. Chem. Ed.*, **40**, 130 (1963).

Dewar, M. J. S. *An Introduction to Modern Chemistry*. Athlone Press, University of London, 1965.

Frazer, M. J., and N. Singer. "Thermochemical Cycles," *Education in Chemistry*, **1**, 39 (1964).

Haight, G. P. "Energy Cycles," *J. Chem. Ed.*, **45**, 420 (1968).

Howald, R. A. "Bond Energies in the Interpretation of Descriptive Chemistry," *J. Chem. Ed.*, **45**, 163 (1968).

Johnson, D. A. *Some Thermodynamic Aspects of Inorganic Chemistry*. Cambridge University Press, New York, 1968.

Roselaar, L. C. "Solubility of Salts," *Education in Chemistry*, **2**, 135 (1965).

Sanderson, R. T. "On the Significance of Electrode Potentials," *J. Chem. Ed.*, **44**, 95 (1967).

————. "Why Does Methane Burn?" *J. Chem. Ed.*, **45**, 423 (1968).

Chapter 2   The Nontransition Elements

Inspection of the periodic table shown inside the cover of this book and of the electronic configurations shows that the chemical elements can be divided into three classes:

1. Those in which the d and f shells are complete are the *nontransition* elements.

2. Those in which the f shells are complete but the d shells are incomplete are known as *transition* elements. Examples are the elements running from scandium to copper in the fourth period.

3. Those elements belonging to series of successive elements in which there is a building up of the f shells are of two types. There is a series of *lanthanides*, running from cerium to lutecium, and a series of *actinides*, which starts with thorium.

Since these classes of elements exhibit rather characteristic properties, it is convenient to treat them separately. The present chapter deals with the nontransition elements and considers them in the order of the groups. Subsequent chapters deal with the transition elements (Chapter 3) and the lanthanides and actinides (Chapter 4).

Hydrogen

The hydrogen atom has a single electron in the 1s state ($n = 1, l = 0$). It can participate in the formation of several different types of bonds, as follows:

1. *A covalent bond*, which is found in the hydrogen molecule, H_2, in organic compounds such as methane, CH_4, and in hydrogen halides such as hydrogen iodide, HI.

2. *An ionic bond*, in which hydrogen is present as the negative ion, known as the hydride ion. Sodium hydride, NaH, for example, contains the Na^+H^- bond. The H^- ion has the configuration

$$[H_o^x]^-$$

both electrons being 1s electrons; according to the Pauli principle they must have opposite spins. The H^- ion is isoelectronic with the helium atom.

3. *A multicenter covalent bond*, as in diborane, B_2H_6, whose structure is

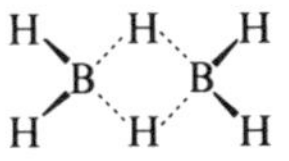

The nature of this bond has been considered in Chapter 1.

4. *A hydrogen bond*, found in the ion

$$[F \ldots H \ldots F]^-$$

and in ice and liquid water, where there are structures of the type

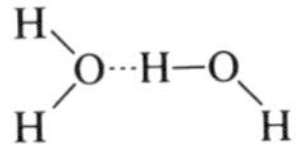

This bond owes its existence largely to electrostatic attractions between atoms which, because of the small size of the hydrogen atom, can come closer together than when other atoms are involved.

A hydrogen atom can also lose an electron to form a proton:

$$H^\circ \rightarrow H^+ + e$$

This process requires a very large amount of energy and therefore occurs readily only when the proton can become attached to some other molecule present. In liquid water, for example, a proton is attached to a water molecule to form the structure

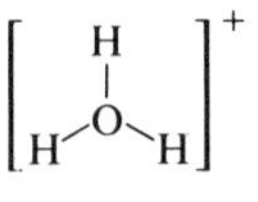

in which each O–H bond is a normal covalent bond.

Hydrogen Isotopes

Three isotopes of hydrogen exist. In ordinary hydrogen, or protium, the nucleus is a single proton and the mass number is 1. In deuterium, given the symbol $^2_1$H or D, the nucleus is one proton and one neutron, and the mass number is 2. Hydrogen in nature consists of about 99.984% protium and about 0.016% deuterium. A very much rarer form is tritium, $^3_1$H or T, which has a mass number of 3 and whose nucleus consists of one proton and two neutrons. Tritium can be prepared artificially, for example, by bombarding ordinary lithium atoms with neutrons:

$$^6_3Li + ^1_0n \rightarrow ^3_1H + ^4_2He \text{ (an } \alpha \text{ particle)}$$

Whereas protium and deuterium are stable, tritium is radioactive, emitting β particles (electrons),

$$^3_1H \rightarrow ^3_2He + \beta$$

This emission process has a "half-life" of 12.4 years; that is to say, if we start with a given amount of $^3_1$H, half of it will be converted into $^3_2$He in 12.4 years.

Since all of these isotopic forms have the same nuclear charge ($+1$) and one valence electron, their chemical properties are the same. Indeed, *qualitatively* the three forms are chemically identical; they form the same compounds, which undergo the same reactions. *Quantitatively*, however, the three isotopic forms exhibit some differences. Thus the free elements H_2, D_2, and T_2 show differences in boiling points, vapor densities, and other physical properties, as do corresponding compounds such as CH_4, CD_4, and CT_4. Differences of equilibrium constants and of reaction rates are also found when the three forms, or their compounds, are compared; for example, chemical processes in which an H atom is transferred from one molecule to another usually occur more rapidly than those in which a D or a T atom is transferred. However, the kinds of reactions that occur are the same with all three forms.

Deuterium and tritium are often used to "label" chemical compounds. For example, in a biochemical experiment it might be necessary to know what happens to a particular organic compound when it is metabolized. This can be determined by preparing a compound in which some of the H atoms are replaced by D or T and finding out what happens to these atoms. With D atoms, this must be done by use of the mass spectrometer, but the radioactivity of T atoms provides a convenient way of tracing them.

Molecular Hydrogen   The hydrogen molecule consists of two atoms held together by a covalent bond; a region of high electron density between the nuclei tends to bind the nuclei together. Because of the existence of isotopes, a number of hydrogen molecules are possible—for example, H_2, HD, D_2, and HT.

Apart from this, the molecule H_2 exists in two forms which arise as a consequence of the spins of the *nuclei*. These spins may occur in the same direction, in which case the molecule is known as *ortho-hydrogen*:

In the other form, *para-hydrogen*, the nuclear spins are opposed:

Ortho-hydrogen and para-hydrogen differ slightly in certain properties, such as specific heats.

The following methods may be used for preparing hydrogen in the laboratory:

(a) *Reactions of metals with mineral acids.* Zinc, for example, dissolves in sulfuric acid with the liberation of hydrogen, and the reaction is

$$2H_{aq}^+ + 2e \rightarrow H_2$$

Whether or not a metal will bring about such a reaction depends on both equilibrium and kinetic factors. The more electropositive the metal, the greater its tendency to react with acids; indeed only metals with positive standard oxidation potentials (cf. Table 2-1) are able to react in this way. Kinetic factors enter in the sense that the rate of attack of a metal by an acid will be much decreased if a layer of protective oxide is formed on its surface (as with aluminum) or if an insoluble salt is formed on the metal (as with lead, which forms lead sulfate, $PbSO_4$, with H_2SO_4).

(b) *Reactions of metals with alkaline solutions.* Elements which form amphoteric oxides (oxides that have both acidic and basic properties) are able to liberate hydrogen from solutions of strong alkalis such as sodium hydroxide; for example

$$Zn + 2OH^- + 2H_2O \rightarrow Zn(OH)_4^{2-} + H_2$$

Table 2-1   Standard Oxidation Potentials.[a]

Half-Reaction	ε^0, Volts
$Li \rightarrow Li^+ + e$	3.04
$K \rightarrow K^+ + e$	2.92
$Ca \rightarrow Ca^{2+} + 2e$	2.87
$Na \rightarrow Na^+ + e$	2.71
$Mg \rightarrow Mg^{2+} + 2e$	2.34
$Al \rightarrow Al^{3+} + 3e$	1.67
$Zn \rightarrow Zn^{2+} + 2e$	0.76
$Cr \rightarrow Cr^{3+} + 3e$	0.74
$Fe \rightarrow Fe^{2+} + 2e$	0.44
$Co \rightarrow Co^{2+} + 2e$	0.28
$Ni \rightarrow Ni^{2+} + 2e$	0.25
$Sn \rightarrow Sn^{2+} + 2e$	0.14
$Pb \rightarrow Pb^{2+} + 2e$	0.13
$H_2 \rightarrow 2H^+ + 2e$	0.00 (by definition)
$Sn^{2+} \rightarrow Sn^{4+} + 2e$	-0.15
$Cu \rightarrow Cu^{2+} + 2e$	-0.34
$2I^- \rightarrow I_2 + 2e$	-0.54
$H_2O_2 \rightarrow O_2 + 2H^+ + 2e$	-0.68
$Fe^{2+} \rightarrow Fe^{3+} + e$	-0.77
$2Hg \rightarrow Hg^{2+} + 2e$	-0.79
$Ag \rightarrow Ag^+ + e$	-0.80
$Hg \rightarrow Hg^{2+} + 2e$	-0.85
$2Br^- \rightarrow Br_2 + 2e$	-1.06
$Pt \rightarrow Pt^{2+} + 2e$	-1.20
$2H_2O \rightarrow O_2 + 4H^+ + 4e$	-1.23
$2H_2O + Mn^{2+} \rightarrow MnO_2 + 4H^+ + 2e$	-1.23
$7H_2O + 2Cr^{3+} \rightarrow Cr_2O_7^{2-} + 14H^+ + 6e$	-1.33
$2Cl^- \rightarrow Cl_2 + 2e$	-1.36
$4H_2O + Mn^{2+} \rightarrow MnO_4^- + 8H^+ + 5e$	-1.52
$Au \rightarrow Au^+ + e$	-1.68
$2H_2O \rightarrow H_2O_2 + 2H^+ + 2e$	-1.77
$2F^- \rightarrow F_2 + 2e$	-2.87

[a] Standard electrode potentials are the negatives of the values given above, since the reactions are written in the opposite direction.

Aluminum, tin, silicon, and zinc are all able to act in this way to form hydrogen gas and a complex ion derived from the metal and hydroxide ion. These reactions can be considered as combining two half-cell reactions and a subsequent reaction between the metal cation and hydroxide ions; for example

$$Zn \quad \rightarrow \quad Zn^{2+} + 2e$$
$$2OH^- + 2H_2O + 2e \quad \rightarrow \quad 4OH^- + H_2$$
$$Zn^{2+} + 4OH^- \quad \rightarrow \quad Zn(OH)_4^{2-}$$

(c) *Electrolysis of an aqueous solution of a mineral acid or a strong base.* All reductions carried out by metals can equally well be performed electrolytically. When a current is passed through a solution of an acid or base, with inert electrodes, hydrogen is liberated at the cathode and oxygen at the anode. The reactions at the two electrodes may be represented as shown below.

At the cathode

$$2H^+ + 2e \;\rightarrow\; H_2$$

At the anode

$$2OH^- \;\rightarrow\; H_2O + \tfrac{1}{2}O_2 + 2e$$

(d) *Reaction of certain hydrides with water.* Hydrides that contain the H^- anion react very rapidly with water:

$$H^- + H_2O \;\rightarrow\; H_2 + OH^-$$

Examples are

$$CaH_2 + 2H_2O \;\rightarrow\; Ca(OH)_2 + 2H_2$$
$$LiAlH_4 + 4H_2O \;\rightarrow\; LiOH + Al(OH)_3 + 4H_2$$

($LiAlH_4$ is lithium aluminum hydride; see p. 60).

Another way of carrying out this type of reaction is to electrolyze calcium hydride, CaH_2, in a molten mixture of lithium chloride and potassium chloride, at a temperature of about 360°C. Hydrogen is liberated at the *anode*, by the process

$$2H^- \;\rightarrow\; H_2 + 2e$$

This is in contrast to the electrolysis of aqueous acidic solutions, when hydrogen is liberated at the *cathode*, and it emphasizes the difference between the reduction of H^+ to $\tfrac{1}{2}H_2$ and the oxidation of H^- to $\tfrac{1}{2}H_2$. It should be noted that H^- is one of the most powerful reducing agents known; the standard oxidation potential for H^- is 2.3 volts. This relates to the process

$$H^- \;\rightarrow\; \tfrac{1}{2}H_2 + e$$

Hydrogen is a colorless, odorless gas with a very low boiling point ($-253°C$). It reacts, usually only when heated, with most metals and nonmetals to give hydrides; for example

$$H_2 + Cl_2 \;\rightarrow\; 2HCl$$
$$2Na + H_2 \;\rightarrow\; 2NaH$$

Hydrogen is a reducing agent and can be used to reduce some metal oxides to the metal; an example is

$$CuO + H_2 \rightarrow Cu + H_2O$$

The Hydrides

Hydrogen combines with most elements in the periodic table. On the basis of their properties, the resulting hydrides can be divided into different types, which differ in the type of bonding. The main types are:

1. saline hydrides, including the anions of complex hydrides
2. covalent hydrides
3. interstitial hydrides

The distribution of these three types of hydrides among the elements of the periodic table is illustrated in Figure 2-1.

Saline hydrides. These are formed by the most electropositive elements in the periodic table, and contain the H^- anion. Examples are: lithium hydride, LiH, and calcium hydride, CaH_2. The saline hydrides are usually prepared by direct reaction between the metal and hydrogen, at elevated temperatures; for example

$$Na + \tfrac{1}{2}H_2 \rightarrow NaH$$

They are white crystalline solids when pure and have properties typical of ionic solids. They react with water to yield hydrogen; for example

$$NaH + H_2O \rightarrow NaOH + H_2$$

This reaction is essentially a reduction of water by the H^- anion:

$$H^- + H_2O \rightarrow H_2 + OH^-$$

The saline hydrides are important in chemistry because of the following properties:

1. They are very powerful reducing agents. They are capable, for example, of reducing organic acids, of formula RCOOH, to alcohols, RCH_2OH:

$$RCOOH + 2LiH \rightarrow RCH_2OH + Li_2O$$

2. They are a convenient source of hydrogen gas; this results, as already seen, from their strong reducing properties.

3. They can be used to prepare complex hydrides, and hydrides of other metals. For example, in alcohol solution lithium hydride reacts with aluminum chloride to form lithium aluminum hydride:

$$4LiH + AlCl_3 \rightarrow 3LiCl + LiAlH_4$$

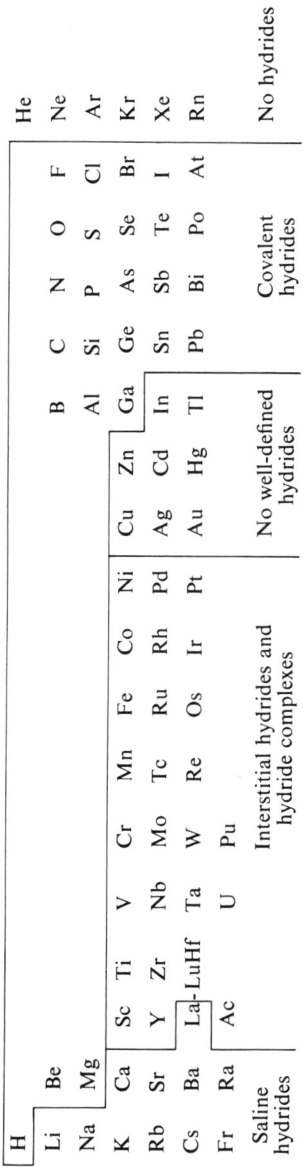

H																	He
Li	Be											B	C	N	O	F	Ne
Na	Mg											Al	Si	P	S	Cl	Ar
K	Ca	Sc	Ti	V	Cr	Mn	Fe	Co	Ni	Cu	Zn	Ga	Ge	As	Se	Br	Kr
Rb	Sr	Y	Zr	Nb	Mo	Tc	Ru	Rh	Pd	Ag	Cd	In	Sn	Sb	Te	I	Xe
Cs	Ba	La–Lu Hf	Ta	W	Re	Os	Ir	Pt	Au	Hg		Tl	Pb	Bi	Po	At	Rn
Fr	Ra	Ac	U	Pu													

Saline hydrides

Interstitial hydrides and hydride complexes

No well-defined hydrides

Covalent hydrides

No hydrides

Fig. 2-1 Classification of hydrides.

Lithium aluminum hydride reacts further with aluminum chloride to form aluminum hydride:

$$3LiAlH_4 + AlCl_3 \quad \rightarrow \quad 3LiCl + 4AlH_3$$

Covalent hydrides. These are compounds like H_2, HF, and CH_4, where the bonds involving the hydrogen atoms are largely covalent. Their properties depend on the electronegativity of the atom bonded to hydrogen. If it is approximately the same as the electronegativity of hydrogen, the resultant bond will be nonpolar; this is so in the case of carbon, so that methane, CH_4, and other paraffin hydrocarbons are nonpolar. If the electronegativity of the other atom is much greater than that of hydrogen, the molecule will be polarized in the direction

$$M^{\delta-} - H^{\delta+}$$

Such a hydride will tend to have acidic properties and will release hydrogen ions when dissolved in water; for example

$$HCl \quad \rightarrow \quad H^+_{aq} + Cl^-_{aq}$$

It is to be noted, however, that the polarity of the M–H bond is not a good measure of its acid strength, since other factors are involved; thus HF is a weaker acid than HCl, although the H–F bond is more polar than the H–Cl bond.

Hydrides formed by very electronegative elements, such as H_2O, NH_3, and HF, tend to exhibit hydrogen bonding, which results from the highly polar nature of the bond.

If the electronegativity of the atom connected to hydrogen is much less than that of hydrogen, the bond will be polarized in the direction

$$M^{\delta+} - H^{\delta-}$$

The acidic properties will then be negligible, and the behavior approaches the situation found in the saline hydrides.

Interstitial hydrides. Many metals absorb hydrogen to yield compounds in which the hydrogen atoms occupy interstitial positions in the metal lattice; that is to say, they reside in the spaces that exist between neighboring metal atoms. The ratio of the numbers of hydrogen and metal atoms is not a simple ratio of small whole numbers; consequently, they are known as *nonstoichiometric* compounds.

Their exact composition depends on the conditions of preparation, such as the temperature, pressure of hydrogen, and the state of division of the metal.

The bonding between hydrogen and the metal in such compounds is not properly understood, but neutron diffraction and other experimental techniques indicate that the arrangement is somewhat as shown in Figure 2-2. The metal atoms are arranged in a more-or-less

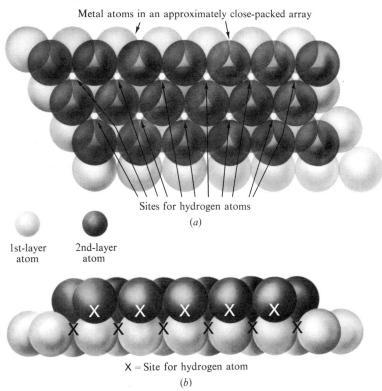

Metal atoms in an approximately close-packed array

Sites for hydrogen atoms

(a)

1st-layer atom   2nd-layer atom

X = Site for hydrogen atom

(b)

Fig. 2-2 The structure of some interstitial hydrides.

close-packed array, but it is slightly expanded so that the hydrogen atom is surrounded octahedrally by six metal atoms. Since a considerable amount of electron transfer takes place from the hydrogen to the metal atoms, the situation approaches that of an assembly of protons embedded in a negatively charged metal lattice.

Group IA. The Alkali Metals

There are six alkali metals, and the chemical and physical properties of all of them are similar. Table 2-2 shows all six and some of their properties. Francium is of little chemical importance, since every isotope of it is radioactive and of short life.

The nuclear charge (atomic number) of each of the alkali metals is one greater than that of a noble gas; this additional charge of $+1$ is balanced by an extra valence electron. The effect of atomic and ionic size on physical and chemical properties can be seen in the behavior of the alkali metals and their compounds. A number of properties, such as the atomic radius and the melting point of the metal, show a

Table 2-2   Properties of The Group-IA Elements—the Alkali Metals.

Property	Lithium (Li)	Sodium (Na)	Potassium (K)	Rubidium (Rb)	Cesium (Cs)	Francium (Fr)
Atomic number	3	11	19	37	55	87
Electronic configuration	[He]2s	[Ne]3s	[Ar]4s	[Kr]5s	[Xe]6s	[Rn]7s
Atomic radius, Å	1.23	1.57	2.03	2.16	2.35	—
Ionic radius, Å	0.78	0.98	1.33	1.49	1.65	—
Electronegativity	0.97	1.01	0.91	0.89	0.86	0.86
Ionization energy, kcal/mole	124.2	118.4	100.0	96.2	89.6	—
Melting point, °C	180	98	64	39	29	27
Standard potential oxidation at 25°C, volts	3.04	2.71	2.92	2.99	3.02	—

steady gradation through the group. Certain other properties, however, such as the oxidation potential, depend less consistently on size, and lithium is frequently out of line. The properties of these elements show less variation than do those in any other group of the periodic table. Lithium shows some kinship with magnesium, the Group-IIA element diagonally to its lower right. Some details are given later (p. 43), and we shall meet other examples of this diagonal relationship.

Alkali-metal atoms can form compounds in one of two ways.

1. *They can form an ionic bond* by donating the single valence electron to a more electronegative element:

$$Na + Cl \rightarrow Na^+ + Cl^-$$

The energetics of such a reaction will depend on both of the atoms involved, as illustrated by the Born–Haber cycle (see p. 21). The ionization energies, listed in Table 2–2, show that the alkali metals have an increasing readiness to lose one electron as the atomic number increases. This important general trend in most groups of the periodic table is caused by the increasing distance of the valence electron from the nucleus as the principal quantum number of the orbital increases.

It is much more difficult to remove a second electron from an atom than to remove the first one. The main reason for this is electrostatic attraction. Once one electron is taken away, the species is positively charged, and the removal of the second electron has to be done against an additional electrostatic attraction. In the case of the alkali metals, the first electron to be removed is a valence electron, but the second is an electron from an inner shell. With sodium, for example, the first electron to be removed is a 3s valence electron, and its removal requires 118 kcal/mole (this is the first ionization energy). The next electron, however, is a 2p electron, which, being closer to the nucleus, is much harder to remove; its removal requires 1085 kcal/mole (the second ionization energy). As a result, the chemistry of the alkali metals is almost entirely the chemistry of singly-charged cations, in either solid compounds or aqueous solution.

2. *They can form a covalent bond.* An alkali-metal atom can share its unpaired electron with another atom possessing an unpaired electron, thus forming a covalent bond:

$$M^\circ + {}_xA \quad \rightarrow \quad M^\circ_xA$$

The electronegativities of the alkali metals are among the lowest known; this means that molecules formed by alkali metals with most other elements are strongly polarized in the direction $M^{\delta+}—A^{\delta-}$. The polarization of most elements is so great that the compounds are ionic. However, when an alkali metal is combined with an atom of equally low electronegativity, a nonpolar molecule results. Examples of nonpolar covalent molecules formed by the alkali metals are the diatomic molecules of the elements; these are found in fairly low concentration in the vapor above the heated metals (the vapor mostly consists of alkali-metal atoms). The heats of dissociation of these diatomic molecules are given in Table 2-3. Notice that the heats of dissociation (which can be called the *bond dissociation energies*) decrease with increasing molecular weight. This illustrates another important general trend in the periodic table; for a given group, bond strengths usually decrease with increasing atomic weight.

The chemistry of the alkali metals is very similar for all the six elements; it is not necessary to deal in detail with each element. Since

Table 2-3 Heats of Dissociation of Diatomic Molecules.

	$\Delta H_{diss}(M_2(g) \rightarrow 2M(g))$, kcal/mole
Li–Li	26
Na–Na	18
K–K	12
Rb–Rb	11
Cs–Cs	10

sodium is the most common member of the group, the chemistry of sodium will be used to illustrate the chemistry of the alkali metals generally.

The Elements

The alkali metals are prepared by electrolysis of their molten salts. Sodium is prepared by electrolysis of fused $CaCl_2/NaCl$ mixtures (the $CaCl_2$ is used simply to lower the melting point of the NaCl). The processes occurring are

At the cathode

$$2Na^+ + 2e \rightarrow 2Na$$

At the anode

$$2Cl^- \rightarrow Cl_2 + 2e$$

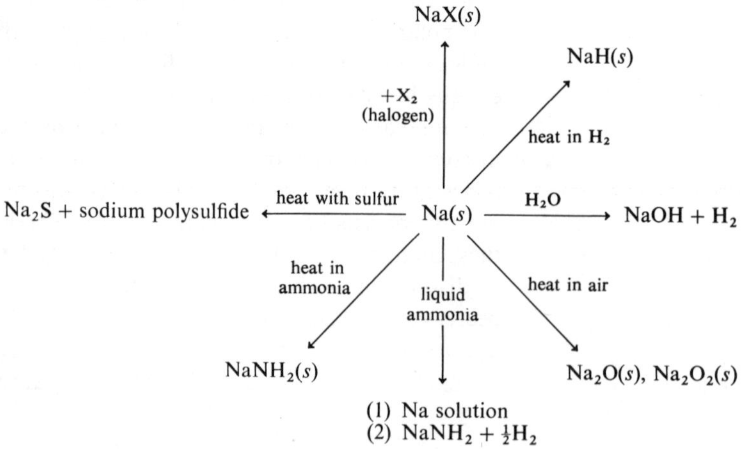

Fig. 2-3 The reactions of sodium.

Electrolysis of aqueous solutions of alkali-metal salts with platinum electrodes cannot be used to prepare the elements, because the standard oxidation potentials (given in Table 2-2) are all large and positive; this means that hydrogen will be liberated at a platinum cathode in preference to the alkali metal. However, if a *mercury* cathode is used, the alkali metal is liberated in preference to hydrogen, and an amalgam (or alloy of mercury) is produced.

The alkali metals are soft, low-melting solids (the melting point of sodium is 97.5°C) which react readily with a great number of elements and compounds. The more important reactions of sodium are shown in Figure 2-3.

Reactions of the Alkali Metals with Liquid Ammonia

All the alkali metals dissolve in liquid ammonia to give solutions that are dark blue when dilute and copper colored when concentrated. The blue color of the dilute solutions arises from absorption of light by *solvated electrons*. Solutions of the alkali metals in liquid ammonia consist of solvated alkali-metal cations and electrons:

$$M(s) \xrightarrow{\text{liquid NH}_3} M(NH_3)_x^+ + e^-(NH_3)_y$$

Such solutions can be kept with little change for some time. The solvated electron reacts slowly with ammonia to liberate hydrogen gas:

$$e^- + NH_3 \rightarrow NH_2^- + \tfrac{1}{2}H_2$$

This reaction can be greatly accelerated if a small amount of a catalyst, such as ferric chloride, is added. The solutions of alkali metals in liquid ammonia are useful in preparative chemistry because of their great reducing power.

Alkali-Metal Hydroxides, MOH

Sodium hydroxide, or caustic soda, NaOH, is the most important of these compounds; the other hydroxides resemble it closely in their reactions. A convenient laboratory preparation, which is also used commercially, involves first making sodium amalgam by electrolysis of aqueous sodium chloride using a mercury cathode, followed by reaction of the amalgam with water.

1. Electrolytic preparation of sodium amalgam.

At the cathode

$$Na_{aq}^+ + e^- \rightarrow Na(\text{dissolved in mercury})$$

At the anode

$$Cl^- \quad \rightarrow \quad \tfrac{1}{2}Cl_2 + e^-$$

2. Reaction of the sodium amalgam with water.

$$Na(\text{dissolved in mercury}) + H_2O \quad \rightarrow \quad NaOH + \tfrac{1}{2}H_2$$

Sodium hydroxide is a corrosive white solid which is very soluble in water. Solutions of sodium hydroxide are very strongly basic, and in aqueous solutions sodium hydroxide is completely dissociated into Na^+ and OH^- ions. It reacts with any acid to produce a salt,

$$NaOH + HA \quad \rightarrow \quad NaA + H_2O$$

and absorbs carbon dioxide to produce either sodium bicarbonate or sodium carbonate, both of which are salts of carbonic acid, H_2CO_3:

$$NaOH + CO_2 \quad \rightarrow \quad NaHCO_3 \text{ (sodium bicarbonate)}$$
$$2NaOH + CO_2 \quad \rightarrow \quad H_2O + Na_2CO_3 \text{ (sodium carbonate)}$$

Sodium hydroxide does not decompose on heating to liberate water and give the oxide.

Lithium hydroxide differs from the hydroxides of the other alkali metals in two important ways:

1. Lithium hydroxide is *not* completely dissociated in aqueous solution.
2. Lithium hydroxide loses water on heating, giving the oxide:

$$2LiOH \quad \rightarrow \quad Li_2O + H_2O$$

Alkali-Metal Salts   Each of the alkali metals forms a great number of salts, most of which can be prepared by causing the metal hydroxide or carbonate to react with an acid. For example

$$LiOH + H_2SO_4 \quad \rightarrow \quad LiHSO_4 + H_2O$$
$$\text{Sulfuric} \qquad\qquad \text{Lithium}$$
$$\text{acid} \qquad\qquad\quad \text{bisulfate}$$

$$2LiOH + H_2SO_4 \quad \rightarrow \quad Li_2SO_4 + 2H_2O$$
$$\text{Lithium}$$
$$\text{sulfate}$$

$$KOH + HNO_3 \quad \rightarrow \quad KNO_3 + H_2O$$
$$\text{Nitric} \qquad\qquad \text{Potassium}$$
$$\text{acid} \qquad\qquad \text{nitrate}$$

$$Na_2CO_3 + 2HCl \quad \rightarrow \quad 2NaCl + H_2CO_3 \quad \rightarrow \quad 2NaCl + H_2O + CO_2$$

The alkali-metal carbonates are, in comparison with other carbonates, exceptionally stable to heat. The decomposition reaction $M_2CO_3 \rightarrow M_2O + CO_2$ does not occur readily, and the dissociation pressure of carbon dioxide in equilibrium with heated alkali-metal carbonates is quite small even when the salts are strongly heated. Thermal stability is least for Li_2CO_3 and increases down the group.

The alkali-metal nitrates are also stable up to quite high temperatures, but thermal decomposition to the metal nitrite does occur:

$$MNO_3 \quad \nrightarrow \quad MNO_2 + \tfrac{1}{2}O_2$$

Most other metal nitrates decompose quite readily on heating, to give oxides of nitrogen and the metal oxide.

In general, compounds of the alkali metals are soluble in water but only very sparingly soluble in nonaqueous solvents such as benzene.

The first member of Group I, lithium, resembles magnesium in Group II in some of its chemistry. This is an example of a *diagonal relationship*. Similar diagonal relationships exist between Be and Al, and B and Si:

Group I   Group II   Group III   Group IV

Li   Be   B   C

Na   Mg   Al   Si

Examples of the similarity between magnesium and lithium are:

1. both form nitrides, Li_3N and Mg_3N_2
2. both form carbides, Li_2C_2 and MgC_2
3. the amides give imides on heating: $2LiNH_2 \quad \nrightarrow \quad Li_2NH + NH_3$
4. the hydroxides decompose on heating to give oxides:

$$2LiOH \quad \nrightarrow \quad Li_2O + H_2O$$

5. the carbonates decompose comparatively readily on heating:

$$Li_2CO_3 \quad \nrightarrow \quad Li_2O + CO_2$$

These examples of similarities in the chemistry of lithium and magnesium are also examples of the differences between lithium and the other alkali metals. Diagonal relationships are sometimes explained in terms of similar charge densities on the ions, but these explanations are not very satisfactory.

Group IIA.   The Alkaline-Earth Elements

The alkaline-earth elements are listed in Table 2-4, which shows some of their more important properties. Four of the elements in this group, calcium, strontium, barium, and radium, are very closely related to one another in chemical properties. Radium differs from the others in being radioactive. As shown in the table, such properties as atomic radius and melting point vary in a regular manner from calcium to radium.

The elements beryllium and magnesium do not closely resemble the remaining elements in the group. Magnesium stands in relation to the others somewhat as does lithium to the rest of the alkali metals. Its hydroxide is markedly less soluble than those of calcium, barium, strontium, and radium, and its salts are more highly hydrated. Beryllium resembles aluminum, which is diagonally to the right of it in the periodic table, at least as much as it does the other members of Group IIA. The two ions Be^{2+} and Al^{3+} have very high charge-to-radius ratios, namely 6.4 and 6.0 unit charges per Ångström; Ca^{2+} has a ratio of only 2.0. In aqueous solution, an ion having a very high ratio of charge to radius will be close to the surrounding water molecules, and it can exert a strong electrostatic effect on them. One result is that the surrounding water molecules can more easily give up protons, so that the hydroxides exhibit acidic as well as basic properties; they are said to be *amphoteric*. Moreover, a number of the salts of Be and Al, such as $BeCl_2$ and $AlCl_3$, are covalent rather than ionic.

As we go down this group there is a steady decrease in electronegativity, which means an increase in electropositive character. The

Table 2-4   Properties of the Group-IIA Elements—the Alkaline-Earth Metals.

Property	Beryllium (Be)	Magnesium (Mg)	Calcium (Ca)	Strontium (Sr)	Barium (Ba)	Radium (Ra)
Atomic number	4	12	20	38	56	88
Electronic configuration	[He]2s^2	[Ne]3s^2	[Ar]4s^2	[Kr]5s^2	[Xe]6s^2	[Rn]7s^2
Atomic radius, Å	0.89	1.36	1.74	1.91	1.98	—
Ionic radius, Å	0.31	0.78	1.06	1.27	1.43	—
Electronegativity	1.47	1.23	1.04	0.99	0.97	—
First ionization energy, (kcal/mole)	215	176	141	131	120	121
Melting point, °C	1283	650	850	770	725	700
Standard oxidation potential at 25°C, volts	1.85	3.34	2.87	2.89	2.92	2.92

metals become more reactive, and the hydroxides become stronger bases.

The Group-II elements can form bonds in four different ways.

1. *They can lose two electrons to form an ionic bond*. As always, the second ionization potentials for these elements (corresponding to the process $M^+(g) \rightarrow M^{2+}(g) + e$) are greater than the first ionization potentials; in spite of this, however, it is energetically more favorable for the alkaline-earth metals to form $M^{2+}X^{2-}$ or $M^{2+}2X^-$ compounds (for example, $Ca^{2+}O^{2-}$, $Sr^{2+}2Cl^-$) than it is for them to form M^+X^- compounds. *Both* $M^{2+}2X^-$ and M^+X^- compounds are formed exothermically from the elements M and X; however, the disproportionation reaction $2M^+X^- \rightarrow M^{2+}2X^- + M$ is also exothermic, so that M^+ compounds cannot be prepared. The main reason for $M^{2+}2X^-$ being more stable than $2M^+X^-$ is that the M^{2+} ions (with their noble gas electronic configurations) are much smaller than the M^+ ions, and the large lattice energies of the $M^{2+}2X^-$ compounds more than cancel the extra ionization energy required to form M^{2+} ions from M^+ ions.

Group-II metals form ionic compounds with the more electronegative elements of Groups V, VI, and VII, and many of their oxyacid salts are ionic solids and contain M^{2+} ions. Examples of such compounds are MgO, $CaCO_3$, $SrCl_2$, and $BaSO_4$.

2. *They can share two electrons with separate atoms and form two covalent bonds*. In Group-II elements in the ground (lowest energy) states, all of the electrons are paired. In their ground states they are, therefore, unable to form ordinary covalent bonds. However, they are able to form covalent bonds after one of the two valence electrons in an s orbital has been excited into the orbital of next highest energy. For beryllium this involves excitation from the configuration $1s^2 2s^2$ to $1s^2 2s 2p$. Beryllium now has two unpaired electrons and can form two covalent bonds—for example, with chlorine to give beryllium chloride, $BeCl_2$. It is energetically more favorable for beryllium to form two equivalent hybrid sp orbitals in such compounds as $BeCl_2$ than it is for it to use unhybridized atomic orbitals. The combination of one s and one p orbital gives two sp hybrid orbitals with an angle of 180° between them. $BeCl_2$ is therefore a linear molecule.

The first member of the group, beryllium, forms the greatest number of covalent molecules. With increasing atomic weight the electronegativities of the atoms decrease, and this is reflected in an increasing ionic character in the compounds. This means that the elements are increasingly metallic in character.

3. *They can participate in a dative (or coordinate) bond.* When a Group-II element forms a covalent molecule of the type MX_2, it uses of all its valence electrons but does not use two empty p orbitals in the valence shell. These molecules can act as electron acceptors if they are mixed with molecules containing pairs of nonbonding electrons. An adduct or donor-acceptor compound is formed from an electron acceptor and an electron donor, a dative bond being formed between them:

Electron acceptor   Electron donor   Adduct

Since there are *two* empty p orbitals on beryllium in BeX_2 compounds, one molecule of BeX_2 can react with one or two molecules of an electron donor. The above is an example of a reaction with one molecule of donor in which the adduct still has an empty p orbital on the Be atom. An example of an adduct formed by addition of two donor molecules is furnished by the molecule formed from $BeCl_2$ and two molecules of diethyl ether, $C_2H_5OC_2H_5$ (cf. p. 215; for the time being it is enough to regard this as a water molecule in which the two H atoms have been replaced by organic groups). The adduct is

There are now no empty orbitals on the Be atom.

The hybridization of the beryllium atom is altered when electrons are accepted. In the 1 : 1 compounds such as $BeCl_2 \cdot NH_3$, the beryllium atom adopts sp^2 hybridization and the two chlorine atoms and the beryllium and nitrogen atom are all in one plane.

In the $1:2$ compounds such as $BeCl_2 \cdot 2(C_2H_5)_2O$, the beryllium atom is sp^3 hybridized and the two chlorine atoms and the two oxygen atoms are at the corners of a tetrahedron with the beryllium atom at the center.

Beryllium chloride, $BeCl_2$, is a solid at room temperature, and is polymerized, as shown on p. 11; the structure is held together by dative bonds.

4. *They can participate in three-center bonding.* Another consequence of the fact that BeX_2 compounds have empty low-energy p orbitals is the formation of three-center bonds, which were considered in Chapter 1. These are formed only (for example, in hydrides) when a lack of electrons makes dative bonding impossible. Examples of three-center bond compounds are BeH_2 and MgH_2. BeH_2 is a polymerized solid of structure

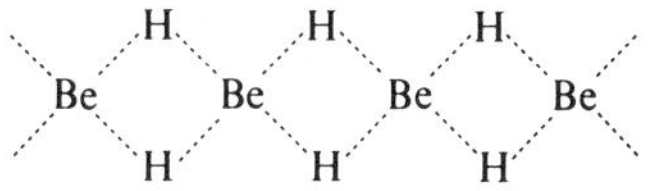

Although the BeH_2 polymer resembles the $BeCl_2$ polymer in structure, the bonding is different. In BeH_2 there are not enough electrons present for us to write

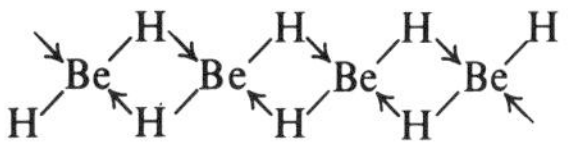

because all the Be and H valence electrons are already used in forming BeH_2. Instead, in $(BeH_2)_n$ only *one* pair of electrons holds each

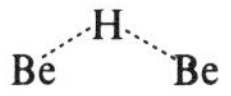

system together.

General Chemistry of Group II

As in Group I, the first member of the group, beryllium, differs in its chemistry from the other elements in the group, which are all closely similar; in some respects, beryllium resembles its diagonal neighbor, aluminum.

Oxides and hydroxides. Beryllium oxide, BeO, is amphoteric and can react as an acid or a base.

As a base

$$BeO + 2H_{aq}^+ \quad \rightarrow \quad Be_{aq}^{2+} + H_2O$$

As an acid

$$BeO + 2OH^- + H_2O \rightarrow Be(OH)_4^{2-}$$

MgO, CaO, SrO, BaO, and RaO have only basic properties.

$Be(OH)_2$ and $Mg(OH)_2$ are weak bases, whereas the other hydroxides are strong. If we consider the processes

$$Be_{aq}^{2+} + 2H_2O \rightleftharpoons Be(OH)_2 + 2H_{aq}^+$$
$$Ca_{aq}^{2+} + 2H_2O \rightleftharpoons Ca(OH)_2 + 2H_{aq}^+$$

the equilibrium for Be^{2+} (and Mg^{2+}) lies to the right, while that for Ca^{2+} (and Sr^{2+}, Ba^{2+}, and Ra^{2+}) lies to the left. In other words, $Be(OH)_2$ is not dissociated to a great extent in water, whereas $Ca(OH)_2$ is. Another result of this difference in behavior is that salts of beryllium and magnesium give acidic solutions when dissolved in water, whereas salts of calcium and the rest of the alkaline-earth elements give neutral aqueous solutions.

The oxides react reversibly with water:

$$MO + H_2O \rightleftharpoons M(OH)_2$$

Heating the hydroxide drives off water to give back the oxide. The solubilities of the hydroxides increase down Group II.

Group-II elements dissolve in liquid ammonia (like the alkali metals) to give blue solutions containing solvated electrons.

Carbonates. The carbonates of the Group-II elements, for example, $CaCO_3$, are insoluble in water and may be prepared by bubbling carbon dioxide gas through an aqueous solution of a Group-II metal hydroxide or soluble salt:

$$CO_2 + H_2O \rightarrow H_2CO_3$$
$$M_{aq}^{2+} + H_2CO_3 \rightarrow MCO_3 + 2H^+$$

The carbonates dissolve in acid to give solutions of bicarbonates; if excess acid is added, the bicarbonate ion is decomposed to give carbon dioxide gas:

$$2MCO_3 + 2H^+ \rightarrow M_{aq}^{2+} + M(HCO_3)_2$$
$$2MCO_3 + 4H^+ \rightarrow 2M_{aq}^{2+} + 2CO_2 + 2H_2O$$

Group-II bicarbonates, unlike Group-I bicarbonates, cannot be isolated as solids because they decompose. Their solutions also decompose on heating:

$$M(HCO_3)_2 \rightarrow MCO_3 + CO_2 + H_2O$$

Group IIIA.
Boron, Aluminum,
Gallium, Indium,
and Thallium

Some properties of the five elements belonging to Group IIIA of the periodic table are shown in Table 2-5. By and large these elements are not so strongly electropositive as the ones in Groups IA and IIA. They show a stronger tendency to form covalent compounds, in which they show a valency of 3. By forming dative bonds, in which they act as acceptors, the elements can exhibit higher covalencies, the maximum being 4 in the case of boron and 6 for the others. Thus, boron can form the ion BF_4^-, whereas aluminum can form the six-covalent ion AlF_6^{3-}.

As we pass down the group, the electropositive character increases, as usual. Thus boron forms no ordinary salts, while aluminum forms hydrated salts and its hydroxide has amphoteric properties. Gallium, indium, and thallium form normal salts. We also find, on passing down the table, an increasing tendency to form univalent ions; thallium, for example, forms the stable ion Tl^+.

Reference to the periodic table shows that, in passing to the right from Group II to Group III, all the transition elements and the lanthanides appear between these groups, corresponding to the filling of d and f orbitals, respectively. The first two elements in Group III, boron and aluminum, contain one extra electron compared to the first two elements in Group II, beryllium and magnesium. However, gallium

Table 2-5 Properties of the Group-IIIA Elements.

Property	Boron (B)	Aluminum (Al)	Gallium (Ga)	Indium (In)	Thallium (Tl)
Atomic number	5	13	31	49	81
Electronic configuration	$[He]2s^22p$	$[Ne]3s^23p$	$[Ar]3d^{10}4s^24p$	$[Kr]4d^{10}5s^25p$	$[Xe]4f^{14}5d^{10}6s^26p$
Atomic radius, Å	0.80	1.25	1.25	1.50	1.55
Ionic radius, M^{3+}, Å	(0.20)	0.51	0.62	0.81	0.95
Electronegativity	2.01	1.47	1.82	1.49	1.44
First ionization energy, (kcal/mole)	191	139	138	133	141
Melting point, °C	2030	660	30	156	303
Standard oxidation potential at 25°C, ε^0, volts $(M(s) \rightarrow M^{3+}(aq) + 3e)$	—	1.66	0.53	0.34	−0.72

and indium each contain 11 extra electrons compared to calcium and strontium, while thallium contains 25 more electrons than barium. These differences are responsible for the irregularities found in some properties of Group-III elements (in contrast to the smooth gradation of properties found in Group II), as illustrated in Table 2-5; note in particular the electronegativities, and the first ionization potentials.

Group-III elements form bonds in the following ways.

1. *They can lose three electrons and form ionic bonds.* The first element in the group, boron, never behaves in this way under chemical conditions, but the four other elements all form compounds containing M^{3+} ions. However, none of the compounds that are loosely considered as containing M^{3+} ions have purely ionic bonding. For instance, many aluminum salts are hydrated and contain the $Al(H_2O)_6^{3+}$ cation, with some degree of covalent bonding between the oxygen atoms of the water molecules and the Al^{3+} ion. Aluminum fluoride, AlF_3, would be expected to be one of the most ionic of solids containing M^{3+} cations (because of the large electronegativity difference between Al (1.5) and F (4.1)), yet recent measurements indicate that the bond between Al and F in AlF_3 is only about 2/3 ionic and 1/3 covalent.

This tendency for the bonding to be covalent can be related to the small sizes of the M^{3+} ions and to their high charges—in other words, to their high charge-to-radius ratios. As a result, electrons are attracted into the empty s and p orbitals, and this favors covalent bond formation. This effect is reflected in the large amounts of energy required to remove all three valence electrons from the neutral atoms. Thus for aluminum this energy, equal to the sum of the first three ionization energies, is

$$138 + 434 + 658 = 1230 \text{ kcal/mole.}$$

2. *They can form three covalent bonds.* In their ground states (lowest energy states), these elements have only one unpaired electron (the valence electron in a p orbital) and, therefore, can form only one ordinary covalent bond. No compounds of this type exist at normal temperatures; instead, the elements form three covalent bonds. In order to form three bonds, one s electron must first be promoted to a p orbital to produce three valence electrons with unpaired spins. The energy released on forming the two extra bonds must in every case exceed the energy required to promote one electron and form sp^2-hybrid orbitals.

All the MX_3 compounds are planar, corresponding to sp^2 hybridization of the central atom with $120°$ between the bonds:

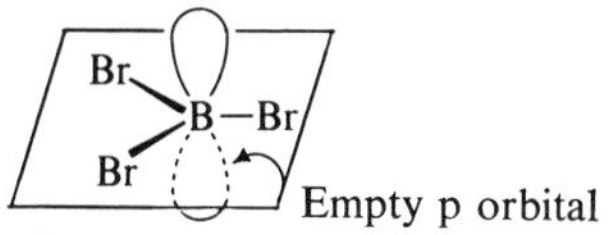

Empty p orbital

The number of simple MX_3 molecules known is rather limited. Such molecules are very powerful electron acceptors, because they possess an empty p orbital; this leads to ready formation of addition compounds with electron donors.

In many cases, the MX_3 molecule can act as an electron donor as well as an acceptor, and this leads either to the formation of dimers or to the formation of internal donor-acceptor bonds. An example of dimer formation is

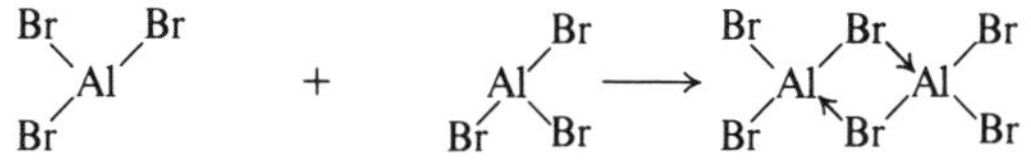

$AlBr_3$ is dimerized in the solid state and in many organic solvents. In the vapor there is considerable dissociation into monomers, which are planar:

$$Al_2Br_6 \;\rightleftharpoons\; 2AlBr_3$$

The extent of the dissociation increases with rise in temperature. Dimerization of trihalides occurs for Al, Ga, and In trihalides.

The boron trihalides do not form dimers; instead there is internal donation of electron density from the halogen atoms to the empty p orbital of boron:

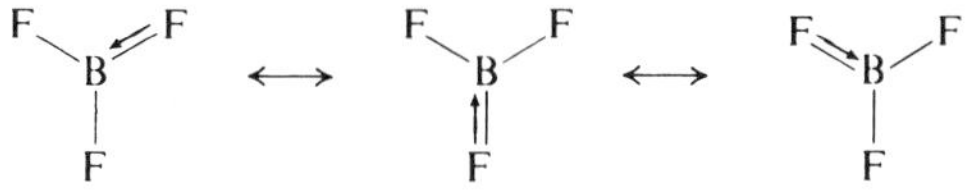

This leads to some double bonding between fluorine and boron.

In the case of BH_3 (which cannot be isolated), dimerization also occurs; but it occurs by the formation of three-centered bonds, which make use of the empty p orbital of boron, as discussed on p. 15.

Donor-acceptor bond formation would be impossible here because there are no nonbonding electrons in BH_3. The dimer of BH_3, B_2H_6, is a well-known example of multicenter bonding.

In B_2H_6, Al_2Cl_6, and similar compounds, the boron and aluminum atoms are sp^3-hybridized, in contrast to the monomers where the centered atom is sp^2-hybridized. This means that the dimers are non-planar molecules.

3. *They can form two covalent bonds and an ionic bond at the same time.* Thallium alone forms a series of compounds of the general type $TlR_2^+X^-$, which contains linear $[R–Tl–R]^+$ ions: R is an organic radical and X a halogen. In these ions, thallium has lost one valence electron by ionization and has used the remaining two valence electrons to form covalent bonds with organic groups. Since these ions are linear, thallium must use sp-hybrid orbitals to form the covalent bonds.

4. *They can lose one electron to form ionic bonds.* Some Group-III elements can form both M^{3+} and M^+ ions; in other words, they have a variable oxidation state. Compared with the M^{3+} ions, the M^+ ions become increasingly favored as Group III is descended. No B^+ or Al^+ compounds are known; however, Ga^+ and In^+ are known in solid compounds but not in solution, while Tl^+ has an extensive chemistry in both solid compounds and in solution.

This ability of nontransition elements to exhibit variable oxidation states involves the *inert-pair effect* (cf. p. 13); two valence electrons do not participate in bonding in these lower-oxidation-state compounds. It occurs only among the heavier elements of Group III, Group IV, and Group V—for instance, in TlCl, $PbCl_2$, and $SbCl_3$. Ga^+ and In^+ compounds can be prepared as solids, for example $GaCl_2$ (which should be written as $Ga^+ GaCl_4^-$) and InCl. However, the Ga^+ and In^+ ions are not stable in aqueous solution and they disproportionate (sometimes slowly) to give metal and Ga^{3+} or In^{3+}:

$$3Ga^+(aq) \rightarrow 2Ga + Ga^{3+}(aq)$$

The Tl^+ ion is more stable; it sometimes resembles Ag^+ and sometimes K^+ and Rb^+ in its properties.

The Elements   Impure boron can be obtained as an amorphous powder by reducing the oxide B_2O_3 with magnesium.

$$B_2O_3 + 3Mg \rightarrow 2B + 3MgO$$

Pure crystalline boron can be prepared by reducing BBr_3 vapor with hydrogen on an electrically heated tungsten filament:

$$2BBr_3 + 3H_2 \;\rightarrow\; 2B + 6HBr$$

Aluminum is prepared industrially by the electrolytic reduction of Al_2O_3 dissolved in molten Na_3AlF_6 (which is an electrical conductor), using carbon electrodes. The electrode processes are:

At the cathode

$$Al^{3+} + 3e \;\rightarrow\; Al$$

At the anode

$$O^{2-} \;\rightarrow\; \tfrac{1}{2}O_2 + 2e$$

Since $\varepsilon^0 = +1.66$ volts for $Al(s) \rightarrow Al^{3+}(aq) + 3e$, hydrogen and not aluminum is liberated if aqueous solutions of aluminum salts are electrolyzed.

Aluminum dissolves slowly in acids

$$Al + 3H_{aq}^+ \;\rightarrow\; Al_{aq}^{3+} + \tfrac{3}{2}H_2$$

and in alkalis

$$Al + OH^- + 3H_2O \;\rightarrow\; Al(OH)_4^- + \tfrac{3}{2}H_2$$

Aluminum is normally less reactive than its oxidation potential would suggest, because it is covered with a thin layer of oxide. If this is destroyed, by amalgamation with mercury, for example, aluminum reacts readily with oxygen, water, and so forth.

Group III Halides

Boron trifluoride, BF_3. This is the most important of the boron trihalides, and it is prepared by treating boric oxide with HF and heating:

$$B_2O_3 + 6HF \;\rightarrow\; 2BF_3 + 3H_2O$$

In practice, HF itself is not used, but is generated in the reaction vessel, for example by heating CaF_2 with H_2SO_4:

$$B_2O_3 + 3CaF_2 + 3H_2SO_4 \;\rightarrow\; 2BF_3 + 3CaSO_4 + 3H_2O$$

BF_3 is a gas (bp $-101°C$), but it is often used in the form of its adduct with diethyl ether, $F_3B \leftarrow O(C_2H_5)_2$, which is a liquid at room temperature. It reacts vigorously with water and fumes in moist air because of the formation of an adduct with water:

$$BF_3 + H_2O \;\rightarrow\; F_3B{\leftarrow}OH_2$$

It undergoes hydrolysis to yield BF_4^- and $B(OH)_3$:

$$4BF_3 + 3H_2O \rightleftharpoons B(OH)_3 + 3BF_4^- + H_3O^+$$

$$BF_3 + 3H_2O \rightleftharpoons B(OH)_3 + 3HF$$

BF_3 is important as the starting point for the preparation of many boron compounds, particularly the boranes:

$$3NaBH_4 + 4BF_3 \rightarrow 3NaBF_4 + 2B_2H_6$$

It is a powerful electron acceptor and forms a large number of adducts with electron donors. An example of this is the reaction with fluoride ion:

$$BF_3 + F^- \rightarrow BF_4^-$$

BF_4^- is isoelectronic with CF_4 and has a tetrahedral arrangement of fluorine atoms around the central boron atom:

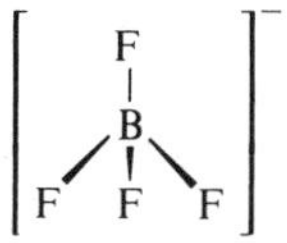

Salts of BF_4^- are known; they are sometimes isomorphous with perchlorates, $M^+ClO_4^-$. The acid $H_3O^+BF_4^-$, fluoroboric acid, which is also known, is a strong acid, completely dissociated in water.

The complex ions BCl_4^-, BBr_4^-, and BI_4^- are also known, but they are increasingly unstable because of crowding of the large halogen atoms round the rather small boron atom.

Boron trichloride, BCl_3. This gas (bp 12°C) can be prepared directly from the elements.

$$2B + 3Cl_2 \xrightarrow{\text{heat}} 2BCl_3$$

It is the source of the lower chlorides of boron. If BCl_3 vapor is passed through a silent discharge and the product collected below 0°C, a colorless liquid is obtained; this is B_2Cl_4. The structure of B_2Cl_4 is

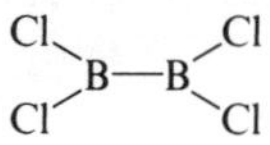

This substance is probably obtained in the discharge by combination of two BCl_2 radicals. Derivatives of it can be obtained, for example

$$\begin{array}{c}Cl\\ \\ Cl\end{array}\!\!>\!\!B\!\!-\!\!B\!\!<\!\!\begin{array}{c}Cl\\ \\ Cl\end{array} + 4H_2O \rightarrow \begin{array}{c}HO\\ \\ HO\end{array}\!\!>\!\!B\!\!-\!\!B\!\!<\!\!\begin{array}{c}OH\\ \\ OH\end{array} + 4\,HCl$$

If B_2Cl_4 is allowed to warm up above $0°C$, decomposition occurs and two other chlorides, B_4Cl_4 and B_8Cl_8, can be isolated from the products of the reactions.

Complex halide ions.   We have already seen that BF_3 reacts with F^- to give the complex ion BF_4^- and that the stability of the BX_4^- ions depends upon the halogen concerned. If BF_4^- is treated with excess of F^-, one does *not* obtain higher complexes, for example BF_5^{2-} or BF_6^{3-}. The maximum coordination number of boron, like all the first-row elements from Li to F, is 4; boron in BF_3 has only one empty orbital of low energy, and this is filled when BF_4^- is formed.

When AlF_3 is dissolved in fluoride solutions, however, AlF_4^-, AlF_5^{2-}, and AlF_6^{3-} are all formed. Aluminum and the rest of the Group-III elements (like all second-row elements and heavier elements) are not restricted to a maximum coordination number of 4. There are two reasons for this. First, Al is a larger atom than B and there is more room for atoms to be attached to Al than to B. Second, aluminum in AlX_3 compounds has more than one empty orbital of low energy— it has one empty 3p orbital of lowest energy and, in addition, five empty 3d orbitals. Similarly, gallium has empty 4d orbitals, indium 5d, and thallium 6d. These empty d orbitals are able to accept electrons from electron donors. For steric and other reasons, the maximum coordination number of the elements from Al to Tl is 6. AlF_6^{3-} is formed by the reaction

$$AlF_3 + 3F^- \rightarrow AlF_6^{3-}$$

and three dative bonds and three ordinary covalent bonds hold the complex together (though in reality all six bonds between Al and F are exactly the same). The complex ion is octahedral in shape

and the aluminum atom is sp^3d^2-hybridized.

The importance of spatial or *steric* factors in determining the maximum coordination number of a particular element is well illustrated by the halogen complexes of Group-III elements. AlX_4^- ions are known for $X = F, Cl, Br,$ and I, but AlX_5^{2-} and AlX_6^{3-} ions are known only for $X = F$, the smallest of the halogen atoms.

As the size of the Group-III elements increases, it is possible to get more of the larger halogen atoms around the central atoms. Gallium and indium are both able to form MF_6^{3-}, MCl_6^{3-}, and MBr_6^{3-} ions, but not MI_6^{3-}, while the largest of the Group-III atoms, thallium, can even form the TlI_6^{3-} ion.

Aqueous Solutions of Group-III Compounds

Important aspects of the chemistry of the elements of Group III are revealed when we consider the behavior of their salts in aqueous solution. When these salts are dissolved, the M^{3+} ions become strongly hydrated, being surrounded by a group of water molecules; the hydrated ions may be represented as $M^{3+}(H_2O)_n$, when n, usually 6, is the number of water molecules packed around the ion. However, these ions are hydrolyzed in solution, successively splitting off protons according to the following equations:

$$M(H_2O)_n^{3+} \rightleftharpoons M(H_2O)_{n-1}(OH)^{2+} + H^+ \tag{1}$$

$$M(H_2O)_{n-1}(OH)^{2+} \rightleftharpoons M(H_2O)_{n-2}(OH)_2^+ + H^+ \tag{2}$$

$$M(H_2O)_{n-2}(OH)_2^+ \rightleftharpoons M(H_2O)_{n-3}(OH)_3 + H^+ \tag{3}$$

$$M(H_2O)_{n-3}(OH)_3 \rightleftharpoons M(H_2O)_{n-4}(OH)_4^- + H^+ \tag{4}$$

and so on. The magnitudes of the equilibrium constants for these reactions determine whether the elements have metallic or nonmetallic characteristics.

In the case of boron compounds, the hydrolysis is very extensive, the equilibrium constants for reactions 1 to 3 being very large. In other words, if we dissolve a compound like BCl_3 in water, very few $B(H_2O)_n^{3+}$ ions are present; three protons are split off, and $B(OH)_3$ (which is surrounded by a layer of water molecules) is produced. The over-all reaction may be written as

$$BCl_3 + 3H_2O \rightleftharpoons B(OH)_3 + 3HCl$$

The solution is acidic as a result of the HCl produced. Reaction 4, *viz.*

$$B(OH)_3 + H_2O \rightleftharpoons B(OH)_4^- + H^+$$

also occurs to a small extent, so that $B(OH)_3$ is a weakly acidic substance. Thus, the oxide and hydroxide of boron are acidic rather than basic in properties, and boron is rather nonmetallic.

These processes occur to a smaller extent with aluminum salts. If aluminum chloride, $AlCl_3$, is added to water, reaction 1 occurs to some extent and the solution contains both $Al(H_2O)_6^{3+}$ and $Al(H_2O)_5OH^{2+}$ ions:

$$Al(H_2O)_6^{3+} \rightleftharpoons Al(H_2O)_5OH^{2+} + H^+$$

Addition of acid reverses this process so that strongly acid solutions contain very little $Al(H_2O)_5OH^{2+}$. Addition of alkali, by the removal of H^+, produces $Al(H_2O)_4(OH)_2^+$ and $Al(H_2O)_3(OH)_3$ and even small amounts of $Al(H_2O)_2(OH)_4^-$. However, the equilibrium constants for reactions 2 to 4, which produce these species, are very small—much smaller than with boron. Aluminum is, therefore, more metallic than boron, and its oxide is less acidic. The oxide is described as *amphoteric*, since it has both acidic and basic properties; it can react to an appreciable extent with acids and with bases.

This tendency for reactions (1) to (4) to occur decreases steadily as we go down the group. When thallium trichloride, $TlCl_3$, is added to water, for example, there is some hydrolysis (reaction 1) to form $Tl(H_2O)_5OH^{2+}$. Addition of alkali leads to $Tl(OH)_3$ (or Tl_2O_3), but $Tl(OH)_4^-$ cannot be produced. In other words, thallium trioxide cannot react with alkali and is a basic oxide.

Oxides, Hydroxides, and Oxyacids

$B(OH)_3$, orthoboric acid, is a molecule in which the bonds emanating from the boron atom lie in a plane

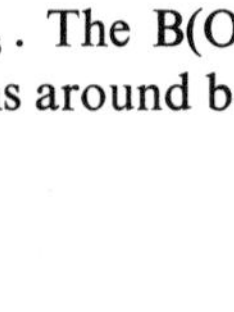

with boron using sp^2-hybrid orbitals for bonding and having an empty 2p orbital, as in BF_3. The $B(OH)_4^-$ anion has a tetrahedral arrangement of oxygen atoms around boron, with one OH^- attached by a dative bond:

There is no difference between the four B–O bonds. Solid orthoboric acid has a layer structure in which $B(OH)_3$ molecules are hydrogen bonded together into very large planar sheets, while separate sheets are only weakly attached to other sheets (by van der Waals forces):

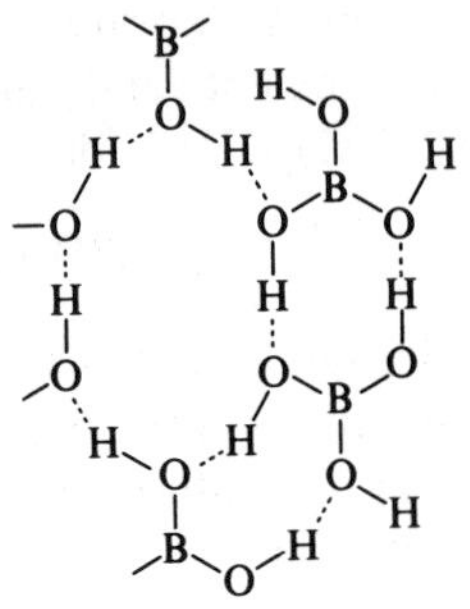

One result of such a structure is that orthoboric acid is a good lubricant, the sheets being easily separated from one another.

When solid $B(OH)_3$ is heated, metaboric acid is produced as an intermediate before the oxide is obtained:

$$6B(OH)_3 \underset{H_2O}{\overset{Heat}{\rightleftharpoons}} 2(HBO_2)_3 \underset{H_2O}{\overset{Heat}{\rightleftharpoons}} 3B_2O_3$$

| Orthoboric acid | Metaboric acid | Boric oxide |

Metaboric acid has a ring structure obtained by eliminating the elements of water from orthoboric acid:

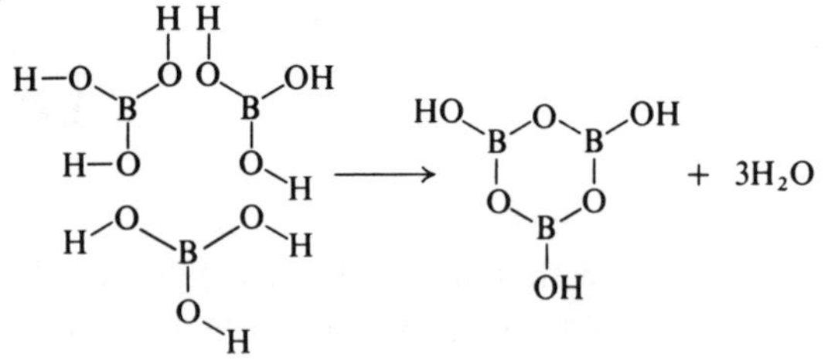

Salts of both orthoboric acid (for example, $La^{3+}BO_3^{3-}$) and metaboric acid (for example, $Na_3B_3O_6$) are known, but most known borates have more complex anions, which can be considered to be formed by elimination of water from $B(OH)_3$ or $B(OH)_4^-$. Some examples are:

Pyroborates (e.g. $Mg_2B_2O_5$)

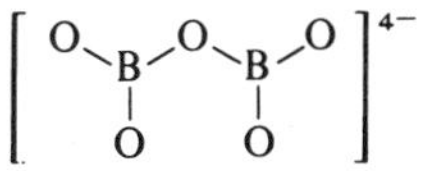

$$\left[\begin{array}{c} O \diagdown_{B} \diagup^{O} \diagdown_{B} \diagup^{O} \\ | \qquad | \\ O \qquad O \end{array} \right]^{4-}$$

Chain borates (also called metaborates) (e.g. CaB_2O_4)

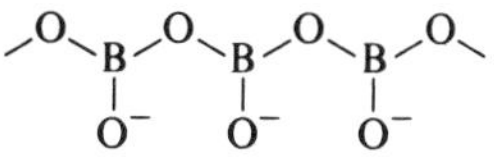

$$\diagup^{O} \diagdown_{B} \diagup^{O} \diagdown_{B} \diagup^{O} \diagdown_{B} \diagup^{O} \diagdown$$
$$| \qquad | \qquad |$$
$$O^- \qquad O^- \qquad O^-$$

Borax, $Na_2[B_4O_5(OH)_4] \cdot 8H_2O$, a common boron compound, contains an anion which can be visualized as being produced from $2B(OH)_3 + 2B(OH)_4^-$ by elimination of five molecules of water:

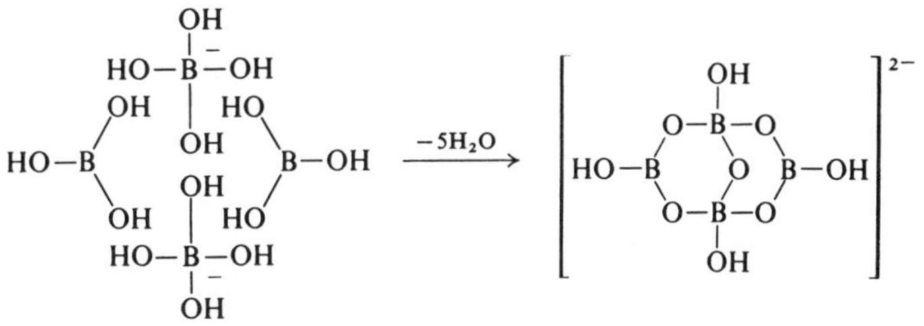

Because the borax anion contains two sp^3 hybridized boron atoms, the anion is not planar. These are examples of condensed oxyacid anions.

The equilibrium constant for the reaction

$$Al(H_2O)_6^{3+} \rightleftharpoons Al(H_2O)_5OH^{2+} + H^+$$

is about 1×10^{-5}, and $Al(H_2O)_6^{3+}$ is, therefore, of similar acid strength to acetic acid ($K_a = 1.86 \times 10^{-5}$). If alkali is added to Al_{aq}^{3+} solutions, $Al(OH)_3$ (or hydrated Al_2O_3) is precipitated; it is then redissolved if excess OH^- is added to form an aluminate solution containing $Al(OH)_4^-$. Well-defined condensed aluminates corresponding to the borates are not known, though condensed aluminates have been detected in solution, for example $Al_{13}(OH)_{32}^{7+}$.

Group-III Hydrides

Boron forms a great variety of hydrides (called boranes) and hydride anions (called boronates); aluminum forms one polymeric hydride and one hydride anion. Gallium, indium, and thallium form either very unstable hydrides and hydride anions or none at all.

Diborane, B_2H_6, is an extremely reactive compound that is hydrolyzed by water,

$$B_2H_6 + 6H_2O \quad \rightarrow \quad 2B(OH)_3 + 6H_2$$

and reacts even more violently with alkali. It burns readily in air,

$$B_2H_6 + 3O_2 \quad \rightarrow \quad B_2O_3 + 3H_2O$$

and reacts violently with halogens to given boron trihalides:

$$B_2H_6 + 6X_2 \quad \rightarrow \quad 2BX_3 + 6HX$$

Since it is electron deficient, it is particularly sensitive to attack by electron donors; for example

$$B_2H_6 + 2CO \quad \rightarrow \quad 2H_3B \leftarrow CO$$

See Chapter 1 for a discussion of the structure of diborane.

Aluminum hydrides are prepared as follows:

$$4LiH + AlCl_3 \xrightarrow{\text{ether}} 3LiCl + LiAlH_4$$
$$3LiAlH_4 + AlCl_3 \longrightarrow 3LiCl + 4[AlH_3]$$

The product depends on the initial proportions of LiH and $AlCl_3$.

Lithium aluminum hydride, $LiAlH_4$, is an important reducing agent in preparative chemistry. It is soluble in ether, and in inorganic chemistry it is used to prepare hydrides of other elements; for example

$$LiAlH_4 + SiCl_4 \quad \rightarrow \quad LiCl + AlCl_3 + SiH_4$$

Borazine and Related B–N Compounds

An interesting compound of boron is borazine, whose structure is

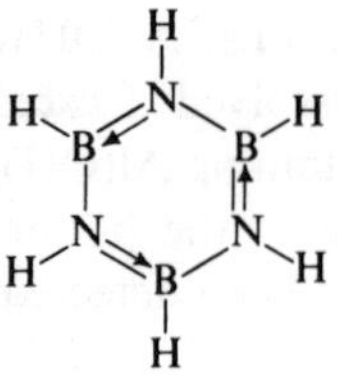

When ammonium chloride, NH_4Cl, and boron trichloride, BCl_3, are heated together in chlorobenzene solution, a ring compound of structure

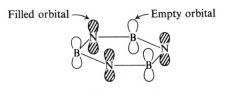

is formed. If this compound is heated with sodium borohydride, $NaBH_4$, *borazine* is produced:

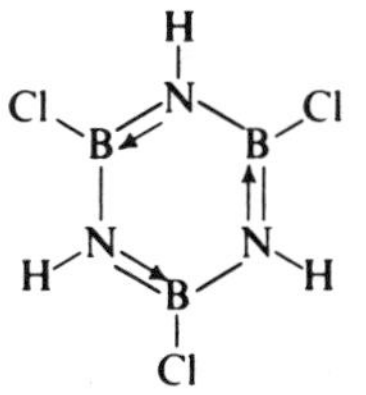

Borazine is isoelectronic with benzene, and the compounds resemble each other in some of their properties. Like benzene, borazine is a planar molecule, and both the boron and nitrogen atoms must be sp^2 hybridized. All the B–N distances are the same and the distance is somewhat less than that for a single B–N bond, because there is some delocalization of π electrons. The structure can be represented in terms of the following resonance states:

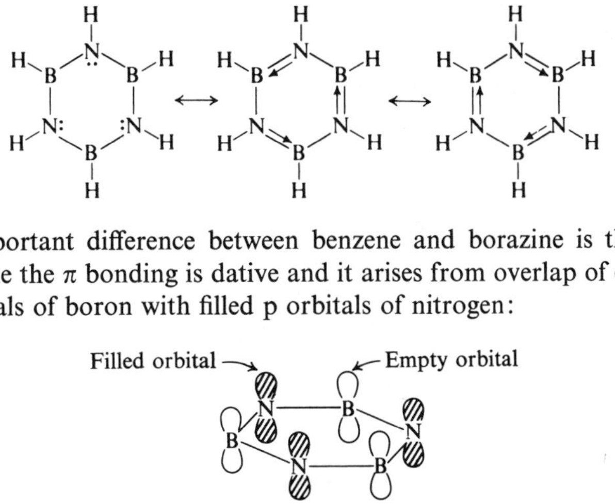

An important difference between benzene and borazine is that in borazine the π bonding is dative and it arises from overlap of empty p orbitals of boron with filled p orbitals of nitrogen:

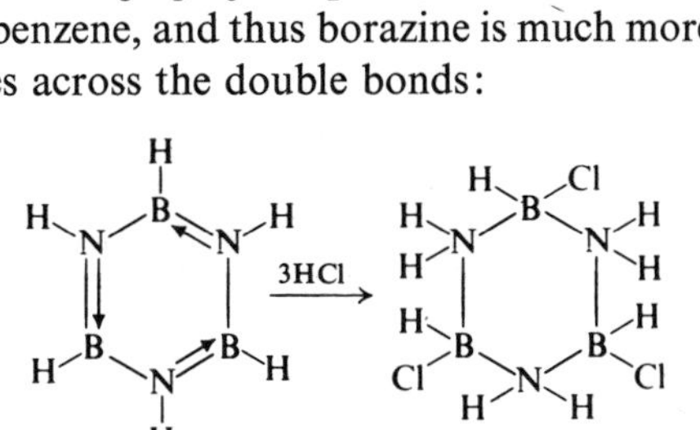

Filled orbital →   ← Empty orbital

The B–N bonds in $B_3N_3H_6$ are polar, in contrast to the nonpolar C–C bonds in benzene, and thus borazine is much more ready to add polar molecules across the double bonds:

3HCl

The addition compounds no longer have planar B_3N_3 skeletons because boron and nitrogen are now sp^3 hybridized.

Group IVA.
Carbon, Silicon,
Germanium, Tin,
and Lead

Some of the characteristics of the five elements belonging to Group IVA are shown in Table 2-6. A valency of 4 is exhibited by all five elements in Group IV. As the group is descended, there is a general change from nonmetallic to metallic properties, but this is not a smooth trend, as is illustrated by the electronegativities listed in Table 2-6.

Table 2-6 Properties of the Group-IVA Elements.

	Carbon (C)	Silicon (Si)	Germanium (Ge)	Tin (Sn)	Lead (Pb)
Electronic configuration	$[He]2s^22p^2$	$[Ne]3s^23p^2$	$[Ar]3d^{10}4s^24p^2$	$[Kr]4d^{10}5s^25p^2$	$[Xe]4f^{14}6s^26p^2$
Electronegativity	2.50	1.74	2.02	1.72	1.55
M–H bond dissociation energy, kcal/mole	99	75	74	71	42
M–M bond dissociation energy, kcal/mole	83	53	40	37	14

The fact that the element carbon occurs in Group IV means that a large proportion of descriptive chemistry is related to this group, an enormous number of carbon compounds being known. In this chapter, however, the chemistry of carbon will be considered only in an "inorganic" context, in relation to the chemistry of the other elements of the group.

The Group-IV elements form compounds in the following ways.

1. *They can form four covalent bonds to four other atoms.* This is the most usual way in which Group-IV elements form compounds, and all five members of the group do so. Examples of such compounds are: CH_4, SiF_4, $GeBr_4$, $SnCl_4$, and $PbCl_4$.

Since the elements in their ground states (the lowest energy states) have only two unpaired electrons, promotion of an s electron to a p orbital is necessary before the atoms can be tetracovalent.

$$s^2p^2 \rightarrow s^1p^3$$

2 unpaired   4 unpaired
electron spins   electron spins

The atoms use sp^3-hybrid orbitals in covalent bonding, and the MX_4 compounds are tetrahedral in shape.

When dissimilar atoms are present, as in CH_3Cl, there are small distortions from a perfectly regular tetrahedral arrangement of atoms.

Because of the different electronegativities of the Group-IVA elements, the polarity of bonds in these MX_4 compounds will be different for different elements. If we consider the hydrides, MH_4, where hydrogen has an electronegativity of 2.1, we find that the C–H bonds in CH_4 should be slightly polarized in the direction $\overset{\longleftarrow +}{C{\rule{1.2em}{0.4pt}}H}$, that Si–H bonds in SiH_4 should be slightly polarized in the direction $\overset{+\longrightarrow}{Si{\rule{1.2em}{0.4pt}}H}$, while the Ge–H bonds in GeH_4 should be practically nonpolar. Regardless of the polarity of the bonds, however, all of these MX_4 compounds must have zero dipole moments for reasons of symmetry.

One important difference between carbon and the other elements of the group can be seen in the MX_4 compounds. Carbon in CX_4 compounds (CH_4, CCl_4, and so forth) is covalently saturated, which means that it has neither any empty orbitals of low energy (as boron has in BX_3 compounds) nor any nonbonding pairs of valence-shell electrons (as nitrogen has in NX_3 compounds). The result is that carbon in CX_4 compounds can neither donate nor accept electron pairs from other molecules. This makes CX_4 compounds resistant to chemical attack by electron acceptors (or *electrophiles* as they are sometimes called) and electron donors (or *nucleophiles*), and this resistance gives carbon compounds great stability. Many reactions of carbon compounds are very slow, involving very large activation energies, while corresponding reactions for silver, germanium, tin, and lead compounds are often very fast and involve small activation energies.

Carbon is the only Group-IV element that is covalently saturated in its MX_4 compounds. Si, Ge, Sn, and Pb all have empty d orbitals of reasonably low energy in such compounds; for example, silicon has empty 3d orbitals in $SiCl_4$. This means that the silicon atom in SiX_4 can act as an electron acceptor, and compounds of the SiX_4 type are readily attacked by electron donors.

Carbon, like all the elements in the first short period, is therefore restricted to a coordination number of 4, while the heavier Group-IV elements can increase their coordination number to 6 by making use of d orbitals. For example

$$SnCl_4 + 2Cl^- \rightarrow SnCl_6^{2-}$$

<table>
<tr><td>sp³ hybridized;
coordination
number = 4</td><td>sp³d² hybridized;
coordination
number = 6</td></tr>
</table>

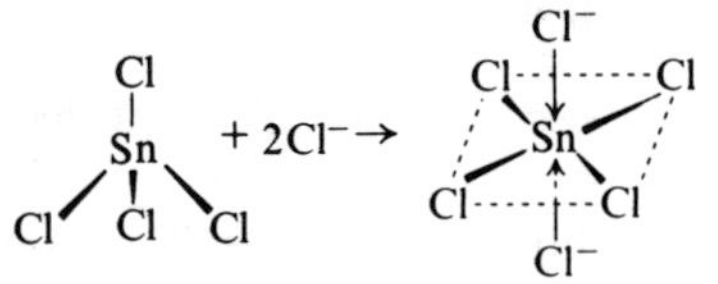

Tetrahedral   Octahedral

Similar reactions occur with pyridine, of structure

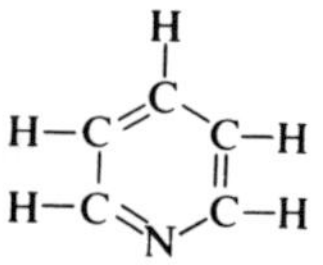

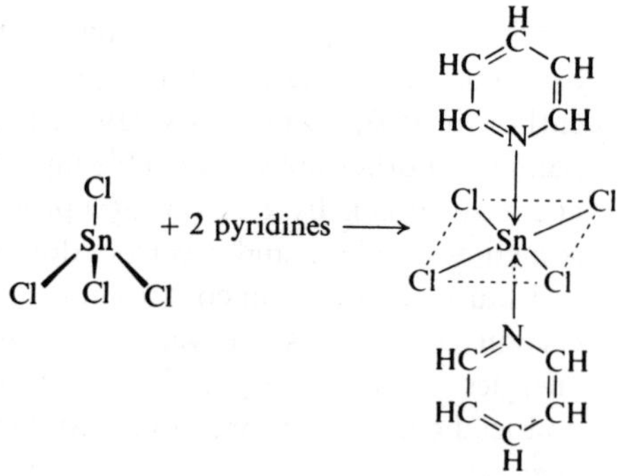

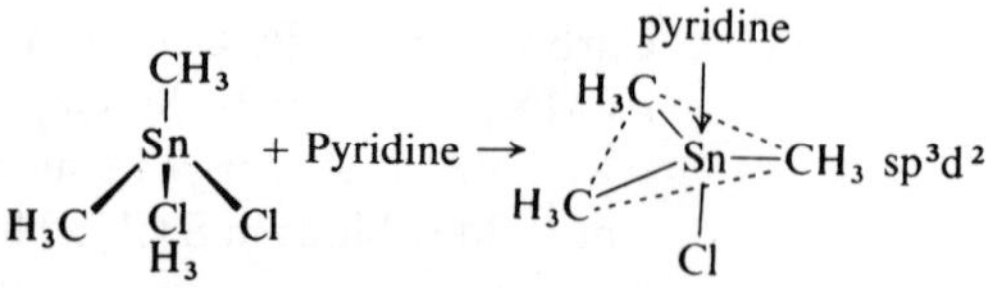

+ 2 pyridines $\longrightarrow$

+ Pyridine $\rightarrow$ sp³d²

Coordination   Coordination
number = 4   number = 5

Another consequence of these empty d orbitals in MX_4 compounds formed by silicon and other Group-IV elements is that there is the possibility of double bonding. In SiF_4, fluorine can act as an electron donor while silicon can accept electrons, so that double bonding occurs through the overlap of the empty d orbitals of silicon with the filled p orbitals of fluorine. This is an example of *intramolecular* dative π bonding:

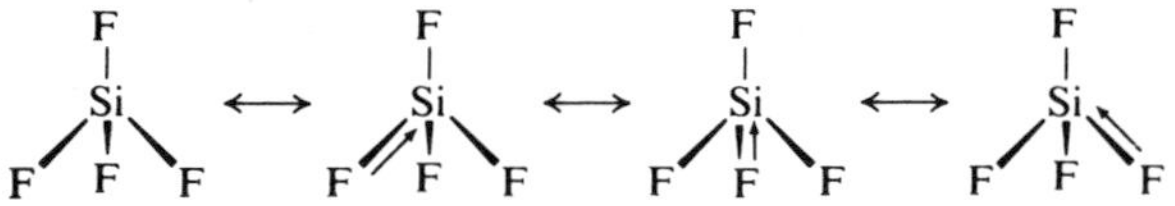

This bond formation is similar to the double bonding between boron and fluorine in BF_3, where there is overlap of the empty boron p orbital with the filled p orbitals of the fluorine atoms (cf. p. 51).

2. *They can lose electrons to form ionic bonds.* The energies required to form M^{4+} ions from Group-IV atoms are so great $(C(g) \rightarrow C^{4+}(g) + 4e : \Delta H = +3420$ kcal/mole; $Pb(g) \rightarrow Pb^{4+}(g) + 4e : \Delta H = +2230$ kcal/mole) that ionic $M^{4+}4X^-$ compounds do not exist. However, compounds such as PbO_2 and PbF_4 contain lead atoms with considerable positive charge on them because of the large differences in the electronegativities of lead (1.55) and fluorine (4.1) and oxygen (3.5):

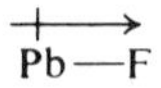

In SnF_4 and PbF_4 there are four highly electronegative atoms each attracting electron density from Sn and Pb, so that the total positive charge on them would be $+2$ if, for instance, each fluorine has a charge of $-\frac{1}{2}$:

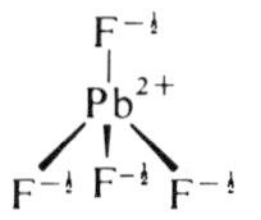

If three of the atoms attached to tin or lead are much less electronegative than the fourth atom, a different result is obtained. For example, in $Sn(CH_3)_3F$ the carbon–tin bonds are very much less polar than the tin–fluorine bond, and, as a result, the compound has three covalent bonds and one ionic bond:

$$Sn(CH_3)_3^+ F^-$$

The $Sn(CH_3)_3^+$ ion is planar in solid $Sn(CH_3)_3^+ F^-$, and the Sn atom is sp^2 hybridized:

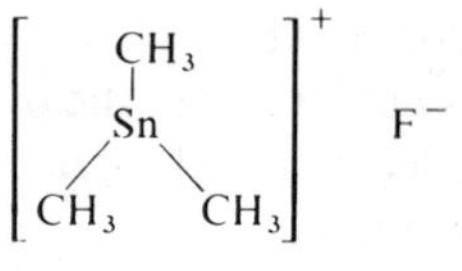

$$
\left[
\begin{array}{c}
CH_3 \\
| \\
Sn \\
\diagup \quad \diagdown \\
CH_3 \qquad CH_3
\end{array}
\right]^+ \qquad F^-
$$

In aqueous solution the ion is hydrated and the $Sn(CH_3)_3(H_2O)^+$ ion is probably sp^3 hybridized:

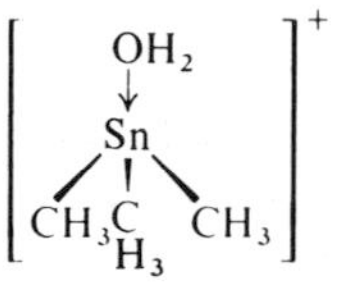

$$
\left[
\begin{array}{c}
OH_2 \\
\downarrow \\
Sn \\
\diagup \; | \; \diagdown \\
CH_3C \quad CH_3 \\
H_3
\end{array}
\right]^+
$$

An extensive chemistry of the $Sn(CH_3)_3^+$ and $Pb(CH_3)_3^+$ ions is known in both the solid state and in aqueous solution. These ions should be compared with the $Tl(CH_3)_2^+$ ion formed by the heaviest Group-III element, thallium.

3. *They can form compounds of oxidation state* +2, *involving ionic or covalent bonds.* The usual oxidation state is +4, as in the MX_4 compounds. Some Group-IV elements, like the Group-III elements, have a variable valency; in some of their compounds they have the group oxidation state of +4 and in others they have an oxidation state of +2:

Oxidation state +4	Oxidation state +2
GeF_4, GeS_2	GeF_2, GeS
$SnCl_4$, $SnCl_6^{2-}$	$SnCl_2$, $SnCl_3^-$
PbO_2	PbO

As was the case in Group III, it is found in Group IV that the relative stability of the two possible oxidation states changes as one descends the group. The +2 oxidation state is unusual for carbon and silicon. With the heaviest member of the group, lead, one finds that most of the common compounds are compounds of oxidation state +2. This is the *inert-pair effect*; in the +2 oxidation-state-compounds, a pair of valence electrons either is not used to form covalent bonds or is not lost to form +4 ions.

The compounds of oxidation state +2 are of two types: ionic compounds containing M^{2+} ions and covalent compounds. Whether a particular compound will be covalent or essentially ionic will, as usual, depend on the relative electronegativities of the atoms involved in compound formation.

Although in molecules of the type MX_2 there is a pair of nonbonding valence electrons (the *inert pair*), these compounds are not strong electron donors. More commonly, in fact, they act as electron acceptors, as in the formation of hydrates and complex anions:

$$SnCl_2 \ + \ Cl^- \ \longrightarrow \ \underset{\underset{Cl^-}{\uparrow}}{Sn}{\overset{\diagup Cl}{-}}Cl$$

$$SnCl_2 \ + \ H_2O \ \longrightarrow \ \underset{\underset{OH_2}{\uparrow}}{Sn}{\overset{\diagup Cl}{-}}Cl$$

4. *They can form double bonds.* We have already seen that double bonding occurs in MX_4 compounds when M is Si, Ge, Sn, or Pb, but not carbon, because of π overlap of empty d orbitals with filled p orbitals. Similar $p\pi$–$d\pi$ double bonding occurs in silicon–oxygen and silicon–nitrogen compounds:

$$Si \overset{\leftharpoondown}{=} F \ \text{in} \ SiF_4$$

$$Si \overset{\leftharpoondown}{=} O \ \text{in} \ Me_3Si \diagdown_{O} \diagup SiMe_3$$

$$Si \overset{\leftharpoondown}{=} N \ \text{in} \ N(SiH_3)_3$$

This type of double bonding is not possible for carbon, which does not possess empty d orbitals of sufficiently low energy.

Carbon is, however, able to form double and triple bonds either with other first-row elements or with another carbon atom; for example

$$\overset{}{\underset{}{>}}C=C\overset{}{\underset{}{<}} , \quad -C\equiv C- , \quad -C\equiv N , \quad \overset{}{\underset{}{>}}C=O$$

The atomic orbital used to form each π bond is a p orbital. Carbon is unique among the Group-IV elements in being able to form such double bonds. It is, in fact, a general rule that only elements in the first short period can form multiple bonds in this way.

As a result of this ability of carbon, alone among the Group-IV elements, to form double and triple bonds, many carbon compounds have no analogies in the rest of the group. For example, there are no compounds of Si and Ge analogous to the aromatic compounds of carbon.

Another consequence of this difference is that compounds of carbon and the other elements of the group may have similar formulas but quite different structures and properties. For example, the oxides CO_2 and SiO_2 (silica) have quite different physical and chemical properties. Carbon dioxide exists in the solid and gaseous states as discrete, linear, CO_2 molecules, $O\!=\!C\!=\!O$, in which there is π bonding between carbon and oxygen; silica, on the other hand, because silicon is unable to form π bonds, has a "giant molecule" structure

As a result, silica has a very high melting point and boiling point, in contrast to CO_2 which is a gas at ordinary temperatures.

Uniqueness of Carbon   We have noted three important respects in which carbon differs from the other members of the group:

1. its inability to form compounds having a covalency higher than 4; this arises from its lack of a sufficiently low-energy d orbital;

2. its inability to undergo reactions in which the carbon atom acts as an electron donor or acceptor; as a result, carbon compounds are more resistant to attack than the compounds of the remaining Group-IVA elements;

3. its marked ability to form double and triple bonds.

There is a *fourth* respect in which carbon differs from the remaining elements of Group IVA. This is its great capacity to form stable, long-chain compounds. Carbon is not unique in its ability to form chains, since silicon and germanium do so to a limited extent; carbon differs from these elements, however, in being able to form long chains of infinite length and of very high stability.

There are two main reasons why carbon differs from silicon and germanium in this respect.

1. The C–C single bond is much stronger than the Si–Si or Ge–Ge single bonds (see Table 2-6). As a result, carbon chains have greater *kinetic* stability, the energy required for the reaction

$$H_3Si–SiH_3 \rightarrow 2SiH_3$$

being much less than for the corresponding reaction of ethane,

$$C_2H_6 \rightarrow 2CH_3$$

2. C–C bonds are about as strong as C–O bonds, whereas Si–O bonds are much stronger than Si–Si bonds. This means that Si–Si chains are unstable with respect to oxidation, while C–C chains are less so; the bond dissociation energies are

$$\diagdown C–C \diagup \quad D_{(C–C)} \quad = 83 \text{ kcal} \qquad \diagdown C–O– \quad D_{(C–O)} \quad = 84 \text{ kcal}$$

$$\diagdown Si–Si \diagup \quad D_{(Si–Si)} \quad = 42 \text{ kcal} \qquad \diagdown Si–O– \quad D_{(Si–O)} \quad = 88 \text{ kcal}$$

The Elements

Carbon exists in two allotropic forms at room temperature: diamond and graphite. At room temperature graphite is slightly more stable than diamond.

$$C_{diamond} \rightarrow C_{graphite} \qquad \Delta H = -0.5 \text{ kcal/mole at } 25°C.$$

However, the rate of the reaction is negligibly slow because of the very high activation energy required for the change in structure (which involves breaking a large number of strong carbon–carbon bonds). At higher temperatures ($>1000°C$) the reaction does occur quite rapidly.

The reverse reaction, the conversion of graphite into diamond, is now an industrial process requiring extremely high pressures, high temperatures, and a catalyst.

The structures of diamond and graphite are shown in Figure 2-4. Diamond has a "giant molecule" structure in which each carbon atom is bonded to four other carbon atoms at the corner of a tetrahedron. Every carbon atom is tetracovalent and saturated. The properties of diamond, such as its extreme hardness and lack of electrical conductivity, can be explained on the basis of this 3-dimensional structure.

Graphite has a layer structure in which sheets of joined carbon hexagons are stacked in a particular way on top of each other. Each

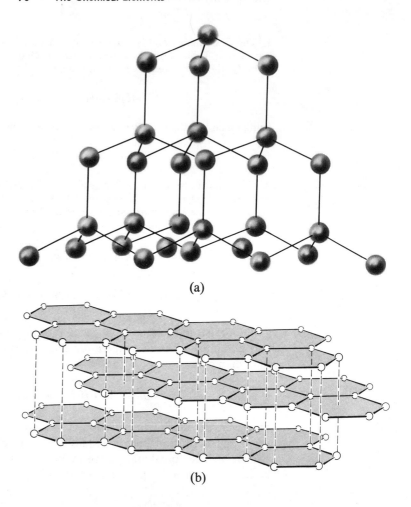

Fig. 2-4   The structures of (a) diamond, (b) graphite.

sheet is flat and every carbon atom is sp^2 hybridized. Only van der Waals forces hold the sheets together and the carbon–carbon distances between two different sheets is much greater than the C–C distances within a sheet. The sheets are stacked on top of each other, and it should be noted that a hexagon of one sheet is not superimposed on a hexagon of a neighboring sheet.

One consequence of the structure of graphite is that the substance is *anisotropic*; that is, properties are different when measured parallel or vertically to the planes of the sheets. The delocalization of π electrons in the sheets means that graphite is a good electrical and thermal conductor in this direction, but a very poor conductor in a direction perpendicular to the plane. It is possible to push the sheets of graphite apart quite easily, since they are only held together by van der Waals forces; for this reason graphite is an important solid lubricant.

Silicon and germanium are unable to form π bonds. Therefore, they do not form structures similar to graphite but only structures corresponding to diamond. Very pure silicon and germanium are used in electronic devices. The preparation of pure silicon illustrates the general methods for preparing pure elements when they have high melting points:

(a) Preparation of the element in an impure form

$$SiO_2 + C \xrightarrow{\text{heat}} Si + CO_2$$

(b) Preparation of a compound that can be purified by, for example, fractional distillation

$$Si + 2Cl_2 \xrightarrow{\text{heat}} SiCl_4$$

followed by reaction of the compound with hydrogen

$$SiCl_4 + 2H_2 \xrightarrow{\text{hot wire}} Si + 4HCl$$

The reduction is brought about on a heated wire of an inert metal, such as tungsten or tantalum; apart from silicon itself, the products of reaction are gaseous and so do not contaminate the silicon.

The Oxides of Carbon

There are three oxides of carbon: carbon monoxide, CO; carbon dioxide, CO_2; and carbon suboxide, C_3O_2.

Carbon monoxide, CO.   This oxide can be prepared in the laboratory by the dehydration of formic acid with concentrated sulfuric acid:

$$HCOOH \xrightarrow{-H_2O} CO$$

Carbon monoxide is an important industrial gas and both "water gas" and "producer gas" contain a high proportion of it:

$$H_2O + C \xrightarrow{\text{heat}} CO + H_2 \quad \text{(water gas)}$$

$$C + \tfrac{1}{2}O_2 \xrightarrow{\text{heat}} CO \quad \text{(producer gas)}$$

Carbon monoxide is a colorless, odorless, and poisonous gas that is metastable at room temperature:

$$2CO \quad \rightleftharpoons \quad C + CO_2 \qquad \Delta H = -40 \text{ kcal/mole of } CO_2 \text{ at } 25°C.$$

The rate of this disproportionation reaction at room temperature in the absence of a catalyst is immeasurably low. Carbon monoxide is a powerful reducing agent which burns in air and reacts with water vapor if heated:

$$2CO + O_2 \quad \rightarrow \quad 2CO_2$$

$$CO + H_2O \quad \rightleftharpoons \quad CO_2 + H_2$$

$$PbO + CO \quad \rightarrow \quad Pb + CO_2$$

With transition metals, it forms a large number of compounds which are called *carbonyls*. Some of these contain only carbon monoxide and the transition metal atom; a few examples are: $Cr(CO)_6$, $Mn_2(CO)_{10}$, $Fe_2(CO)_9$, and $Ni(CO)_4$. Many compounds are known in which carbon monoxide is just one of a number of groups attached to the metal.

Although carbon has an oxidation state of $+2$ in carbon monoxide, it is not divalent, since there is a triple bond between carbon and oxygen:

$$C \equiv O$$

One of the bonds is a σ bond:

One of the bonds is a π bond to which carbon and oxygen each contribute an electron:

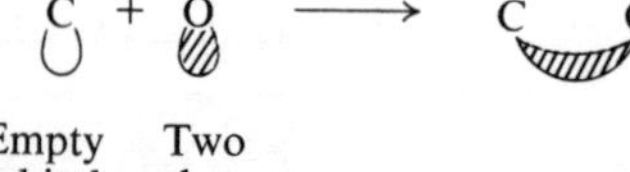

The third bond is a dative π bond to which both bonding electrons are provided by the oxygen atom:

Empty   Two
orbital   electrons

There is a pair of nonbonding valence electrons on both the carbon atom and the oxygen atom, in sp-hybrid orbitals, and carbon monoxide is therefore able to act as an electron donor. It does this in borine carbonyl and the transition-metal carbonyls; in the latter compounds there is additional bonding involving the metal d electrons:

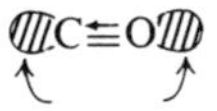

$$C \equiv O$$

Nonbonding
valence electrons

$$H_3B \longleftarrow CO$$

Borine carbonyl

Carbon monoxide reacts with chlorine gas in sunlight to give phosgene,

$$CO + Cl_2 \rightarrow COCl_2$$

and with sodium hydroxide at high temperatures and pressures to give sodium formate:

$$CO + NaOH \rightarrow HCOONa$$

Carbon dioxide, CO_2. Carbon dioxide is prepared by the thermal decomposition of calcium carbonate,

$$CaCO_3 \xrightarrow{\text{heat}} CaO + CO_2$$

or by treating any carbonate with mineral acid:

$$CaCO_3 + 2HCl \rightarrow CaCl_2 + CO_2 + H_2O$$

It is also produced in very large quantities in the fermentation of sugars:

$$\underset{\text{Glucose}}{C_6H_{12}O_6} \xrightarrow{\text{enzyme}} \underset{\text{Ethyl alcohol}}{2C_2H_5OH} + 2CO_2$$

Because carbon dioxide is a linear, symmetrical molecule, it has a zero dipole moment, even though each bond is polar:

$$O=C=O$$

It is moderately soluble in water, but only about 1 % of the dissolved gas is present as carbonic acid, 99 % being present as loosely-hydrated CO_2 molecules:

$$CO_2(g) + H_2O \;\rightleftharpoons\; \underset{\text{Hydrate}}{CO_2(aq)} \;\rightleftharpoons\; \underset{\substack{\text{Carbonic}\\\text{acid}}}{H_2CO_3} \;\rightleftharpoons\; \underset{\substack{\text{Bicarbonate}\\\text{ion}}}{H^+ + HCO_3^-}$$

Carbonic acid cannot be obtained as a pure compound at room temperatures but only as an aqueous solution. It is the parent acid of two series of salts: the *bicarbonates*, which contain the HCO_3^- ion, and the *carbonates*, which contain the CO_3^{2-} ion. The structures of the acid and its ions can be written as

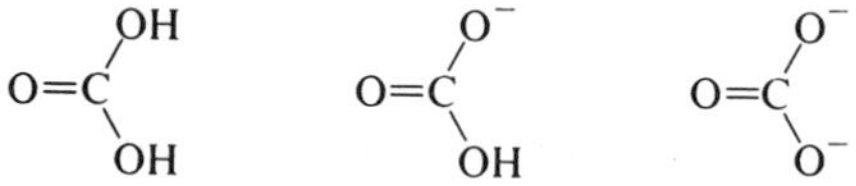

Since in each case the carbon atom is attached to three other atoms, there will be sp^2 hybridization, and therefore a planar configuration. In the free acid the double bond will be composed of a σ bond and a π bond. The same is true of the ions, but there is now the possibility of *resonance* between equivalent structures:

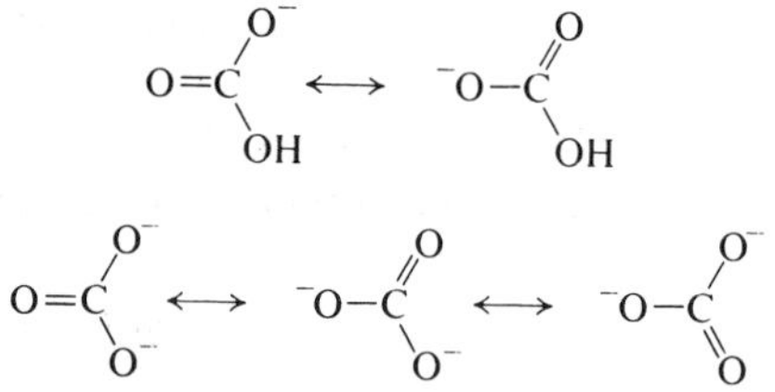

This resonance preserves the planar arrangement, which is confirmed by X-ray evidence.

Carbonic acid is a weak acid, though a slightly stronger one than acetic acid ($K_a = 1.8 \times 10^{-5}$).

$$H_2CO_3 \;\rightleftharpoons\; H^+ + HCO_3^- \qquad K_a = \frac{[H^+][HCO_3^-]}{[H_2CO_3]} = 5 \times 10^{-4}$$

Carbon suboxide, C_3O_2. A rare example of a linear penta-atomic molecule, carbon suboxide can be prepared in rather low yield by dehydrating malonic acid by heating it with phosphorus pentoxide:

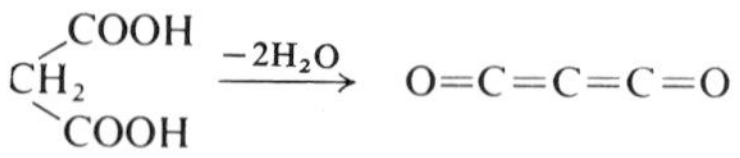

$$\underset{\text{COOH}}{\overset{\text{COOH}}{CH_2}} \xrightarrow{-2H_2O} O=C=C=C=O$$

Silicates

These are salts of condensed oxacids of silicon of great variety and complexity. The parent condensed oxacids have not been isolated but the salts are quite stable. The principles involved in their structures will be considered for a few of the simplest compounds.

The simplest of the silicates are the *orthosilicates*, which contain the SiO_4^{4-} anion and are derived from silicic acid, $Si(OH)_4$, by removing four protons. The SiO_4^{4-} ion is tetrahedral (sp^3 hybridization) with four identically situated oxygen atoms:

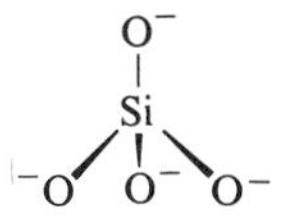

Pyrosilicates. These contain the $Si_2O_7^{6-}$ anion, which can theoretically be obtained by the condensation of two molecules of orthosilicic acid:

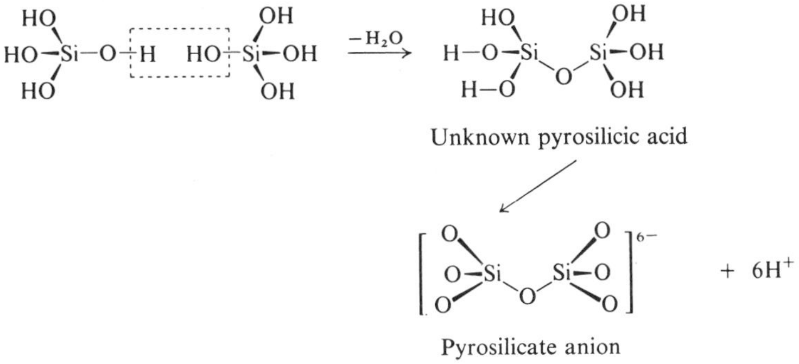

Unknown pyrosilicic acid

$+ 6H^+$

Pyrosilicate anion

A convenient shorthand notation used in writing the structures of the silicates is to represent a SiO_4^{4-} unit as ⧊ , which represents a view of the tetrahedral ion from above one of the apices. The $Si_2O_7^{6-}$ ion can then be written as ⧊⧊ $^{6-}$.

Metasilicates. These contain either linear or ring polymeric anions and they have the general formula $(SiO_3^{2-})_n$:

Minerals containing linear polymeric anions, such as the one illustrated, are called *pyroxenes*. There is also a ring structure.

$$(SiO_3^-)_6$$

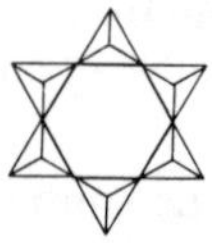

This ring anion is found in the mineral beryl, $3Be^{2+}2Al^{3+}[Si_6O_{18}]^{12-}$. In these polymers, each SiO_4 unit shares two of its four oxygen atoms with neighboring SiO_4 units, and two oxygen atoms are not shared. Other linear polymeric anions exist where two chains are linked together in a variety of ways:

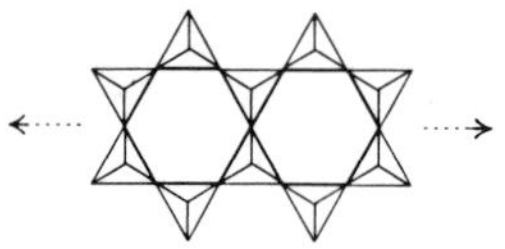

Minerals that contain linear polymeric (one-dimensional) silicate anions often have fibrous properties, as illustrated by the different varieties of asbestos.

Sheet-like (two-dimensional) silicate anions can be thought of as arising from the linking together of a large number of linear polymers:

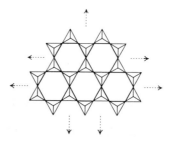

The simplest sheet structure gives rise to the formula $(Si_2O_5^{2-})_n$ for the silicate anion. In this structure, each SiO_4 shares three oxygen atoms with neighboring SiO_4 units, while the fourth oxygen atom is not shared. Such structures are found in materials such as mica, which readily cleave to give thin sheets.

The combination of SiO_4 units into very large three-dimensional structures in which every oxygen atom in one SiO_4 is shared with neighboring SiO_4 units leads to the silica structure, $(SiO_2)_n$. There are a number of different structures known for silica, and these differ in the arrangement of neighboring SiO_4 units relative to each other; for example,

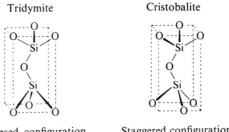

Eclipsed configuration   Staggered configuration

The three types of SiO_2 structures are the quartz, tridymite, and cristobalite structures; at room temperature quartz is the most stable. However, the activation energies required to interconvert any of the structures are so great that all three structures are stable at room temperature and they occur in nature.

The silicate framework structures, illustrated above, all carry negative charges. This charge is exactly balanced by a number of positively charged cations, as with the mineral beryl, referred to earlier. In naturally occurring silicates a great variety of metal cations are found in various proportions. The arrangement of cations around and in the silicate anions affect the properties of the material. This is illustrated schematically in Figure 2-5. Structure (b) will be more easily cleaved than structure (a), because in (b) two of the silicate layers are not

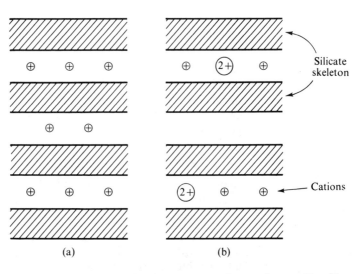

Fig. 2-5 Schematic diagram showing structures of naturally occurring silicates. In (a) each layer is separated by cations; in (b) two of the layers are not separated by cations, and the structure will be more easily cleaved.

bound together with cations (ionic bonding) but are bound only by much weaker van der Waals forces.

Some silicate minerals, called xeolites, are permeable to water, and some of the cations can readily be replaced by other cations in solution. Such minerals have been used as *ion-exchange* materials.

Group VA.   The Nitrogen Family

The elements in Group VA, nitrogen, phosphorus, arsenic, antimony, and bismuth, all exhibit a covalency of three and all have the characteristics of typical nonmetals. With increasing atomic weight there is an increase in metallic character, but this is not very pronounced even with the heaviest element in the group, bismuth. As can be seen in Table 2-7, the electronegativity of nitrogen is much greater than that of any of the other elements of the group.

Table 2-7   Characteristics of the Group-VA Elements.

	Nitrogen (N)	Phosphorus (P)	Arsenic (As)	Antimony (Sb)	Bismuth (Bi)
Electronic configuration	$[He]2s^22p^3$	$[Ne]3s^23p^3$	$[Ar]3d^{10}4s^24p^3$	$[Kr]4d^{10}5s^25p^3$	$[Xe]4f^{14}5d^{10}6s^26p^3$
Electronegativity	3.1	2.1	2.2	1.8	1.7
Covalent radius, Å	0.74	1.10	1.21	1.41	1.52
Melting point, °C	−210	44.2	814.5	630.5	271

Group-VA elements form compounds in the following ways.

1. *They can gain three electrons and form M^{3-} ions.* Nitrogen forms nitrides, e.g. Mg_3N_2, which are ionic compounds containing the nitride ion, N^{3-}. Phosphorus and arsenic similarly form phosphides and arsenides, e.g. Be_3P_2 and Mg_3As_2, but compounds containing Sb^{3-} and Bi^{3-} ions are not known.

Most metals do not form well-defined ionic nitrides, phosphides, and so on. Instead, they form "interstitial" compounds which often have a variable composition and resemble the interstitial hydrides (cf. p. 36) in some aspects of their structures and bonding.

A very large amount of energy is required to produce M^{3-} ions from nitrogen molecules in the gas phase.

$$N_2(g) + 6e \rightarrow 2N^{3-}(g) \qquad \Delta H = 1332 \text{ kcal}$$

This process can be divided conceptually into two stages:
(a) the dissociation of the nitrogen molecule

$$N_2(g) \rightarrow 2N(g) \qquad \Delta H = 226 \text{ kcal}$$

(b) the addition of three electrons to each nitrogen atom

$$2N(g) + 6e \rightarrow 2N^{3-}(g) \qquad \Delta H = 1106 \text{ kcal}$$

The three electrons added to a nitrogen atom to form N^{3-} are added to 2p orbitals that are already occupied by one electron; the second and third electron will be added to singly and doubly charged negative ions, respectively. Repulsion between the electrons in the N^{3-} ion will be very pronounced, which is why so much energy is required to produce the ion. The N^{3-} ion is much larger than the N atom (atomic radius of N $= 0.75$ Å; ionic radius of $N^{3-} = 1.4$ Å). In stable ionic nitrides such as Li_3N and Mg_3N_2, the very large amount of energy required to produce the N^{3-} ion is counterbalanced by the very high lattice energies of compounds that contain triply charged ions.

2. *They can form three covalent bonds.* Examples are NH_3, PH_3, NF_3, and $AsCl_3$. Such molecules are pyramidal, with eight electrons in the valence shell of the Group-V element. All contain a lone pair of valence electrons.

3. *They can form one or two covalent bonds and gain two electrons or one electron, respectively.* The amide ion, NH_2^-, and the imide ion, NH^{2-}, are two members of a series of five isoelectronic species formed by nitrogen:

Number of pairs of	NH_4^+	NH_3	NH_2^-	NH^{2-}	N^{3-}
nonbonding valence electrons	0	1	2	3	4

The four nitrogen–hydrogen species can be thought of as being formed by the successive addition of one, two, three, and four protons to the nitride ion, with the nitride ion forming one, two, three, and four dative bonds using the four pairs of nonbonding electrons*:

---

* The structures are represented for convenience as involving complete sp³ hybridization; the hybridization will, in fact, be complete for the symmetrical N^{3-} and NH_4^+ structures, but incomplete for the remaining ones.

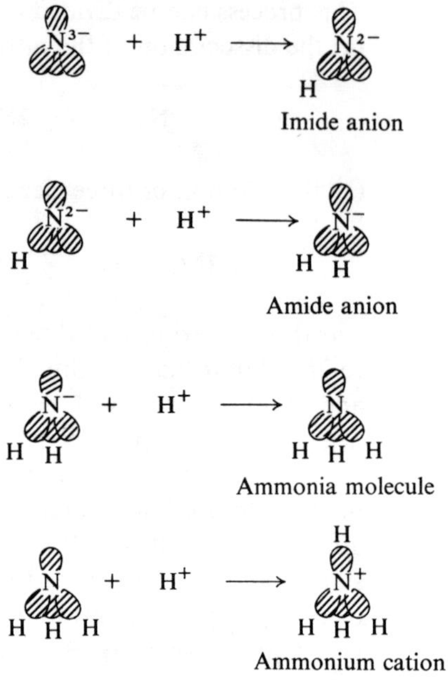

Imide anion

Amide anion

Ammonia molecule

Ammonium cation

The basic strengths decrease smoothly from N^{3-} to NH_4^+.

The nitride, imide, and amide ions are all such strong bases that they cannot exist in water, because they extract protons from water molecules:

$$NH_2^- + H_2O \rightarrow NH_3 + OH^-$$

$$NH^{2-} + 2H_2O \rightarrow NH_3 + 2OH^-$$

$$N^{3-} + 3H_2O \rightarrow NH_3 + 3OH^-$$

This means that the hydroxide ion is a weaker base than N^{3-}, NH^{2-}, or NH_2^- in that it is unsuccessful in competing with these ions for protons.

The ammonia molecule dissolved in water, however, is a weak base, the equilibrium

$$NH_3 + H_2O \rightleftharpoons NH_4^+ + OH^-$$

lying to the left. The ammonium ion is a weak acid, as is shown by the fact that the equilibrium

$$NH_4^+ + H_2O \rightleftharpoons NH_3 + H_3O^+$$

lies to the left.

For the phosphonium ion, PH_4^+, the equilibrium

$$PH_4^+(aq) + H_2O \rightarrow PH_3(aq) + H_3O^+$$

lies to the *right*, which means that phosphonium salts liberate phosphine gas when they are added to water. If one considers the success with which NH_3, PH_3, and H_2O compete with each other for protons, one obtains the following order of base strengths: $NH_3 > H_2O > PH_3$. Because of the acid–base properties, compounds containing ions such as NH_2^-, NH^{2-}, N^{3-}, PH^{2-}, PH_4^+ can be prepared and used only as dry solids or in nonaqueous systems such as liquid ammonia.

Sodamide, $NaNH_2$, the most important of these compounds, can be prepared from sodium and ammonia either by heating the metal in ammonia gas or by dissolving sodium in liquid ammonia with an added catalyst:

$$Na + NH_3 \rightarrow NaNH_2 + \tfrac{1}{2}H_2$$

The imides are obtained from amides by gentle heating:

$$Ca(NH_2)_2 \xrightarrow{\text{heat}} CaNH + NH_3$$

The ionic nature of amides and imides is demonstrated (1) by their moderately high melting points (mp of $NaNH_2$, 210°C), (2) by the fact that sodium amide dissolves in liquid ammonia to give a conducting solution, and (3) by the fact that both $NaNH_2$ and CaNH have the NaCl crystal structure.

4. *They can lose electrons to form cations.* The formation of M^{5+} cations, in which all the valence electrons would be lost by ionization, requires impossibly large amounts of energy ($M(g) \rightarrow M^{5+}(g) + 5e$; $\Delta H = 61,000$ kcal/mole) and, therefore, these ions are not found in chemical systems. The heavier elements of the group do, however, form compounds that contain M^{3+} ions. Salts such as $Sb_2(SO_4)_3$ and $Bi(NO_3)_3$ contain Sb^{3+} and Bi^{3+} ions, but even these cations have only a limited existence in aqueous solution because hydrolysis to give basic salts occurs in all but strongly acidic solutions; for example,

$$Bi^{3+} + H_2O \rightarrow BiO^+ + 2H^+$$

Salts which contain the SbO^+ ion are called antimonyl compounds, and those which contain the BiO^+ ion are called bismuthyl compounds.

5. *They can form three covalent bonds and act as electron donors.* We have seen that in molecules such as NH_3 there is a pair of nonbonding electrons in the valence shell of nitrogen. The ammonia molecule is, consequently, an electron donor and can form a dative bond with an electron-acceptor molecule such as BF_3, as was discussed in Chapter 1.

There are many examples known of adducts formed between Group-V electron-donor molecules and a great variety of electron acceptors; for example

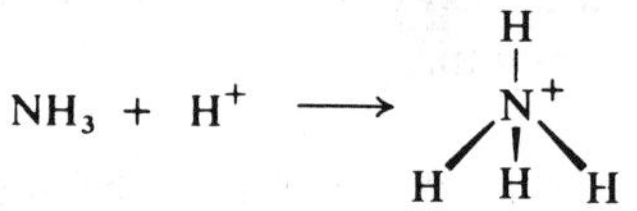

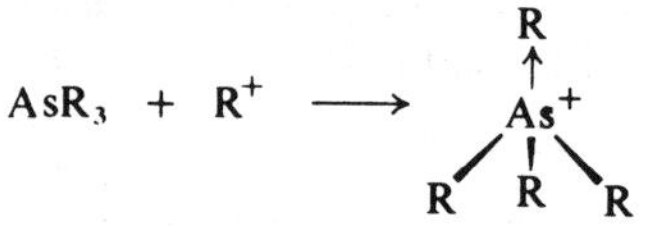

$$NH_3 \ + \ H^+ \ \longrightarrow \ \underset{H \quad H \quad H}{\overset{H}{N^+}}$$

$$AsR_3 \ + \ R^+ \ \longrightarrow \ \underset{R \quad R \quad R}{\overset{R}{As^+}}$$

R = an organic group

$$H_3N \ + BF_3 \ \longrightarrow \ H_3N \longrightarrow BF_3$$

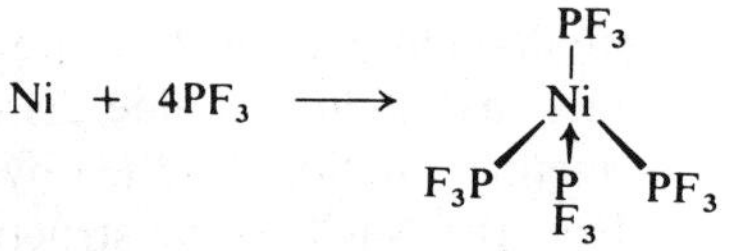

$$Ni \ + \ 4PF_3 \ \longrightarrow \ \underset{F_3P \quad \underset{F_3}{P} \quad PF_3}{\overset{PF_3}{Ni}}$$

The available evidence suggests that when the electron-acceptor atom is a nontransition metal, such as boron or gallium, the strongest dative bonds are formed by nitrogen compounds and the strengths of dative bonds decrease down Group V. This is another example of the general rule that the strengths of covalent bonds decrease with increasing atomic weight; for example

		ΔH, kcal/mole
$Me_3N + GaMe_3^*$ → $Me_3N \rightarrow GaMe_3$		−21
$Me_3P + GaMe_3$ → $Me_3P \rightarrow GaMe_3$		−18
$Me_3As + GaMe_3$ → $Me_3As \rightarrow GaMe_3$		−10

6. *They can form five and six covalent bonds.* All of the Group-V elements except the first member, nitrogen, can use all their five

* Me represents the methyl group, CH_3 (see p. 187).

valence-shell electrons to form covalent bonds with five separate atoms. In their ground states the elements have valence shells with the electronic configuration s^2p^3, there being three unpaired electrons. This means that the elements, if they used only s and p orbitals, could form only three covalent bonds or three covalent bonds and a dative bond; for example

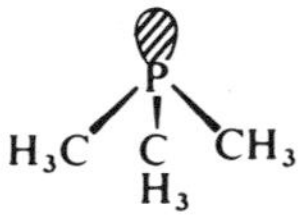

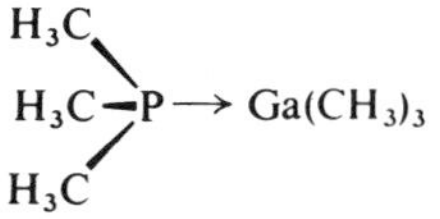

In other words, their coordination number would be limited to four.

However, the elements in Group V other than nitrogen have empty d orbitals of reasonably low energy, and these can also be used for bonding. If an electron is promoted from the s orbital to an empty d orbital, all five valence electrons will have unpaired spins and five covalent bonds can be formed. (Less energy would be required to promote an s electron to a half-filled p orbital than to a d orbital, but it would produce an atom which still had only three unpaired electrons.) Some relevant electronic configurations are:

	3s	3p	3d	Number of unpaired electrons
P in ground state	↑↓	↑ ↑ ↑	☐ ☐ ☐ ☐ ☐	3
P in PH_3	↑↓	↑↓ ↑↓ ↑↓	☐ ☐ ☐ ☐ ☐	0
P in $Me_3P \rightarrow GaMe_3$	↑↓	↑↓ ↑↓ ↑↓	☐ ☐ ☐ ☐ ☐	0
P in sp^3d excited state	↑	↑ ↑ ↑	↑ ☐ ☐ ☐ ☐	5
P in PF_5	↑↓	↑↓ ↑↓ ↑↓	↑↓ ☐ ☐ ☐ ☐	0
P in PF_6^-	↑↓	↑↓ ↑↓ ↑↓	↑↓ ↑↓ ☐ ☐ ☐	0

These block diagrams do not indicate the hybridization of the atom concerned. Phosphorus is sp^3 hybridized in PH_3, sp^3d hybridized in PF_5, and sp^3d^2 hybridized in PF_6^-.

Since nitrogen has no low-energy empty d orbitals, it cannot form MX_5 compounds; like all the elements of the first short period, it is restricted to a maximum coordination number of 4.

The shapes of the MX_5 compounds formed by the rest of the Group-V elements will depend on which d orbital is used in forming the sp^3d-hybrid orbitals. The shapes of the d orbitals are shown in Figure 2-6.

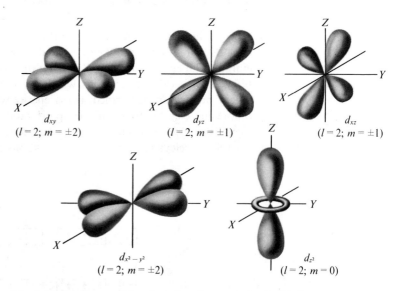

Fig. 2-6   The five possible orientations in space of a *d* orbital.

In practice, only the d_{z^2} or the $d_{x^2-y^2}$ orbitals are used, and of these the d_{z^2} appears to be used in the great majority of known compounds. PF_5 is a trigonal bipyramidal molecule in which phosphorus is $sp^3d_{z^2}$ hybridized:

The same is true with most of the other MX_5 compounds formed by the Group-V elements.

It is a feature of trigonal bipyramidal molecules that the five atoms bonded to the central atom are not all equivalent. In PF_5, the two axial fluorine atoms are in an environment different from that of the three equatorial fluorine atoms, and this is reflected in slightly different bond lengths:

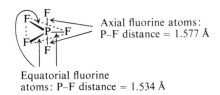

Axial fluorine atoms: P–F distance = 1.577 Å

Equatorial fluorine atoms: P–F distance = 1.534 Å

There are no nonbonding valence electrons on the phosphorus, arsenic, antimony, and bismuth atoms in MX_5 molecules, which therefore, are unable to act as electron donors—unlike the corresponding MX_3 molecules. In contrast, the MX_5 compounds are able to act as electron acceptors; for example

$$PF_5 + F^- \rightarrow PF_6^-$$

In the adducts formed between PF_5 and an electron donor, the phosphorus atom is sp^3d^2 hybridized. The PF_6^- ion is octahedral and every fluorine atom is equivalent:

$$
\left[
\begin{array}{c}
F \\
F\cdots\!\!\!\diagup\!\!\!\cdots F \\
\diagup P \diagdown \\
F\cdots\!\!\!\diagdown\!\!\!\cdots F \\
F
\end{array}
\right]^{-}
$$

All the known pentahalides of the Group-V elements have trigonal bipyramidal shapes in the vapor phase, but many of them form ionic solids:

$2PCl_5 \rightleftharpoons PCl_4^+ PCl_6^-$	$2AsF_3Cl_2 \rightleftharpoons AsCl_4^+ AsF_6^-$	
Vapor Solid	Vapor Solid	

The MX_4^+ ions are tetrahedral and the MX_6^- ions are octahedral.

7. *They can form double and triple bonds.* Group V is no exception to the general rule that only the first member of a group, in this case nitrogen, forms π bonds using p orbitals. Examples in which nitrogen forms π bonds are to be found in N_2, $N\equiv N$, in organic nitriles, $R-C\equiv N$, in azo compounds, $R-N = N-R$, and in borazine, which has already been described on p. 60.

Nitrogen occurs in the atmosphere as N_2 molecules, in which there is a triple bond between nitrogen atoms: a σ bond and two π bonds. As a result, the dissociation energy is very large:

$$N\equiv N(g) \quad \rightarrow \quad 2N(g) \quad \Delta H = 226 \text{ kcal/mole}$$

This has important consequences for the whole chemistry of nitrogen, because it means that many common nitrogen compounds are endothermic and often rather unstable:

			ΔH, kcal/mole
$NH_3(g)$	$\rightarrow$	$\tfrac{1}{2}N_2 + \tfrac{3}{2}H_2$	$+11$
$N_2H_4(g)$	$\rightarrow$	$N_2 + 2H_2$	-12
$HN_3(g)$	$\rightarrow$	$\tfrac{3}{2}N_2 + \tfrac{1}{2}H_2$	-71
$NO(g)$	$\rightarrow$	$\tfrac{1}{2}N_2 + \tfrac{1}{2}O_2$	-21
$N_2O(g)$	$\rightarrow$	$N_2 + \tfrac{1}{2}O_2$	-17
$NO_2(g)$	$\rightarrow$	$\tfrac{1}{2}N_2 + O_2$	-7

From the above heats of decomposition into the elements, it will be seen that of the common hydrides and oxides of nitrogen only ammonia, NH_3, is formed exothermically from the elements. In other words, only ammonia is thermodynamically stable with respect to decomposition into the elements.

The Elements

Phosphorus, arsenic, antimony, and bismuth form diatomic molecules like N_2 only at high temperatures, because of their reluctance to form π bonds. They occur as solids at room temperature, with complicated "giant-molecule" structures. The vapors of phosphorus, arsenic, and antimony contain P_4, As_4, and Sb_4 molecules. The P_4 molecule has the structure

in which the four phosphorus atoms are situated at the corners of a tetrahedron. The P–P–P angles are 60°, and it is probable that the P–P bonds do *not* lie on straight lines between the phosphorus atoms:

In this respect, there is a resemblance with the strained carbon ring in cyclopropane (see p. 191).

The P_4 unit is found to occur in a number of phosphorus compounds, such as the oxides. In these compounds, other atoms form bridges between the phosphorus atoms, and these bridging atoms do not lie on a straight line between neighboring phosphorus atoms; for example,

P_4O_6, phosphorus trioxide
or phosphorous oxide

P_4O_{10}, phosphorus pentoxide
or phosphoric oxide

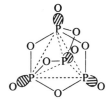

Hydrogen Compounds of Nitrogen

Ammonia. NH_3 is prepared industrially from nitrogen and hydrogen by the Haber process:

$$N_2 + 3H_2 \rightleftharpoons 2NH_3 \qquad \Delta H = -22 \text{ kcal}$$

High pressures, moderately high temperatures, and an iron catalyst are used to obtain the optimum yield of ammonia. In the laboratory, ammonia can be prepared by treating any ammonium salt with an alkali:

$$NH_4^+ + OH^- \rightarrow NH_3 + H_2O$$

Ammonia is a colorless gas with a pungent smell. It is easily liquified (bp, 33.4°C), and the liquid can be contained in an open Dewar flask for some considerable time, the latent heat of evaporation of ammonia being rather large (5.6 kcal/mole), owing to hydrogen bonding between ammonia molecules. Liquid ammonia is sometimes used as a solvent in preparative chemistry.

Ammonia is extremely soluble in water; at 20°C, 1 volume of water dissolves 700 volumes of ammonia gas to give a solution of ammonia in water which is usually called "ammonium hydroxide." Nearly all of the dissolved ammonia is present in solution as a hydrate $H_3N\text{---}H\text{---}O\text{---}H$ and none is present as NH_4OH, which would require nitrogen to be pentacovalent. Ammonia is a weak base:

$$NH_3 + H_2O \rightleftharpoons NH_4^+ + OH^-$$

$$K_b = \frac{[NH_4^+][OH^-]}{[NH_3]} = 1.8 \times 10^{-5} \text{ at } 25°C$$

Ammonia gas will burn in pure oxygen, but not in air, to give nitrogen and steam:

$$4NH_3 + 3O_2 \rightarrow 2N_2 + 6H_2O \tag{1}$$

If the oxidation is carried out under carefully controlled conditions in the presence of a platinum catalyst, nitric oxide is obtained in high yield:

$$4NH_3 + 5O_2 \rightarrow 4NO + 6H_2O \tag{2}$$

Nitric oxide is an endothermic compound, and the only reason for its formation is that the rate of reaction (2) under special conditions is much faster than the rate of reaction (1). In other words, *kinetic* considerations determine the products of reaction. Reaction (2) is important in industry because it is one step in the conversion of ammonia into nitric acid.

Ammonia reacts with acids to give ammonium salts, which contain the NH_4^+ ion. Ammonium salts resemble the salts of the alkali metals, and those of the common acids are all colorless and soluble in water. If the parent acid is volatile, the ammonium salt itself will readily sublime, because it will dissociate into volatile ammonia and hydrogen chloride on heating:

$$NH_4Cl \rightleftharpoons NH_3(g) + HCl(g)$$

Hydrazine, N_2H_4. Hydrazine is prepared industrially by the Raschig process, in which ammonia is oxidized by sodium hypochlorite in the presence of gelatin:

$$NH_3 + OCl^- \rightarrow NH_2Cl + OH^-$$
$$\text{Chloramine}$$

$$NH_2Cl + NH_3 + OH^- \rightarrow NH_2NH_2 + Cl^- + H_2O$$

The gelatin is necessary to prevent other possible reactions of chloramine from occurring, for example

$$2NH_2Cl + OCl^- + 2OH^- \rightarrow N_2 + 3Cl^- + 3H_2$$

Hydrazine sulfate, $N_2H_6^{2+}SO_4^{2-}$, can be obtained as a crystalline salt from aqueous solution after sulfuric acid has been added, and pure hydrazine can be distilled from a mixture of solid KOH and $N_2H_6^{2+}SO_4^{2-}$.

Hydrazine has the nonplanar structure

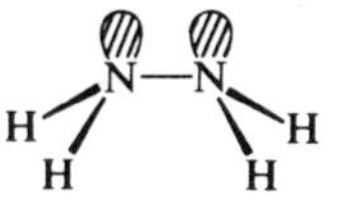

and is a diacidic base, forming $N_2H_5^+$ and $N_2H_6^{2+}$ cations with acids. It can behave as either a reducing agent or an oxidizing agent. This unusual behavior is also shown by hydroxylamine, NH_2OH, and hydrogen peroxide, H_2O_2, which are both isoelectronic with hydrazine. For example:

As an oxidizing agent

$$Zn + N_2H_5^+ + 3H^+ \rightarrow Zn^{2+} + 2NH_4^+$$

As a reducing agent

$$2Br_2 + N_2H_4 \rightarrow N_2 + 4H^+ + 4Br^-$$

The N–N bond in hydrazine is rather weak ($D_{(N-N)} = 39$ kcal/mole), probably because of the repulsion between the two pairs of nonbonding valence electrons in the molecule. This weakening of a bond by repulsions between nonbonding electrons also occurs in hydrogen peroxide and fluorine:

Hydrazoic acid, HN_3. Sodium azide can be prepared by passing nitrous oxide through molten sodamide,

$$NaNH_2 + N_2O \rightarrow NaN_3 + H_2O$$

and hydrazoic acid can be obtained from sodium azide by heating it with sulfuric acid:

$$2NaN_3 + H_2SO_4 \rightarrow 2HN_3 + Na_2SO_4$$

Hydrazoic acid is a colorless liquid, bp 37°C, which readily explodes when pure. In aqueous solution it has greater kinetic stability, though it is still a slightly endothermic species. It is a weak acid, having an acid dissociation constant K_a, of 1×10^{-5}. The azide ion, N_3^-, behaves in many ways like a halide ion and is sometimes termed a pseudohalide. Alkali-metal azides are colorless crystalline solids which are relatively safe to handle, but the heavy metal azides are sparingly soluble, extremely dangerous substances sometimes used as detonators; for example

$$Pb(N_3)_2 \rightarrow Pb + 3N_2 \qquad \Delta H = -104 \text{ kcal/mole}$$

The azide ion is linear and symmetrical with N–N distances that correspond to a bond order of 2.0:

$$[N\equiv\overset{+}{N}-\overset{2-}{N}] \leftrightarrow [\overset{2-}{N}-\overset{+}{N}\equiv N] \leftrightarrow [\overset{-}{N}=\overset{+}{N}=\overset{-}{N}]$$

Hydroxylamine, NH_2OH.   Hydroxylamine can be prepared by the electrolytic reduction of a nitrite or a nitrate using a lead cathode.

At the cathode

$$HONO_2 + 6H^+ + 6e \rightarrow HONH_2 + 2H_2O$$

At the anode

$$3H_2O \rightarrow \tfrac{3}{2}O_2 + 6H^+ + 6e$$

Hydroxylamine is usually isolated as the sulfate $(NH_3OH_2SO_4)$, rather than as the pure solid, which is explosive.

Hydroxylamine has the structure

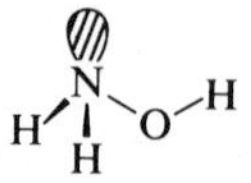

and, like ammonia, it is a monoacidic base that forms the NH_3OH^+ cation with acids. It can act as either an oxidizing or a reducing agent:

As a reducing agent

$$BrO_3^- + NH_2OH \longrightarrow Br^- + NO_3^- + H_3O^+$$
$$4Fe^{3+} + 2NH_2OH \longrightarrow 4Fe^{2+} + N_2O + 4H^+ + H_2O$$
(in acid solution)

Many products are formed when hydroxylamine is oxidized, and mixtures of NO_3^-, N_2O, and N_2 are commonly obtained. Kinetic factors determine what products are obtained in a particular reaction.

As an oxidizing agent

$$2H^+ + NH_2OH + 2Ti^{3+} \rightarrow 2Ti^{4+} + NH_3 + H_2O$$

$$2Fe(OH)_2 + H_2O + NH_2OH \rightarrow 2Fe(OH)_3 + NH_3$$
(in alkaline solution)

The fact that Fe^{3+} oxidizes hydroxylamine in acid solution while Fe^{2+} is oxidized by hydroxylamine in alkaline solution shows the striking effect that pH can have on the relative stabilities of oxidation states of elements. In the example above the effect of pH is particularly marked on the ε^0 of the Fe^{2+}–Fe^{3+} reaction:

$$Fe^{2+} \rightarrow Fe^{3+} + e \qquad \varepsilon^0 = -0.77 \text{ (in acid solution)}$$

$$Fe(OH)_2 + OH^- \rightarrow Fe(OH)_3 + e \qquad \varepsilon^0 = +0.56 \text{ (in alkaline solution)}$$

Oxides and Oxyacids of Nitrogen

Oxides	Oxidation State of Nitrogen	Oxyacids
N_2O, nitrous oxide	+1	$H_2N_2O_2$, hyponitrous acid
NO, nitric oxide	+2	
N_2O_3, dinitrogen trioxide	+3	HNO_2, nitrous acid
NO_2, nitrogen dioxide	+4	
N_2O_4, dinitrogen tetroxide		
N_2O_5, dinitrogen pentoxide	+5	HNO_3, nitric acid
NO_3, nitrogen trioxide	+6	

Nitrous oxide, N_2O.   Nitrous oxide is prepared by heating ammonium nitrate:

$$NH_4NO_3 \rightarrow N_2O + 2H_2O$$

It is a colorless, odorless, and rather unreactive gas which can act as an oxidizing agent when heated:

$$H_2 + N_2O \rightarrow H_2O + N_2$$

$$2NH_3 + 3N_2O \rightarrow 3H_2O + 4N_2$$

It can support combustion, because on heating it decomposes,

$$2N_2O \;\rightarrow\; 2N_2 + O_2$$

and many substances will burn in the oxygen so liberated. As noted earlier, N_2O, like all the other oxides of nitrogen, is an endothermic compound. It is isoelectronic with CO_2, and, like carbon dioxide, it is linear; however it is not symmetrical and therefore, unlike CO_2, it does have a dipole moment. Its structure can be represented as

$$\overset{-}{N}=\overset{+}{N}=O \;\leftrightarrow\; N\equiv\overset{+}{N}-\overset{-}{O}$$

Nitrous oxide is slightly soluble in water, but it is not the anhydride of hyponitrous acid (in which nitrogen is also in the $+1$ oxidation state).

Nitric oxide, NO. Nitric oxide can be prepared by warming a mixture of a nitrate, ferrous sulfate, and concentrated sulfuric acid:

$$2KNO_3 + 5H_2SO_4 + 6FeSO_4$$
$$\rightarrow\; 2KHSO_4 + 3Fe_2(SO_4)_3 + 4H_2O + 2NO$$

In this reaction, iron(II) reduces nitrogen from the $+5$ oxidation state in NO_3^- to the $+2$ oxidation state in NO:

$$4H^+ + NO_3^- + 3Fe^{2+} \;\rightarrow\; 3Fe^{3+} + NO + 2H_2O$$

Nitric oxide is prepared industrially by the catalytic oxidation of ammonia. It is a colorless gas and is only slightly soluble in water; it is not the anhydride of an oxyacid. There is an odd number of electrons in the molecule (15), and it is one of only a very few known stable compounds which do not have even numbers of electrons (NO_2 and ClO_2 are two other examples of "odd-electron" molecules). Since one of the electrons must be unpaired, one would expect the substance to be very reactive and to show a great tendency to dimerize and to attack other molecules. However, NO, NO_2, and ClO_2 are all remarkably unreactive considering that they have an unpaired electron; there is no simple explanation for this.

Because of the unpaired electron, nitric oxide is a paramagnetic gas at room temperature, though at lower temperature it is diamagnetic. It is very readily oxidized,

$$2NO + O_2 \;\rightarrow\; 2NO_2$$
$$2NO + Cl_2 \;\rightarrow\; 2NOCl$$
$$\text{Nitrosyl chloride}$$

and it is almost equally readily reduced, the products of the reduction depending on conditions and reagents; for example

$$NO \ + \ Cr^{2+} \ \xrightarrow[\text{Neutral solution}]{\text{Acid solution}} \begin{array}{l} NH_2OH \\ \text{Hydroxylamine} \\[1em] NH_3 \\ \text{Ammonia} \end{array}$$

The odd electron of nitric oxide is fairly easily removed to give the nitrosyl or nitrosonium ion:

$$NO \ \rightarrow \ NO^+ + e \qquad \text{(oxidation of nitrogen from } +2 \text{ to } +3)$$

Salts containing this ion can be obtained as crystalline solids, for example, $NO^+HSO_4^-$, $NO^+HClO_4^-$, but the NO^+ reacts with water except in very concentrated acid solution:

$$NO^+ + H_2O \ \rightarrow \ HNO_2 + H^+$$
$$\text{Nitrous acid}$$

The N–O distance in NO^+ (1.06 Å) is less than in NO itself (1.14 Å), and this indicates that the electron lost to give NO^+ occupied an antibonding molecular orbital, since its removal is accompanied by a strengthening and shortening of the bond between nitrogen and oxygen. The NO^+ ion is isoelectronic with N_2 and CO and contains a triple bond between nitrogen and oxygen.

It is also possible to add an electron to NO to obtain the NO^- ion. If NO is passed into a solution of sodium in liquid ammonia, Na^+NO^- is obtained:

$$NO + e \ \rightarrow \ NO^- \text{ (reduction of nitrogen from } +2 \text{ to } +1)$$

Nitric oxide resembles carbon monoxide in forming a large number of donor–acceptor complexes with transition metals, and in some of the adducts it is probable that nitric oxide is complexed in the form of the NO^+ ion, having transferred the odd electron to the transitional metal. An example is

$$[Fe(CN)_5(NO)]^{2-},$$

the ion in sodium nitroprusside, $Na_2Fe(CN)_5(NO)$, in which the bonding between NO and Fe can be represented better as $Fe^{2+} \leftarrow \overset{+}{NO}$ than as $Fe^{3+} \leftarrow NO$.

Dinitrogen trioxide, N_2O_3.   This is prepared by condensing together equimolar amounts of NO_2 and NO:

$$NO_2 + NO \;\rightarrow\; N_2O_3$$

It forms a blue liquid and solid, but the vapor is almost entirely dissociated into nitrogen dioxide and nitric oxide. It is the anhydride of nitrous acid:

$$N_2O_3 + H_2O \;\rightarrow\; 2HNO_2$$

Nitrogen dioxide, NO_2, *and dinitrogen tetroxide*, N_2O_4.   Nitrogen dioxide can be prepared by the thermal decomposition of a heavy metal nitrate,

$$2Pb(NO_3)_2 \;\rightarrow\; 2PbO + 4NO_2 + O_2$$

or by allowing nitric oxide to mix with air:

$$2NO + O_2 \;\rightarrow\; 2NO_2$$

The solid is colorless, mp $-11°C$, and consists of pure N_2O_4, the dimer of NO_2. On melting the solid, one obtains a pale brown liquid, bp $20°C$, which darkens in color as the temperature is raised. This liquid is a dilute solution of NO_2 in N_2O_4. The vapor just above the boiling point consists largely of undissociated N_2O_4 molecules, but as the temperature is raised, the equilibrium

$$N_2O_4 \;\rightleftharpoons\; 2NO_2 \qquad \Delta H = +14.7 \text{ kcal}$$

N_2O_4	$2NO_2$
Colorless	Brown
diamagnetic	paramagnetic

is driven to the right and the color of the gas darkens; the dissociation is essentially complete at around $150°C$.

Nitrogen dioxide, a mixed anhydride, dissolves in water to give a mixture of nitric and nitrous acids:

$$2NO_2 + H_2O \;\rightarrow\; HNO_3 + HNO_2$$

Oxidation states of N: $+4$ $+5$ $+3$

Nitrous acid is unstable and decomposes,

$$3HNO_2 \;\rightarrow\; HNO_3 + 2NO + H_2O$$

and the liberated nitric oxide will be oxidized by air to give back nitrogen dioxide, so that one can write the over-all reaction in the presence of air as

$$O_2 + 4NO_2 + 2H_2O \rightarrow 4HNO_3$$

Nitrogen dioxide is a powerful oxidizing agent,

$$NO_2 + 2I^- + H_2O \rightarrow NO + I_2 + 2OH^-$$

and it can be oxidized to the nitrate ion by powerful oxidizing agents such as potassium permanganate:

$$2MnO_4^- + 10NO_2 + 2H_2O \rightarrow 2Mn^{2+} + 4H^+ + 10NO_3^-$$

NO_2, like NO, can either gain or lose an electron (can be either reduced or oxidized by one unit), and both of the ions so produced no longer have an odd number of electrons:

$$NO_2 \quad \overset{+e}{\nearrow} \quad NO_2^- \text{ (nitrite ion, isoelectronic with } O_3\text{)}$$
$$\overset{-e}{\searrow} \quad NO_2^+ \text{ (nitronium ion, isoelectronic with } CO_2\text{)}$$

Solid salts containing NO_2^- and NO_2^+ are known—for example, $Na^+NO_2^-$, $NO_2^+BF_4^-$; but nitrites are soluble in water without decomposition, while nitronium salts can have no existence in the presence of water, because the following reaction occurs:

$$NO_2^+ + H_2O \rightarrow HNO_3 + H^+$$

The nitronium ion, like CO_2 with which it is isoelectronic, is a linear symmetrical species. The shapes of NO_2 and N_2O_4 are

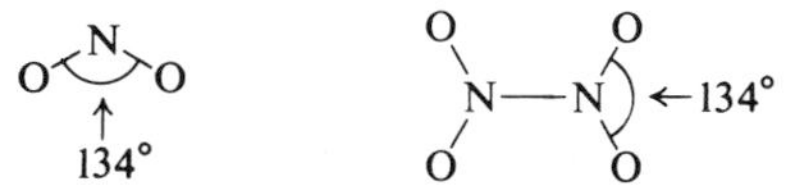

Dinitrogen pentoxide, N_2O_5. This anhydride of nitric acid, can be prepared by dehydrating 100% nitric acid using phosphorus pentoxide (P_4O_{10}):

$$2HNO_3 \xrightarrow{-H_2O} N_2O_5$$

It is a hygroscopic solid which reacts with water to give back nitric acid. The solid has an ionic structure, $NO_2^+NO_3^-$, so that it should perhaps be called nitronium nitrate.

Hyponitrous acid, $H_2N_2O_2$. This acid is prepared by the reduction of a nitrate with sodium amalgam:

$$4H^+ + 2NO_2^- + 4e \rightarrow N_2O_2^{2-} + 2H_2O$$

It is a weak dibasic acid which is unstable, decomposing to give nitrous oxide:

$$H_2N_2O_2 \rightarrow H_2O + N_2O$$

The anion has the structure

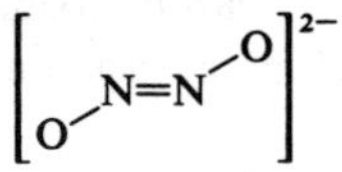

$$\left[\begin{array}{c} O \\ \diagdown \\ N{=}N \\ \diagup \\ O \end{array} \hspace{-2em} \begin{array}{c} O \\ \diagup \\ \\ \diagdown \\ \end{array} \right]^{2-}$$

the oxygen atoms being on the opposite sides of the double bond; it is said to have a *trans* structure, in contrast to a *cis* structure, in which the atoms are on the same side of the double bond.

Nitrous acid, HNO_2. This weak acid cannot be isolated; it is known only in solution. It can be obtained in solution by adding a strong acid to a solution of a metal nitrite, such as sodium nitrite. It is unstable and disproportionates to give nitric oxide and nitrate ion:

Oxidation numbers	$3HNO_2 \rightarrow$	$NO_3^- + H_3O^+ +$	$2NO$
of nitrogen atoms	+3	+5	+2

Sodium nitrite, $NaNO_2$, can be prepared by the thermal decomposition of sodium nitrate:

$$2NaNO_3 \rightarrow 2NaNO_2 + O_2$$

The nitrite ion is nonlinear:

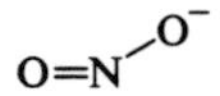

$$O{=}N{\diagup}^{O^-}$$

Nitric acid, HNO_3. Pure nitric acid can be prepared by distillation from a mixture of potassium nitrate and sulfuric acid:

$$H_2SO_4 + KNO_3 \rightarrow KHSO_4 + HNO_3$$

Aqueous solutions of nitric acid have the acidic properties associated with strong acids; for example

$$CaCO_3 + 2HNO_3 \rightarrow Ca(NO_3)_2 + CO_2 + H_2O,$$

combined with powerful oxidizing properties. Because nitric acid is a powerful oxidizing agent, its reactions with many substances yield different products from those obtained with nonoxidizing mineral acids such as HCl or H_2SO_4; for example,

copper + cold 1:1 nitric acid/water mixture:

$$3Cu + 8HNO_3 \rightarrow 3Cu(NO_3)_2 + 2NO + 4H_2O$$

copper + warm concentrated nitric acid:

$$Cu + 4HNO_3 \rightarrow Cu(NO_3)_2 + 2NO_2 + 2H_2O$$

zinc + concentrated nitric acid:

$$4Zn + 10HNO_3 \rightarrow 4Zn(NO_3)_2 + N_2O + 5H_2O$$

Many reactions of nitric acid yield a mixture of products, the proportion of different products depending on conditions. Hydrogen is *not* usually obtained in any reaction of a metal with nitric acid. The nitrate ion is in a resonance state involving the structures

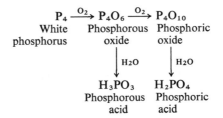

The three oxygen atoms are equivalent. The N^+ ion is isoelectronic with C; it follows that there will be sp^2 hybridization in these structures, which are planar. The arrangement about the N atom in nitric acid is also planar.

Phosphorus Oxides and Oxyacids

Oxides	Oxidation State of Phosphorus	Oxyacids
	+1	H_3PO_2, hypophosphorous acid
P_4O_6	+3	H_3PO_3, orthophosphorous acid
	+4	$H_4P_2O_6$, hypophosphoric acid
P_4O_{10}	+5	H_3PO_4, orthophosphoric acid

Phosphorus oxides. If white phosphorus is treated with a limited supply of air, a mixture of P_4O_6 and P_4O_{10} is obtained. In the presence of excess oxygen P_4O_{10} is the sole product:

$$P_4 \xrightarrow{O_2} P_4O_6 \xrightarrow{O_2} P_4O_{10}$$

White phosphorus · Phosphorous oxide · Phosphoric oxide

$P_4O_6 \xrightarrow{H_2O}$ · $P_4O_{10} \xrightarrow{H_2O}$

$$H_3PO_3 \qquad H_2PO_4$$

Phosphorous acid · Phosphoric acid

P_4O_6 can be prepared pure by the oxidation of white phosphorus with nitrous oxide:

$$P_4 + 6N_2O \xrightarrow{\quad 600° \quad} P_4O_6 + 6N_2$$

As was seen earlier (p. 87), the structures of both oxides are based on the P_4 unit found in elementary phosphorus.

P_4O_6 is the anhydride of orthophosphorous acid, and P_4O_{10} is the anhydride of orthophosphoric acid; the oxides react with water to give aqueous solution of these acids. P_4O_{10} reacts very vigorously with water and with water-containing substances and is used as a powerful dehydrating agent.

Hypophosphorous acid, H_3PO_2. Hypophosphites, the salts of hypophosphorous acid, can be prepared in poor yield by boiling white phosphorus with alkali:

$$P_4 + 4OH^- + 4H_2O \rightarrow 4H_2PO_2^- + 2H_2$$

Other reactions also occur; for example

$$P_4 + 4OH^- + 2H_2O \rightarrow 2HPO_3^{2-} + 2PH_3$$

The pure acid, mp 26°C, can be obtained by precipitating barium hypophosphite from solution and then treating this salt with sulfuric acid:

$$Ba(H_2PO_2)_2 + H_2SO_4 \rightarrow BaSO_4 + 2H_3PO_2$$

The acid is a moderately strong ($K_a = 8 \times 10^{-2}$) *monobasic* acid. The structure of the hypophosphite anion is

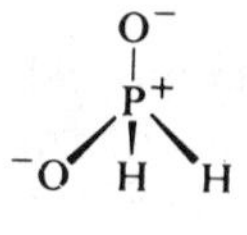

with the arrangement being tetrahedral. The acid and its salts are very powerful reducing agents.

Orthophosphorous acid, H_3PO_3. This acid can be prepared by the hydrolysis of phosphorous trichloride or phosphorus trioxide:

$$PCl_3 + 3H_2O \rightarrow H_3PO_3 + 3HCl$$

Orthophosphorous acid is a moderately strong $(K_a = 5 \times 10^{-2})$ *dibasic* acid which is the parent acid for the normal phosphites (Na_2HPO_3, for example) and acid phosphites (NaH_2PO_3, for example). The normal phosphites contain the tetrahedral anion

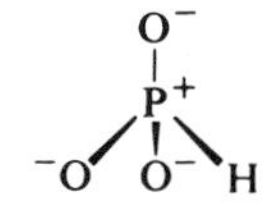

in which one hydrogen is directly bonded to phosphorus.

Orthophosphoric acid, H_3PO_4. This acid can be prepared in the laboratory by the hydrolysis of PCl_5 or P_4O_{10}:

$$PCl_5 + 4H_2O \rightarrow H_3PO_4 + 5HCl$$
$$P_4O_{10} + 6H_2O \rightarrow 4H_3PO_4$$

It is a colorless solid which is very soluble in water. It is a tribasic acid, but not a particularly strong one:

$$H_3PO_4 + H_2O \rightarrow H_2PO_4^- + H_3O^+ \qquad K_1 = 7.5 \times 10^{-3}$$
$$H_2PO_4^- + H_2O \rightarrow HPO_4^{2-} + H_3O^+ \qquad K_2 = 6.2 \times 10^{-8}$$
$$HPO_4^{2-} + H_2O \rightarrow PO_4^{3-} + H_3O^+ \qquad K_3 = 2.2 \times 10^{-13}$$

It should be noted that $H_2PO_4^-$ and HPO_4^{2-} are very much weaker acids than, for instance, acetic acid. Dissociation constants for multibasic acids decrease successively as protons are lost; the main reason is electrostatic.

There are three series of salts derived from orthophosphoric acid—for example, NaH_2PO_4, Na_2HPO_4, and Na_3PO_4. As a result of the different strengths of the acids concerned, Na_3PO_4 gives an alkaline solution, Na_2HPO_4 gives a neutral solution, and NaH_2PO_4 gives an acid solution when the salts are dissolved in water:

Solution	pH
0.1 M H_3PO_4	1.5
0.1 M NaH_2PO_4	4.5
0.1 M Na_2HPO_4	9.2
0.1 M Na_3PO_4	11.7

The structures of the acid and the three anions are

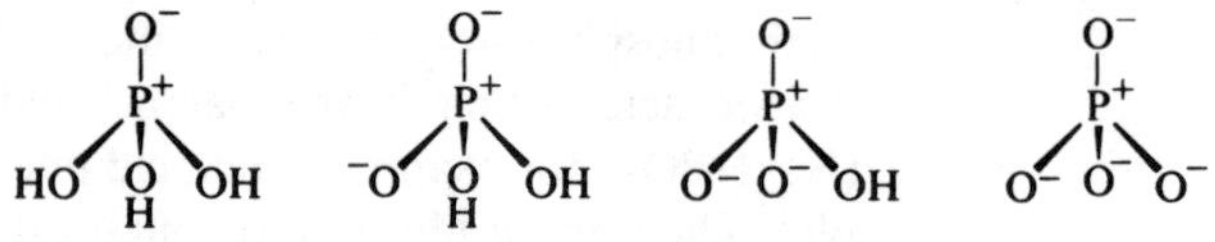

$$H_3PO_4 \qquad H_2PO_4^- \qquad HPO_4^{2-} \qquad PO_4^{3-}$$

All are tetrahedral. Orthophosphoric acid is the parent compound for condensed oxyacids, which resemble the silicates in their structures. For example

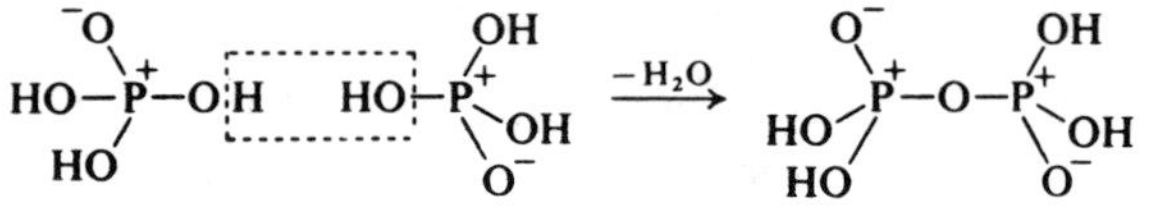

Pyrophosphoric acid, $H_4P_2O_7$

There are many ring and linear condensed oxyacids, the salts of which are all called metaphosphates. For example

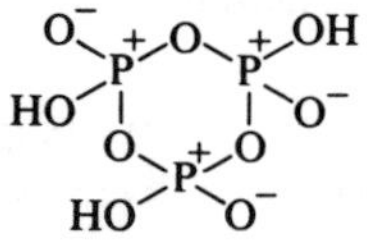

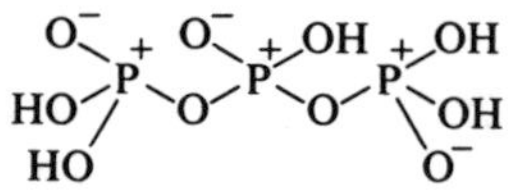

**Group VIA.
Oxygen, Sulfur,
Selenium,
Tellurium, and
Polonium**

Some of the properties of the five elements belonging to Group VIA of the periodic table are shown in Table 2-8. As usual, the first member of the group, oxygen, is much more electronegative than any of the other elements of the group. It is the only element in the group that is gaseous at room temperature. Metallic character becomes more

Table 2-8   Properties of the Group-VIA Elements

Property	Oxygen (O)	Sulfur (S)	Selenium (Se)	Tellurium (Te)	Polonium (Po)
Atomic number	8	16	34	52	84
Electronic configuration	$[He]2s^2sp^4$	$[Ne]3s^23p^4$	$[Ar]3d^{10}4s^24p^4$	$[Kr]4d^{10}5s^25p^4$	$[Xe]4f^{14}5d^{10}6s^26p^4$
Ionic radius, X^{2-}, Å	1.40	1.90	2.02	2.22	2.30
Covalent radius,[a] Å	0.74	1.02	1.16	1.35	1.64
Electronegativity	3.50	2.44	2.48	2.01	1.76
Boiling point, °C	−183	444.6	684.8	1390	962

[a] The covalent radius in divalent molecules, for example, H_2X

pronounced as the group is descended, but even the heaviest element, polonium, has many characteristics of a nonmetal. All the isotopes of polonium are strongly radioactive.

Group-VI elements form bonds in the following ways.

1. *They can gain two electrons to produce* M^{2-} *ions and form ionic bonds.* All the Group-VIA elements can behave in this way. Ionic oxides containing the O^{2-} anion, and ionic sulfides, which contain the S^{2-} anion, are important and common chemical compounds. The electronic configurations of the ions correspond to those of noble gases, there being six p electrons in the valence shell.

The process in which *one* electron is added to a gaseous Group-VI atom is energetically favorable, but the addition of a second electron to the singly charged ion is energetically very unfavorable; for example

$$O(g) + e \rightarrow O^-(g) \qquad \Delta H = -34 \text{ kcal/mole}$$
$$[He]2s^2 2p^4 \qquad [He]2s^2 2p^5$$
$$O^-(g) + e \rightarrow O^{2-}(g) \qquad \Delta H = +191 \text{ kcal/mole}$$
$$[He]2s^2 2p^5 \qquad [He]2s^2 2p^6$$

Overall, the addition of two electrons to the oxygen atom is also energetically unfavorable:

$$O(g) + 2e \rightarrow O^{2-}(g) \qquad \Delta H = (+191 - 34) = +157 \text{ kcal/mole}$$

Since it requires energy to dissociate oxygen molecules into oxygen atoms

$$O_2(g) + 2e \rightarrow 2O(g) \qquad \Delta H = +118 \text{ kcal/mole}$$

the overall process

$$\tfrac{1}{2}O_2(g) + 2e \rightarrow O^{2-}(g) \qquad \Delta H = +216 \text{ kcal/mole}$$

has a very unfavorable ΔH value. Similar large positive ΔH's can be calculated for the corresponding processes with the other Group-VI elements.

The occurrence of compounds containing the O^{2-} ion can be examined by using the Born–Haber cycle, as described in Chapter 1, and is due to the fact that the very high lattice energy of an ionic solid containing this small, doubly charged anion, more than counter-balances the unfavorable enthalpy of its production from oxygen; for example

Compound	Lattice energy
$MgBr_2(Mg^{2+}, 2Br^-)$	575 kcal/mole
$MgO(Mg^{2+}, O^{2-})$	938 kcal/mole

The high lattice energies of ionic oxides make it possible to prepare stable oxides of some metals in which the metal has an unusually high oxidation state. This is because the high lattice energy can compensate for the extra, unfavorable ionization energy required to produce the higher-oxidation-state metal cation. Examples of unusually high oxidation states found in oxides are:

AgO, which contains the Ag^{2+} cation (Ag^+ is the most common oxidation state of silver, for example in Ag_2O);

PrO_2, which contains the Pr^{4+} cation (Pr^{3+} is the most common oxidation state of praseodymium, for example in Pr_2O_3).

Fluorine shares with oxygen this ability to bring out the maximum oxidation states of elements.

The oxide ion is very strongly basic and has no existence in aqueous solution, because the equilibrium

$$O^{2-} + H_2O \rightleftharpoons 2OH^-$$

lies very far to the right. As a result, no oxide simply "dissolves" in water; instead some oxides react with water to give either a solution of the hydroxide (if the hydroxide is soluble) or a precipitate of the hydroxide if the hydroxide is insoluble. For example

$$Na_2O + H_2O \rightarrow 2Na^+(aq) + 2OH^-(aq)$$
$$CaO + H_2O \rightarrow Ca(OH)_2$$

The sulfide ion, S^{2-}, is larger than the oxide ion, and ionic sulfides consequently have smaller lattice energies. One result is that sulfur does not share with oxygen the ability to form stable compounds with elements in exceptionally high oxidation states. The sulfide ion is much less strongly basic than the oxide ion and can exist in aqueous solution:

$$S^{2-}(aq) + H_2O \rightleftharpoons SH^-(aq) + OH^-(aq)$$

The equilibrium constant for the above reaction between sulfide and water has a value of about 1, in contrast to an equilibrium constant of greater than 10^{22} for the corresponding reaction of the oxide ion. Another way of stating the same result is to say that SH^- is a very weak acid in aqueous solution,

$$HS^-(aq) + H_2O \;\; \rightleftharpoons \;\; H_3O^+ + S^{2-}(aq) \qquad K = 10^{-14}$$

while OH^- has essentially no acidic properties at all:

$$OH^-(aq) + H_2O \;\; \rightleftharpoons \;\; H_3O^+ + O^{2-}(aq) \qquad K = 10^{-36}$$

2. *They can form two covalent bonds.* All the Group-VIA elements form compounds in this way; examples are F_2O, H_2O, and H_2S. The molecules are nonlinear, and the Group-VIA element has two pairs of nonbonding electrons in its valence shell. If the bonds involved p orbitals, and if it were not for repulsion between the orbitals, the bond angles would be $90°$. As one descends the group and the bonds become larger, the bond angle gradually approaches a right angle:

$$H\!-\!\overset{\frown}{O}\!-\!H = 104.5°$$

$$H\!-\!\overset{\frown}{S}\!-\!H = \;\; 92.1°$$

$$H\!-\!\overset{\frown}{Se}\!-\!H = \;\; 91°$$

Molecules of this type contain two pairs of nonbonding electrons which are capable of forming dative bonds; for example

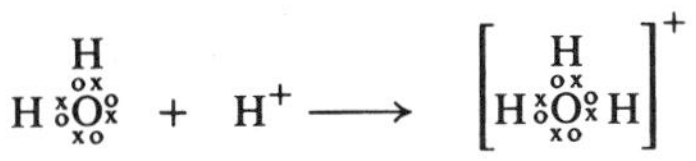

$$\begin{array}{c} H \\[-2pt] \overset{ox}{H\,\overset{\circ}{\underset{xo}{O}}\!\overset{\circ}{}} \end{array} \; + \; H^+ \longrightarrow \left[\, H\,\overset{ox}{\underset{xo}{O}}\!\overset{H}{}\, H \right]^{+}$$

Compounds of oxygen and hydrogen, such as water, ethanol, $C_2H_5\!-\!OH$, and acetic acid, $CH_3CO\!-\!OH$, contain highly polar hydroxyl groups, since oxygen has a much higher electronegativity than hydrogen. Because of this bond polarity, and because the oxygen atom possesses pairs of nonbonding valence electrons, such compounds form *hydrogen bonds* which join together two or more molecules. Acetic acid (and many other carboxylic acids) forms dimers when dissolved in inert solvents such as benzene, and it has been shown that a pair of hydrogen bonds holds the two acetic acid molecules together:

$$H_3C-C \underset{O\cdots H-O}{\overset{O-H\cdots O}{\diagdown}} C-CH_3$$

Hydrogen bonding in pure water, ethanol, and acetic acid leads to anomalously high boiling points for these compounds.

The polarity of –S–H, –Se–H, and –Te–H bonds is very much less than the polarity of the –O–H bond, because the electronegativities of S, Se, and Te are much less than that of oxygen and much closer to the value for hydrogen. As a result, hydrogen bonding is not of much importance for Group-VIA hydrogen compounds other than –O–H compounds.

3. *They can form one covalent bond and gain one electron.* This is a combination of the two methods of bonding described under 1 and 2, in which singly charged anions are formed in combination with at least one other atom. Examples of such ions are:

O–H⁻, the hydroxide ion;   S–H⁻, the hydrosulfide ion;

O–Cl⁻, the hypochlorite ion;   O–O²⁻, the peroxide ion.

The ions contain oxygen and sulfur atoms in which there are three pairs of nonbonding valence electrons. Oxygen forms the following important series of ions and molecules:

$$H_3O^+ \quad H_2O \quad OH^- \quad O^{2-}$$

In this series, protons are successively attached to pairs of nonbonding valence electrons of the oxide ion to form a series similar to the $NH_4^+-N^{3-}$ series of ions already described for nitrogen:

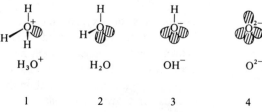

H_3O^+	H_2O	OH^-	O^{2-}
1	2	3	4

(Number of pairs of non-bonding valence electrons)

The H_4O^{2+} ion, which would be isoelectronic with the ammonium ion, NH_4^+, and with methane, CH_4, is not known. This is to be expected, since both pairs of nonbonding electrons would be forming dative bonds:

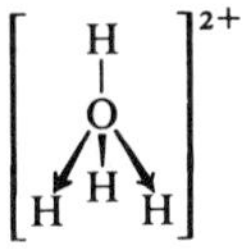

As was the case for the series of nitrogen ions and molecules, with oxygen the acidity increases and the basicity decreases as protons are added to the O^{2-} ion. The species H_3O^+ is very strongly acidic, water is both weakly acidic and weakly basic,

$$H_2O \rightleftharpoons H^+ + OH^-$$

and the hydroxide and oxide ions are increasingly strongly basic species.

We have seen that Group-VIA elements can attain the electronic configuration of a noble gas in three different ways: by accepting two electrons to form M^{2-} ions, by forming two covalent bonds to produce MX_2 molecules, or by accepting one electron and forming one covalent bond to give MX^- ions.

4. *They can form π bonds.* Oxygen is probably the only Group-VIA element which can form π bonds involving p orbitals; it can do this when combined with other elements from the first short period, for example, in O_2, CO_2, and NO. Sulfur forms compounds with carbon which have similar structures to those possessed by analogous carbon–oxygen compounds, for example

S=C=S
Carbon disulfide

O=C=O
Carbon dioxide

H₂N
\
  C=S
/
H₂N

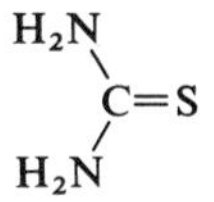

Thiourea

H₂N
\
  C=O
/
H₂N

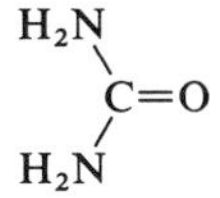

Urea

but it is probable that the π bond between carbon and sulfur is formed by overlap of a p orbital from carbon and a d orbital (rather than a p orbital) from sulfur. Sulfur makes use of its empty 3d orbitals to form double bonds in oxygen compounds such as SO_2 and SO_4^{2-}, but these π bonds are dative ones, since both electrons in the π bond originate from the oxygen atom.

5. *They can lose electrons to form cations.* The formation of M^{6+} cations, in which all the valence electrons would be lost by ionization, is out of the question because of the enormous ionization energies required to produce such ions. Some compounds of the two heaviest elements in Group VIA, tellurium and polonium, for example TeO_2, can be considered to contain the M^{4+} cations Te^{4+} and Po^{4+} in which a pair of valence electrons is not lost. However, none of the Group-VIA elements has an extensive cation chemistry like that of antimony and bismuth in Group VA.

Recently, a series of dioxygenyl compounds has been prepared; these contain the dioxygenyl cation, O_2^+, which is derived from the oxygen *molecule* by the loss of an electron. The bonding in this ion will be considered later, together with that of the oxygen molecule.

6. *They can use* d *orbitals and form four or six covalent bonds with other elements.* Because oxygen is in the first short period, it has no empty d orbitals of low energy and it is restricted to a maximum coordination number of 4, as was explained in Chapter 1. Sulfur and the heavier Group-VIA elements have empty, low-energy, d orbitals, and the promotion of valence electrons into these orbitals produces electronic configurations containing four or six unpaired electrons instead of only the two unpaired electrons of the ground state. They can, as a result, form four or six covalent bonds, for example

SF₄

sp³d-hybridized sulfur

SF₆

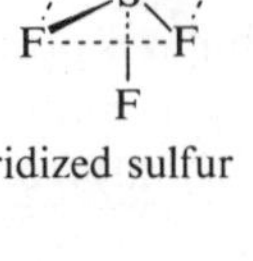

sp³d²-hybridized sulfur

	3s	3p	3d	Number of unpaired electrons
Sulfur atom, $3s^2 3p^4$ (ground state)	↑↓	↑↓ ↑ ↑	☐ ☐ ☐ ☐ ☐	2
Sulfur in H_2S	↑↓	↑↓ ↑↓ ↑↓	☐ ☐ ☐ ☐ ☐	0
Sulfur atom, $3s^2 3p^3 3d^1$ (excited state)	↑↓	↑ ↑ ↑	↑ ☐ ☐ ☐ ☐	4
Sulfur atom in SF_4	↑↓	↑↓ ↑↓ ↑↓	↑↓ ☐ ☐ ☐ ☐	0
Sulfur atom, $3s^1 3p^3 3d^2$ (excited state)	↑	↑ ↑ ↑	↑ ↑ ☐ ☐ ☐	6
Sulfur atom in SF_6	↑↓	↑↓ ↑↓ ↑↓	↑↓ ↑↓ ☐ ☐ ☐	0

Since the sulfur atom in SF_6 has used all its valence electrons to form bonds and has no nonbonding valence electrons, SF_6 is not an electron donor.

The structure of SF_4 is closely related to that of PF_5, except that in SF_4 a pair of nonbonding valence electrons occupies an sp^3d-hybrid orbital which in PF_5 is occupied by a pair of bonding electrons:

7. *The atoms can act as electron acceptors.* The Group-VIA elements can also achieve a noble-gas electronic configuration by accepting a pair of electrons from an electron donor and so forming a dative bond. An example of this is found in a class of organic compounds called amine oxides, $R_3N \rightarrow O$, which can be thought of as being formed from an oxygen atom and an amine (substituted ammonia) molecule:

$$R_3N: \ + \ O \ \longrightarrow \ R_3N \rightarrow O$$

8. *Covalent molecules of Group-VIA elements in the oxidation state* $+4$ *can also act as acceptors*; for example

$$TeI_4 + 2I^- \ \rightarrow \ TeI_6^{2-}$$
$$SeBr_4 + 2Br^- \ \rightarrow \ SeBr_6^{2-}$$

The ions produced are octahedral, although there are seven pairs of electrons in the valence shells of selenium and tellurium. The pair of nonbonding electrons does not participate in the stereochemistry of the ions and must therefore occupy an s orbital rather than an sp^3d^3-hybrid orbital:

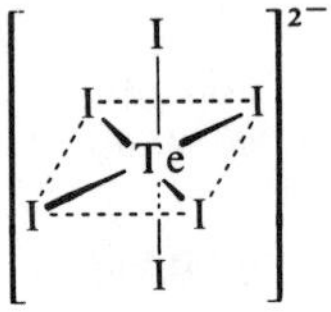

The Elements

Oxygen. Air contains 23 % oxygen by weight, and oxygen is obtained industrially by the fractional distillation of liquid air. In the laboratory it can be obtained by the electrolysis of water (which contains 89 % oxygen by weight) which has been rendered conducting by the addition of acid or alkali:

At the cathode

$$2H^+(aq) + 2e \rightarrow H_2(g)$$

At the anode

$$2OH^-(aq) \rightarrow H_2O + \tfrac{1}{2}O_2(g) + 2e$$

Alternatively, many oxygen-rich compounds decompose on heating. to give oxygen gas. For example,

$$2KClO_3 \rightarrow 2KCl + 3O_2 \text{ (catalyzed by } MnO_2\text{)}$$

Potassium chlorate	Potassium chloride

$$2BaO_2 \rightleftharpoons 2BaO + O_2$$

Barium peroxide	Barium oxide

Oxygen, O_2, is a colorless, paramagnetic gas, bp $-183°C$. Many elements and compounds will react with oxygen, but usually only when heated. White phosphorus burns slowly in the cold in oxygen to give P_4O_6 and P_4O_{10}, and nitric oxide (NO) gas also reacts in the cold with oxygen to give nitrogen dioxide, NO_2.

Combustion of elements in oxygen to give oxides is often a highly exothermic process because of the high lattice energies of ionic oxides or the strong covalent bonds formed by oxygen:

$$2Ca(s) + O_2(g) \rightarrow 2CaO \qquad \Delta H = -304 \text{ kcal}$$

$$4Al(s) + 3O_2(g) \rightarrow 2Al_2O_3 \qquad \Delta H = -800 \text{ kcal}$$

$$4P(s) + 5O_2(g) \rightarrow P_4O_{10} \qquad \Delta H = -720 \text{ kcal}$$

Nearly all carbon compounds will burn in oxygen or air to give carbon dioxide and water among the products. These combustion reactions are of enormous importance because they provide much of the world's energy. For example,

$$C_7H_{16} + 11O_2 \rightarrow 7CO_2 + 8H_2O \qquad \Delta H = -1149 \text{ kcal}$$
Heptane

$$2C_2H_2 + 5O_2 \rightarrow 4CO_2 + 2H_2O \qquad \Delta H = -624 \text{ kcal}$$
Acetylene

Many combustion reactions occur only when the reaction mixture is heated. At room temperature the rate of oxidation is negligibly small because the activation energy for oxidation is large. One cause of this large activation energy is the large bond dissociation energy of the O_2 molecule (118 kcal/mole).

Ozone. The element oxygen exhibits *allotropy*, which is a term used to describe the ability of an element to exist in more than one form. The oxygen molecule, O_2, is one allotrope of the element; ozone, O_3, is the other.

Ozone is less stable than oxygen at room temperature and atmospheric pressure:

$$3O_2 \rightleftharpoons 2O_3 \qquad \Delta H = +68 \text{ kcal}$$

The equilibrium constant

$$K = \frac{[O_3]^2}{[O_2]^3}$$

for the reaction is very small. Very high pressures will favor the production of ozone, since three molecules of oxygen are converted into two ozone molecules, but under normal conditions the equilibrium concentration of ozone is extremely small.

Ozone can be prepared by passing oxygen gas through a silent electric discharge in an apparatus called an ozonizer. The silent discharge in the ozonizer produces oxygen atoms

$$O_2 \;\rightarrow\; 2O \qquad \Delta H = +118 \text{ kcal}$$

and some of the atoms react with oxygen molecules to give ozone:

$$O_2 + O \;\rightarrow\; O_3 \qquad \Delta H = -24 \text{ kcal}$$

The gas produced from an ozonizer contains up to 10% ozone. Pure ozone can be obtained from the ozone–oxygen mixture by passing it through a tube cooled in liquid oxygen; the boiling point of ozone is $-112°C$, much higher than that of O_2.

Ozone is a very reactive substance; it is explosive when pure. It is a very powerful oxidizing agent

$$O_2 + H_2O \;\rightleftharpoons\; O_3 + 2H^+ + 2e \qquad \varepsilon^0 = -2.07 \text{ volts}$$

much more powerful than oxygen itself

$$2H_2O \;\rightleftharpoons\; 4H^+ + O_2 + 4e \qquad \varepsilon^0 = -1.23 \text{ volts}$$

Sometimes ozone will oxidize substances and give oxygen as the product, while with stronger reducing agents the oxygen will be consumed as well. For example,

$$PbS + 4O_3 \;\rightarrow\; PbSO_4 + 4O_2$$
$$Ag + O_3 \;\rightarrow\; AgO + O_2$$
$$6Cr^{2+} + O_3 + 3H_2O \;\rightarrow\; 6Cr^{3+} + 6OH^-$$

Ozone reacts with unsaturated organic compounds containing carbon–carbon double bonds to give ozonides:

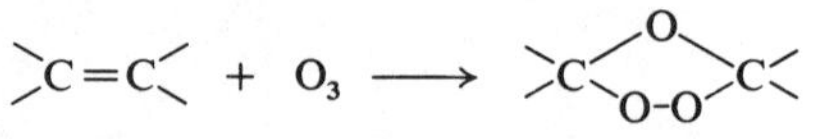

Ozonide

Ozone is a pale blue gas which is very poisonous. Structure determinations have shown that the molecule is nonlinear, with an angle of 116.8°, in agreement with the fact that ozone has a dipole moment. The O–O distance in ozone corresponds to a bond order of 1.5, and the bonding in the molecule can be represented by two resonance structures:

$$O=\overset{+}{\underset{}{O}}\diagdown_{O^-} \quad \longleftrightarrow \quad O=\overset{+}{\underset{}{O}}\diagdown\diagup_{O}$$

Sulfur. Sulfur vapor at high temperatures consists mostly of S_2 molecules, which resemble O_2 molecules in their bonding. At room temperature, however, S_2 molecules are unstable (unlike O_2 molecules), and they polymerize to give a variety of solid structures containing S_8 or S_6 rings or S_n chains. These different solid structures are allotropes of sulfur and they differ only slightly in stability; for example

$$S_{(rhombic)} \quad \rightarrow \quad S_{(monoclinic)} \qquad \Delta H = 0.76 \text{ kcal mole}$$

Rhombic sulfur, which contains S_8 rings, is the stable form of sulfur under ordinary conditions, the other allotropes all being metastable. Above the transition temperature (95.5°C) monoclinic sulfur (which also contains S_8 rings, but arranged differently) is more stable. However the rate at which one allotrope of sulfur can be converted into another allotrope is very often low. Yet another solid allotrope of sulfur, called Engel's sulfur, contains S_6 rings:

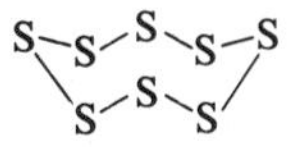

S_8 ring in rhombic
and monoclinic sulfur

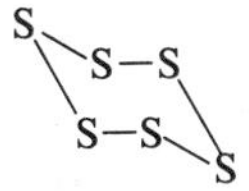

S_6 ring in
Engel's sulfur

Liquid sulfur consists of a mixture of S_8 and other rings and polymeric chains of sulfur atoms,

$$\ldots S—S—(S)_n—S—S \ldots$$

the composition depending on the temperature. Sudden chilling of the liquid produces another metastable form of sulfur called plastic sulfur.

The Group-VIA Hydrides

Each Group-VIA element forms a hydride of the general formula H_2X. Some of the properties of these hydrides are listed in Table 2-9. Polonium hydride has only been detected in minute quantities. Oxygen forms a second hydride, H_2O_2 (hydrogen peroxide), whose properties will be considered separately.

Table 2-9 Properties of the Group-VIA Hydrides

Property	Water (H$_2$O)	Hydrogen Sulfide (H$_2$S)	Hydrogen Selenide (H$_2$Se)	Hydrogen Telluride (H$_2$Te)
Boiling Point, °C	100.00	−60.7	−41.5	−1.8
Latent heat of evaporation at the bp, (kcal/mole)	9.7	4.5	4.8	5.7
Heat of formation at 20°C (ΔH_f), kcal/mole	−68	−5	+21	+37
First acid dissociation constant, 18°C $H_2X(aq) \rightleftharpoons H_3O^+(aq) + HX^-(aq)$	1.3×10^{-16}	8.7×10^{-8}	1.9×10^{-4}	2.3×10^{-3}
H–X–H (g) angle, °	104.5	92.1	91	
Heat of atomization, D_{H_2X}, kcal/mole	222	162	122	116

Water.   Many properties of water, such as its boiling point and latent heat of evaporation, are anomalously high compared with the values for the other hydrides. Thus, a simple molecular weight trend would lead to a *lower* boiling point for water than for H$_2$S, and, similarly, the latent heat of vaporization for water would be expected to be *less* than 4.5 kcal/mole, the value for H$_2$S, rather than 9.7, the actual value. These anomalies arise from the association of water molecules in the liquid phase.

The heats of formation listed in Table 2-9 show that H$_2$O and H$_2$S are formed *exothermally* from the elements, whereas H$_2$Se and H$_2$Te are *endothermic* molecules. H$_2$Se and H$_2$Te are unstable with respect to the elements, but they have considerable *kinetic* stability and do not decompose until raised to a fairly high temperature. The trend in $\Delta H_f°$ values from −68 to +37 kcal/mole on passing from H$_2$O to H$_2$Te is caused principally by the decreasingly strong bonds formed between Group-VIA elements and hydrogen as the atomic weight increases. This is a general trend we have already met in several groups.

Hydrogen peroxide, H$_2$O$_2$.   One method of preparing hydrogen peroxide is to hydrolyze perdisulfuric acid, which can be prepared by the electrolytic oxidation of sulfate ions in aqueous solution:

1. Preparation of perdisulfate:

At the anode

$$2SO_4^{2-} \rightarrow S_2O_8^{2-} + 2e$$

At the cathode

$$2H^+ + 2e \rightarrow H_2$$

2. The hydrolysis of perdisulfate:

$$H_2S_2O_8 + H_2O \rightleftharpoons H_2SO_4 + H_2SO_5$$
$$\text{(Permonosulfuric acid)}$$

$$H_2SO_5 + H_2O \rightleftharpoons H_2SO_4 + H_2O_2$$

Hydrogen peroxide is obtained as an aqueous solution by distilling it from the sulfuric acid–hydrogen peroxide reaction mixture, and the sulfuric acid can be used again in the electrolysis stage.

The hydrogen peroxide molecule is nonplanar, having the structure

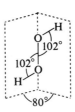

The fact that the two O–H bonds lie in different planes is due to repulsion between the various bonding and nonbonding orbitals.

Hydrogen peroxide is rarely used in the pure state because it is dangerously explosive. Aqueous solutions, however, have much greater kinetic stability. Hydrogen peroxide is *not* endothermic with respect to the elements

$$H_2O_2 \rightarrow H_2 + O_2 \qquad \Delta H = +44 \text{ kcal/mole}$$

but its decomposition into water and oxygen *is* an exothermic reaction:

$$H_2O_2 \rightarrow H_2O + \tfrac{1}{2}O_2 \qquad \Delta H = -23 \text{ kcal/mole}$$

This decomposition reaction is catalyzed by a very large number of solids and ions in solution and by light.

Hydrogen peroxide is a very weak dibasic acid

$$H_2O_2(aq) \quad \rightleftharpoons \quad H^+(aq) + HO_2^-(aq)$$

$$HO_2^-(aq) \quad \rightleftharpoons \quad H^+(aq) + O_2^{2-}(aq)$$

$$K_1 = 1.5 \times 10^{-12}$$

and two series of ionic salts are known, one series being derived from HO_2^-, for example, $NaHO_2$, and the other from the peroxide ion O_2^{2-}, for example, Na_2O_2. Ionic peroxides have already been described in the sections of this chapter dealing with the alkali and alkaline earth metals.

Hydrogen peroxide is a powerful oxidizing agent.

In acid solution

$$2H_2O \quad \rightleftharpoons \quad H_2O_2 + 2H^+ + 2e \qquad \varepsilon^0 = -1.77 \text{ volts}$$

In alkaline solution

$$3OH^- \quad \rightleftharpoons \quad HO_2^- + H_2O + 2e \qquad \varepsilon^0 = -0.88 \text{ volts}$$

It is particularly useful as an oxidizing agent in preparative chemistry, because it introduces into solution no ions that might contaminate the product (unlike $KMnO_4$, K_2CrO_4, Cl_2, and so forth). Excess hydrogen peroxide is readily removed by catalytic decomposition.

The oxidation of Fe^{2+} (and other reducing agents which can only increase their oxidation states by one unit) by H_2O_2 is an important reaction, since hydroxyl free radicals are produced as intermediates in the reaction:

$$Fe^{2+} + H_2O_2 \quad \rightarrow \quad Fe^{3+} + OH^- + OH$$

$$Fe^{2+} + OH \quad \rightarrow \quad Fe^{3+} + OH^-$$

These hydroxyl radicals contain an odd number of electrons and can be used to initiate polymerization reactions of organic molecules.

Hydrogen peroxide shares with hydrazine and hydroxylamine (cf. p. 90) the ability to act as both an oxidizing and a reducing agent:

$$H_2O_2 \quad \rightarrow \quad O_2 + 2H^+ + 2e \qquad \varepsilon^0 = -0.68 \text{ volts}$$

While hydroxylamine and hydrazine are, as is indicated by their ε^0 values, chiefly of use as reducing agents, hydrogen peroxide is not a powerful reducing agent. However, powerful oxidizing agents do oxidize hydrogen peroxide to oxygen:

$$H_2O_2 + 2Ce^{4+} \rightarrow 2Ce^{3+} + O_2 + 2H^+$$
$$7H_2O_2 + 2MnO_4^- + 6H^+ \rightarrow 2Mn^{2+} + 6O_2 + 10H_2O$$

Other peroxides. In addition to the ionic peroxides such as Na_2O_2 and BaO_2, many covalent derivatives of hydrogen peroxide are known. These can be very briefly listed under three headings.

1. *Permono acids*, which contain the –O–H grouping and are in theory derived from oxyacids and hydrogen peroxide:

$$H_2O + 2H_2O_2 + P_2O_5 \rightarrow 2H_3PO_5$$

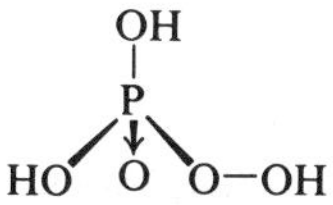

Permonophosphoric acid

Permonosulfuric acid was described above as an intermediate in the preparation of hydrogen peroxide, and it can be similarly prepared from sulfuric acid and hydrogen peroxide:

$$H_2SO_4 + H_2O_2 \rightleftharpoons H_2SO_5 + H_2O$$

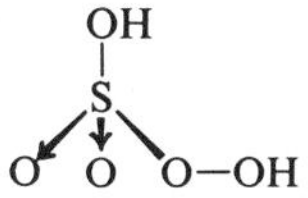

Permonosulfuric acid

Perborates are of importance as bleaching agents in modern detergents.

2. *Perdi-acids*, which contain the M–O–O–M grouping, are hydrogen peroxide derivatives of pyro acids in which the –O– bridge group is replaced by the –O–O– of hydrogen peroxide; for example

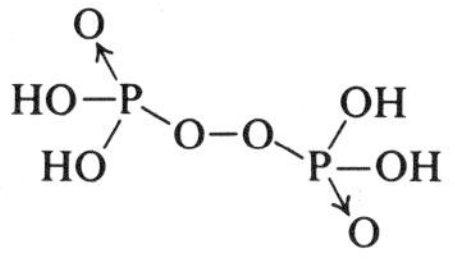

$H_4P_2O_8$

Perdiphosphoric acid

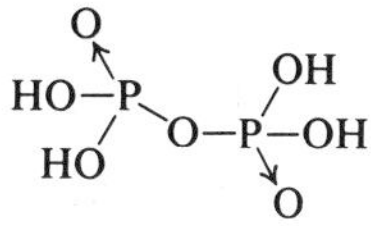

$H_4P_2O_7$

Pyrophosphoric acid

Perdisulfuric acid, an intermediate in the preparation of hydrogen peroxide, has the structure

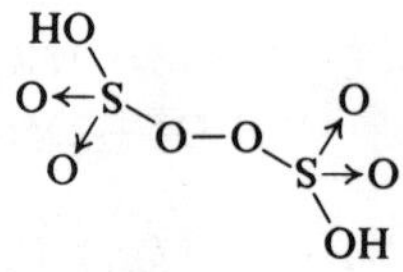

$H_2S_2O_8$
Perdisulfuric acid

This should be compared with the structure of pyrosulfuric acid, $H_2S_2O_7$:

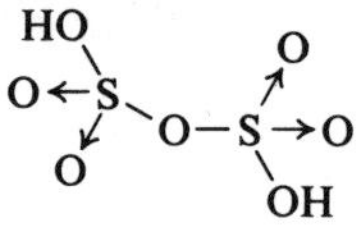

Perdi-acids are usually prepared by anodic oxidation, as has been illustrated earlier for $H_2S_2O_8$ in the preparation of hydrogen peroxide.

3. *Peroxide derivatives of transition metals* have many known varieties. They may contain either the M–O–O–H or the M–O–O–M groupings as described above, or the peroxide group can be linked to the same metal ion by two bonds,

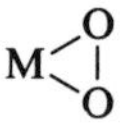

The single example that follows illustrates the type of compound that can be obtained:

$$CrO_4^{2-} + H_2O_2 \xrightarrow{\text{conc KOH}} K_3CrO_8$$

The CrO_8^{3-} ion has been shown to have the structure

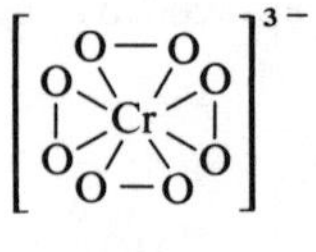

each O–O^{2-} ion being joined by two bonds to the Cr^{5+} ion.

All peroxides are powerful oxidizing agents and are often used as such in preparative chemistry.

Oxides of Sulfur

There are four known oxides of sulfur, S_2O, SO, SO_2, and SO_3, but of these only SO_2 and SO_3 are obtainable at room temperature.

Sulfur dioxide, SO_2.　This is obtained by burning sulfur or metal sulfides in air or oxygen:

$$S + O_2 \ \rightarrow \ SO_2$$
$$2PbS + 3O_2 \ \rightarrow \ 2PbO + 2SO_2$$

Sulfur dioxide is a gas, bp $-10°C$, which is easily liquified. It reacts with chlorine in the presence of charcoal, which acts as a catalyst for the reaction, to give sulfuryl chloride, SO_2Cl_2:

$$SO_2 + Cl_2 \ \rightarrow \ SO_2Cl_2$$

Sulfur dioxide dissolves in water to give a solution of sulfurous acid

$$SO_2 + H_2O \ \rightarrow \ H_2SO_3$$

and dissolves in alkaline solutions to give sulfites or bisulfites

$$NaOH + SO_2 \ \rightarrow \ NaHSO_3$$

Sulfur dioxide is a reducing agent, for example

$$2SO_2 + O_2 \ \rightarrow \ 2SO_3$$

but it is usually used in aqueous solution, and then sulfurous acid is the active species, not SO_2 itself.

The sulfur dioxide molecule has a bent configuration; it may be represented as involving the following type of resonance:

Its structure is analogous to that of ozone (p. 111).

Sulfur trioxide, SO_3.　Sulfur trioxide is obtained industrially by the oxidation of sulfur dioxide with air:

$$2SO_2 + O_2 \ \rightarrow \ 2SO_3 \qquad \Delta H = -45 \text{ kcal}$$

Although this reaction is exothermic and has a negative free energy change ($\Delta G = -33$ kcal), the rate of the reaction is very low; a platinum or vanadium pentoxide catalyst must therefore be used and the mixture heated to 400–500°C, even though this reduces the equilibrium yield of sulfur trioxide.

Sulfur trioxide can be obtained in the laboratory by dehydrating concentrated sulfuric acid with phosphorus pentoxide:

$$H_2SO_4 \xrightarrow{\;-H_2O\;} SO_4$$

Sulfur trioxide is a solid which exists in three allotropic modifications. One form contains S_3O_9 rings

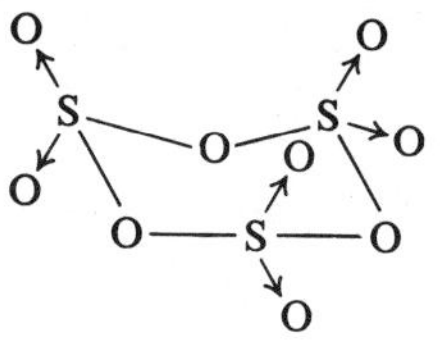

while the other two forms exist as asbestos-like needles and contain linear polymeric chains

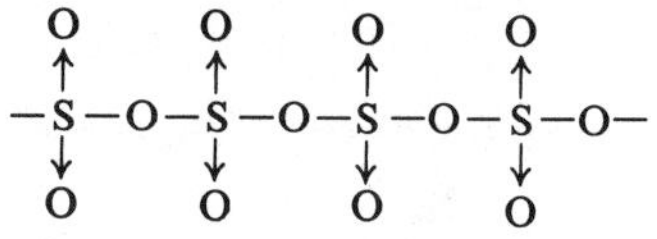

in which each sulfur atom is surrounded by four oxygen atoms in a tetrahedral arrangement. Sulfur trioxide vapor contains planar symmetrical SO_3 molecules, the angles between the S-O bonds being 120°. Its shape can be understood if one regards it as formed from S^{2+}, which is isoelectronic with Si. Since the S^{2+} is attached to three atoms, there will be sp^2 hybridization; two of the bonds will be σ bonds and the other a double bond involving σ and π bonds. There will be resonance between the three equivalent structures

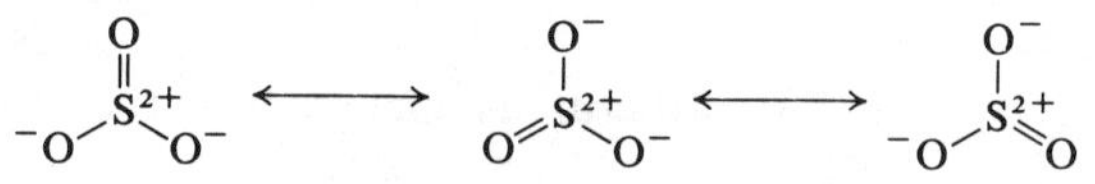

or

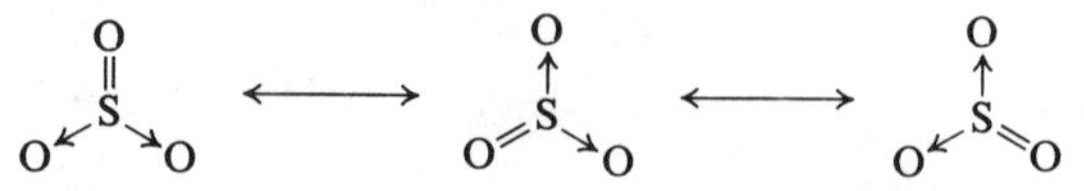

so that all of the bonds are the same.

Sulfur trioxide reacts violently with water to give sulfuric acid

$$SO_3 + H_2O \rightarrow H_2SO_4$$

and dissolves in sulfuric acid to give pyrosulfuric acid:

$$H_2SO_4 + SO_3 \rightarrow H_2S_2O_7$$

The sulfur atom in SO_3 possesses an empty 3p orbital and empty 3d orbitals, and the molecule is a powerful electron acceptor, as is illustrated by the polymer formation described above and by many reactions with electron donors.

Oxyacids of Sulfur

Sulfur forms a remarkably large number of oxyacids and oxyacid anions, which will be considered briefly because they illustrate the different types of oxyacids that can exist.

1. *Simple oxyacids and their anions.* Sulfurous and sulfuric acids are both simple and dibasic oxyacids of sulfur in which sulfur has the oxidation states + 4 and + 6, respectively:

Sulfurous acid, H_2SO_3

Bisulfite anion, HSO_3^-

Sulfite anion, SO_3^{2-}

Sulfuric acid, H_2SO_4

Bisulfate anion, HSO_4^-

Sulfate anion, SO_4^{2-}

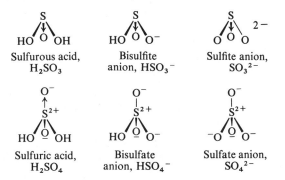

The tetrahedral shapes of these species can be understood if one regards them as built up from S^{2+}, which is isoelectronic with Si. There will be sp^3 hybridization, and when the four monovalent species O^- or OH are attached, the resulting molecule is tetrahedral.

2. *Peracids.*

Permonosulfuric acid, H_2SO_5

Perdisulfuric acid, $H_2S_2O_8$

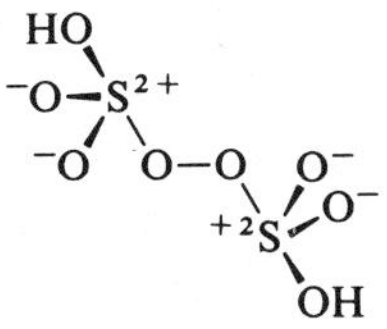

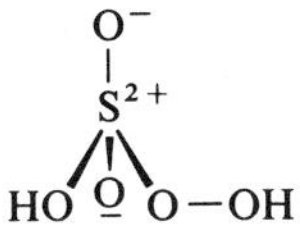

As has already been explained, these peracids can be considered to be derivatives of sulfuric or pyrosulfuric acid and hydrogen peroxide, and both contain the –O–O– (peroxide) group.

3. *Thiosulfates*, $S_2O_3^{2-}$. Thiosulfuric acid, $H_2S_2O_3$, is unknown, but salts derived from it are important chemicals. The thiosulfate ion can be thought of as being derived from the sulfate ion by substituting a sulfur atom for one of the oxygen atoms:

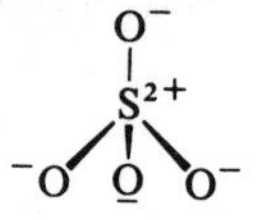

Sulfate anion 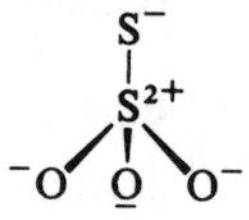   Thiosulfate anion

Thiosulfates are in fact prepared by boiling *sulfites* with sulfur,

$$SO_3^{2-} + S \rightleftharpoons S_2O_3^{2-}$$

The reaction is reversed by acid, which is why thiosulfuric acid cannot be isolated.

4. *Pyro acids.* These are condensed oxyacids, similar in kind to borates, silicates, and phosphates.

Pyrosulfuric acid, $H_2S_2O_7$, can be obtained by removing a molecule of water from two molecules of sulfuric acid:

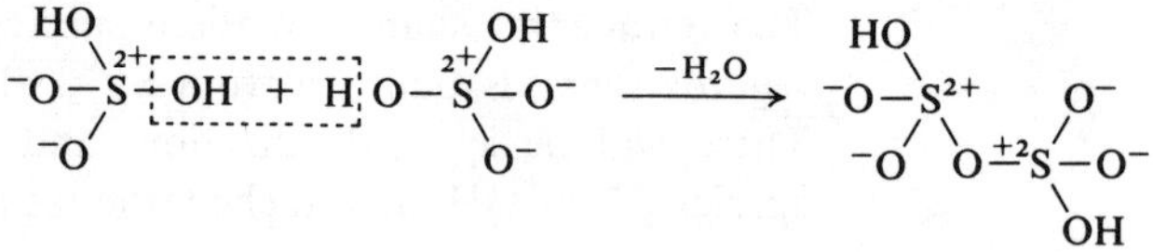

Other, less well-defined, condensed oxyacids are known which contain more than two sulfur atoms, each linked by a single oxygen atom.

5. *Thionates and polythionates.* As we have seen from the structures found in elemental sulfur, sulfur readily forms sulfur chains. A large number of thionates are known in which a number of sulfur atoms are joined in a chain and terminated at each end with –SO_3 groups.

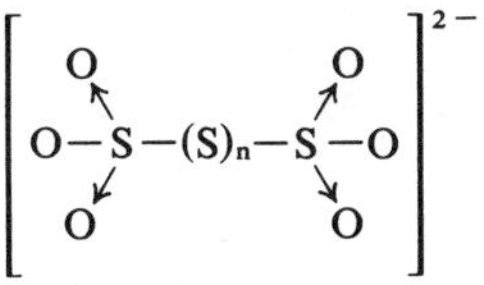

$$\left[\begin{array}{c} O \\ \uparrow \\ O-S-(S)_n-S-O \\ \downarrow \qquad \downarrow \\ O \qquad\qquad O \end{array}\right]^{2-}$$

The simplest thionate is dithionate, $S_2O_6^{2-}$, in which $n = 0$:

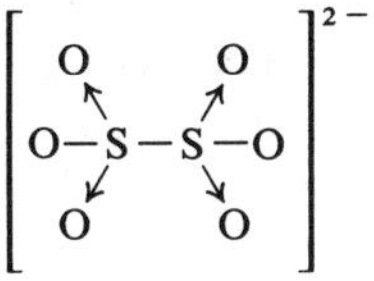

$$\left[\begin{array}{c} O \qquad O \\ \uparrow \qquad \uparrow \\ O-S-S-O \\ \downarrow \qquad \downarrow \\ O \qquad O \end{array}\right]^{2-}$$

Another well-known representative of this class of compound is tetra-thionate, in which $n = 2$; this is obtained as a product in the volu-metric estimation of iodine with thiosulfate:

$$I_2 + 2S_2O_3^{2-} \rightarrow 2I^- + S_4O_6^{2-}$$

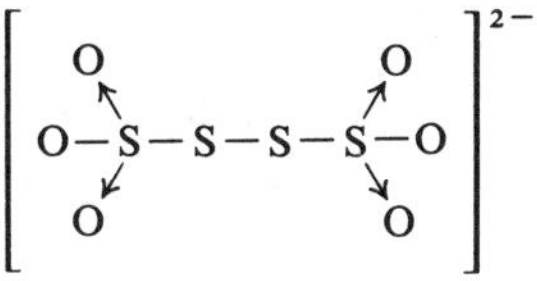

$$\left[\begin{array}{c} O \qquad\qquad O \\ \uparrow \qquad\qquad \uparrow \\ O-S-S-S-S-O \\ \downarrow \qquad\qquad \downarrow \\ O \qquad\qquad O \end{array}\right]^{2-}$$

6. *Thionites.* The product of the reduction of a sulfite in the presence of sulfur dioxide with, for example, zinc dust, is a thionite:

$$SO_3^{2-} + SO_2 + 2H^+ + 2e \rightarrow S_2O_4^{2-} + H_2O$$

Thionites contain the $S_2O_4^{2-}$ anion

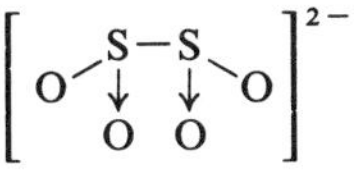

$$\left[\begin{array}{c} S-S \\ O \quad \downarrow \quad \downarrow \quad O \\ O \quad O \end{array}\right]^{2-}$$

and are very powerful reducing agents in alkaline solution:

$$2SO_3^{2-} + 2H_2O \rightarrow 4OH^- + S_2O_4^{2-} \qquad \varepsilon^0 = +1.12 \text{ volts}$$

They can be used to absorb oxygen from the air.

The S–S bond in the dithionite ion is rather long and weak, and dissociation into the radical ion SO_2^- can be detected in solution.

$$S_2O_4^{2-} \quad \rightleftharpoons \quad 2SO_2^-$$

In some ways this system resembles the $N_2O_4/2NO_2$ system.

The products of many reactions of the oxyacids of sulfur are determined by kinetic considerations rather than by thermodynamic ones. In other words, the product obtained is the one which is produced most rapidly rather than the one that is obtained with the greatest evolution of heat. In many reactions a mixture of products is obtained. The reaction of iodine with thiosulfate is such a reaction; tetrathionate is produced quantitatively, although the reaction to give sulfate is more exothermic:

$$I_2 + 2S_2O_3^{2-} \quad \rightarrow \quad I^- + 2S_4O_6^{2-} \qquad \Delta H = -27 \text{ kcal/mole}$$
$$5H_2O + 4I_2 + S_2O_3^{2-} \quad \rightarrow \quad 8I^- + 2SO_4^{2-} + 10H^+ \quad \Delta H = -48 \text{ kcal/mole}$$

Bromine and chlorine differ from iodine in that they do not oxidize thiosulfate to tetrathionate but instead give a mixture of products, the proportions depending on the conditions. The thermodynamically favored sulfate is one of the products obtained.

Halides of Sulfur

The important sulfur halides are the three fluorides SF_4, SF_6, and S_2F_{10} and the chloride S_2Cl_2.

All of the fluorides are obtained from the reaction between fluorine and sulfur.

$$S + 2F_2 \quad \rightarrow \quad SF_4$$
$$S + 3F_2 \quad \rightarrow \quad SF_6 \qquad \Delta H = -262 \text{ kcal/mole}$$
$$2S + 5F_2 \quad \rightarrow \quad S_2F_{10}$$

They have the structures

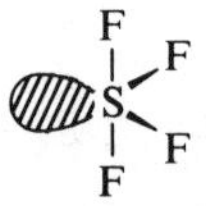

SF_4

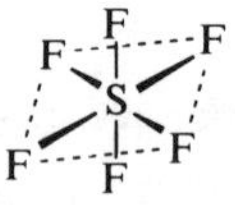

SF_6

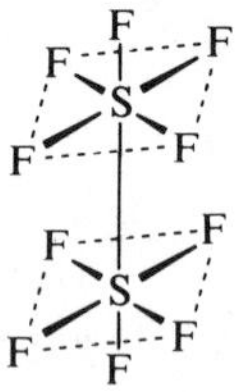

S_2F_{10}

Sulfur is sp^3d hybridized in SF_4 and sp^3d^2 hybridized in both SF_6 and S_2F_{10}.

The main interest in these compounds is their differing reactivities. For instance, SF_4 is rapidly hydrolyzed by water

$$SF_4 + 2H_2O \rightarrow SO_2 + 4HF$$

while SF_6 and S_2F_{10} are not attacked by water at all. In many ways SF_6 is as unreactive as a noble gas and reacts only with the most powerful reagents (for example, molten sodium) under the most extreme conditions, even though it is possible to calculate that many reactions of SF_6 are exothermic. An example is the hydrolysis

$$SF_6 + 3H_2O \rightarrow SO_3 + 6HF \qquad \Delta H^\circ = -17 \text{ kcal/mole}$$

In other words, SF_6 and S_2F_{10} have great kinetic stability, while SF_4 does not have such kinetic stability. The main reason for the differences in reactivity is that in SF_6 and S_2F_{10} fluorine atoms shield the sulfur atoms from attack, while there is incomplete shielding by fluorine atoms in SF_4. In addition, the S–F bonds in all three fluorides are strong bonds, and this will make a reaction depending on the step

$$SF_6 \rightarrow SF_5 + F$$

energetically very unfavorable. SF_5Cl is considerably more reactive than SF_6, and this presumably is because the S–Cl bond is weaker than the S–F bond, the reaction step

$$SF_5Cl \rightarrow SF_5 + Cl$$

being more favorable energetically.

Disulfur dichloride, S_2Cl_2, can be prepared by passing dry chlorine gas over molten sulfur:

$$2S + Cl_2 \rightarrow S_2Cl_2$$

Disulfur dichloride is a pale yellow liquid, bp 138°C, which is readily hydrolyzed by water:

$$S_2Cl_2 + 3H_2O \rightarrow 2HCl + H_2S + SO_3^{2-} + 2H^+$$

The S_2Cl_2 molecule is nonlinear, its structure being

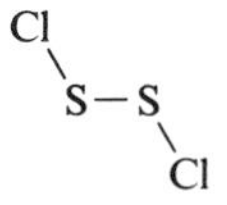

$$\begin{array}{c} Cl \\ \backslash \\ S-S \\ \qquad \backslash \\ \qquad Cl \end{array}$$

Group VIIA.   The
Halogens:
Fluorine, Chlorine,
Bromine, Iodine,
and Astatine

The Group-VII elements, fluorine, chlorine, bromine, iodine, and astatine, exhibit a continuous gradation of properties; this is illustrated in Table 2-10. As is true for every group, the first member of Group VII, fluorine, differs in several important respects from the other halogens because of differences in size and electronic configuration.

Table 2-10   Properties of the Halogens

	Fluorine (F)	Chlorine (Cl)	Bromine (Br)	Iodine (I)	Astatine (At)
Atomic number	9	17	35	53	85
Electronic configuration	$[He]2s^22p^5$	$[Ne]3s^23p^5$	$[Ar]3d^{10}4s^24p^5$	$[Kr]4d^{10}5s^25p^5$	$[Xe]4f^{14}5d^{10}6s^26p^5$
Ionic radius of halide ion, X^-, Å	1.36	1.81	1.95	2.16	—
Electronegativity	4.10	2.83	2.74	2.21	1.9
Ionization potential, kcal/mole	401.5	299.8	272.9	240.8	220
Electron affinity, kcal/mole	79.5	83.2	77.4	70.5	—
Boiling point, °C	-188	-34	58.8	183	—
ε^0, volts $2X^-(aq) \rightarrow X_2 + 2e$	-2.87	-1.36	-1.06	-0.54	—
Heat of dissociation $X_2(g) \rightarrow 2X(g)$, kcal/mole	38	57	45	36	—
Heat of dissociation $HX(g) \rightarrow H(g) + X(g)$ kcal/mole	134	103	88	71	—
Acid dissociation constant, K_a $HX(aq) \rightleftharpoons H^+(aq) + X^-(aq)$	10^{-3}	10^7	10^9	10^{10}	—

All the isotopes of the heaviest element of the group, astatine, are radioactive, and the element occurs in nature only as a short-lived intermediate in certain radioactive decay series. As a result, the chemistry of astatine has been little investigated, and we shall confine our attention to the four nonradioactive halogens. The known chemistry of astatine indicates that its properties are those to be expected for a halogen which has a higher atomic weight than iodine.

The halogens, and in particular fluorine, have high electronegativities. The ionization potentials, as usual, decrease with increasing atomic weight, because the electron being removed is in a p orbital of increasing principal quantum number, which corresponds to the electron being, on the average, farther from the nucleus.

The high electronegativities of the halogens mean that they form ionic solids with many metals; in the compounds, the halogen is present as the halide ion, X^-, and in covalent molecules the bonds are nearly always quite polar:

$$\overset{\text{\tiny $+$}\longrightarrow}{M\text{------}X}$$

We have already noted in considering the chemistry of earlier groups that, in general, there is an increase in metallic character with increasing atomic weight down a group. A simple measure of this metallic character is the tendency of atoms to form cations; for instance, in Group IV, the tendency to form M^{2+} and M^{4+} ions increases down the group. As we move *across* the periodic table, there is a general *increase* in electronegativity of the elements, so that each group is less metallic than the group further to the left. This effect is illustrated in Table 2-11. When Group VII is reached, the result is

Table 2-11   Increase in Electronegativity across the Periodic Table

Group	I	II	III	IV	V	VI	VII
4th-period elements	Rb	Sr	In	Sn	Sb	Te	I
Electronegativity	0.89	0.99	1.49	1.72	1.82	2.01	2.21

the almost complete disappearance of metallic character, even in the heaviest elements of the group, iodine and astatine. While there is the usual decrease in electronegativity down Group VII, iodine still has the quite high electronegativity of 2.21; it thus has very few metallic properties, in spite of being more metallic than any other halogen. It is possible to obtain solutions of I^+ and I^{3+} in certain solvents, but these cationic species are usually present as positively charged complexes such as $I(\text{pyridine})_2^+$. The ions Cl^+ and Br^+ have not yet been detected in solution.

As distinct from this rare occurrence of the halogens as cations, all the halogens except fluorine occur in compounds in which they have positive formal oxidation states; for example

$+1$ oxidation state: ClF, Cl_2O, $HClO$, $HBrO$, HOI

$+3$ oxidation state: ClF_3, BrF_3, $HClO_2$

$+5$ oxidation state: BrF_5, IF_5, I_2O_5

$+7$ oxidation state: Cl_2O_7, $HClO_4$, IF_7, H_5IO_6

The halogens form compounds in the following ways.

1. *They can gain an electron to give the halide ion,* X^-, *and form ionic bonds.* The electron affinities, given in Table 2-10, give the exothermicities of the processes

$$X(g) + e \rightarrow X^-(g)$$

It should be noted that this process is most favorable for chlorine and least favorable for iodine. However, if we consider the process

$$\tfrac{1}{2}X_2(g) + e \rightarrow X^-(g)$$

we have to combine these electron-affinity values with half the heat of dissociation, ΔH_{diss}, of the halogen molecules to obtain the heat change in forming a mole of X^- ions from half a mole of X_2 molecules:

	Electron affinity, kcal/mole	$\tfrac{1}{2}\Delta H_{\text{diss}}$, kcal/mole	$\tfrac{1}{2}X_2(g) + e \rightarrow X^-(g)$ kcal/half-mole of X_2
F	82	19	$\Delta H = -63$
Cl	87	29	-58
Br	82	23	-59
I	75	18	-57

It is seen from the above figures that the process yielding the halide ion from the halogen *molecule* is energetically most favorable for fluorine; this is because of the low value for the heat of dissociation of the fluorine molecule. This heat of dissociation is anomalously low; in general, one expects that bond strengths will decrease with increasing atomic weight. However, the bonds in I_2 and F_2 have almost the same strengths and the bond strengths in Br_2 and Cl_2 are greater than the bond strength of F_2. This anomaly has already been mentioned in connection with the similar anomalies found for O–O and N–N bonds. It is probable that all three bonds are anomalously weak because of repulsion between pairs of nonbonding valence electrons; one might, therefore, expect that the weakening should be greatest for F_2 and least for $>$N–N$<$, and this is so. The low value for the bond energy of F_2 compared with the other halogens is largely responsible for the great reactivity of fluorine: fluorine gas reacts violently with most elements and compounds at room temperature, while the other halogens usually react only on heating, and with fewer substances. In addition, fluorine will displace other halogens from their compounds.

2. *They can form a covalent bond with another atom possessing an unpaired electron,* examples are: F_2, Cl_2, Br_2, I_2, ICl, CCl_4, $CHCl_3$, and HF. The halogen atoms in their ground (lowest energy) states possess only one electron with unpaired spin, and so can form only one covalent bond unless electrons are promoted to d orbitals.

Because the halogens are highly electronegative elements, halogen covalent bonds are often very polar, with the electron density concentrated toward the halogen atom; for example

$$\overset{+\quad\longrightarrow}{\underset{/}{\overset{\diagdown}{\rule{0pt}{0pt}}}C\!-\!\!-\!\!-\,F}$$

The diatomic halogen molecules are polar when two different halogen atoms form the molecule; for example

$$\overset{\longleftarrow\quad+}{F\!-\!\!-\!\!-\,Cl}$$

3. *Except for fluorine, they can use d orbitals to form 2, 3, 4, 5, 6, or 7 covalent bonds.* This important distinction between the first member of a group and the rest of the group has been met in all previous groups, and results from the lack of empty d orbitals of low energy for the first-period elements. The simplest examples of halogen covalencies higher than one are found among groups of molecules called interhalogen compounds, or ions called polyhalide ions, shown in Table 2-12. The shapes of some of these molecules and ions are

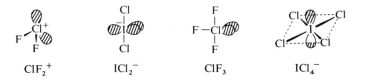

Some aspects of the chemistry of these species will be mentioned later in this chapter.

4. *The halide ions can act as electron donors and form a very large number of complex halide ions with metal ions;* for example

$$BF_3 + F^- \longrightarrow F^- \longrightarrow BF_3$$

$$SiF_4 + 2F^- \longrightarrow$$

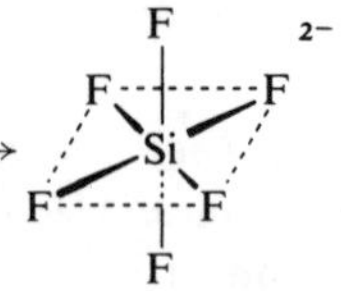

$$Tl^{3+} + Cl^- \longrightarrow [Tl \longleftarrow Cl]^{2+}$$

$$TlCl^{2+} + Cl^- \longrightarrow [Cl—Tl \longleftarrow Cl]^-$$

$$TlCl_2{}^+ + Cl^- \longrightarrow Cl \longrightarrow Tl \overset{Cl}{\underset{Cl}{\Big\langle}}$$

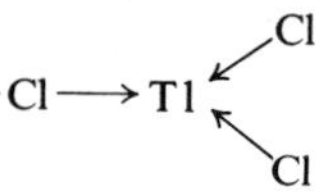

$$TlCl_3 + Cl^- \longrightarrow$$

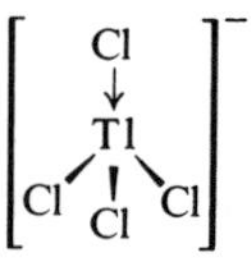

It is found experimentally that some metal ions form more stable complexes in the order $F^- > Cl^- > Br^-$, while others show the reverse order.

A halogen atom which is already covalently bonded to one metal can sometimes donate a pair of nonbonding electrons to another metal atom and so act as a "bridge" between the two metal atoms. Examples of halogen bridges have been given for beryllium (p. 11)

Table 2-12   Interhalogen Compounds Having Covalency Greater Than One.

Species	Covalency of central halogen atom	Number of pairs of electrons in valence shell of central halogen atom	Hybridization of central halogen atom
ClF_2^+	2	4	sp^3
ICl_2^-	2	5 ⎫	
ClF_3	3	5 ⎬	sp^3d
IF_4^+	4	5 ⎭	
ICl_4^-	4	6 ⎫	
IF_5	5	6 ⎭	sp^3d^2
IF_6^-	6	7 ⎫	
IF_7	7	7 ⎭	sp^3d^3

and aluminum (p. 51), and many other examples are known, for example

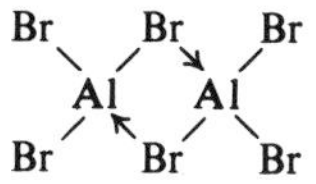

It has already been pointed out that in reality there is no difference between the two bonds to the bridging halogen atoms in such species, though there is a difference (in length, for example) between the bridging and nonbridging bonds.

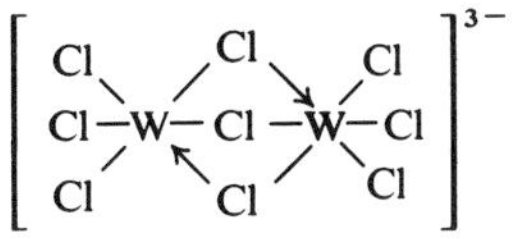

5. *Hydrogen bonds can be formed to the halide ions, or to halogen atoms when they are covalently bonded to other atoms*; for instance

$$F-H \quad + \quad F^- \quad \longrightarrow \quad [F\cdots H\cdots F]^-$$

$$F-H \quad + \quad F-H \quad \longrightarrow \quad F-H\cdots F-H$$

$$\underset{/}{\overset{\backslash}{>}}C-OH \quad + \quad Br- \quad \longrightarrow \quad \underset{/}{\overset{\backslash}{-}}C-O-H\cdots Br-$$

The requirements for hydrogen bonding have already been considered (see p. 29). In this section we consider structures where the halogen atom is acting as the negatively charged atom to which the hydrogen atom is weakly bonded. There is evidence that the hydrogen atom is attracted to the nonbonding electrons on the halogen atom; thus HF forms a polymer in the gas phase which has been shown to be nonlinear

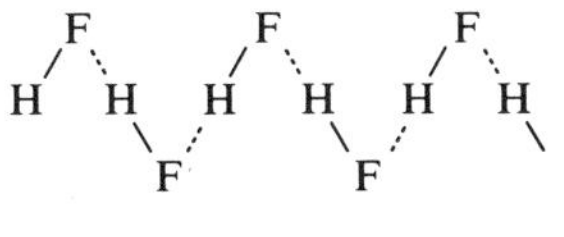

rather than linear

$$\cdots H-F\cdots H-F\cdots H-F\cdots H-F\cdots H-F\cdots$$

The strongest hydrogen bond known is found in HF_2^-, and from the reaction

$$Me_4N^+F^-(s) + HF(g) \quad \rightarrow \quad Me_4N^+HF_2^-(s) \qquad \Delta H = -37 \text{ kcal/mole}$$

it is possible to put a lower limit of 37 kcal/mole on the bond strength in HF_2^-. Similar, but less stable, ions to HF_2^- have been prepared with the other halogens, for example, HI_2^-, and all are symmetrical species:

$$[I \cdots H \cdots I]^-$$

Unsymmetrical ions containing two different halogen atoms have also been prepared, for example

$$[Br \cdots H \cdots Cl]^-$$

6. *Iodine can lose an electron to form the I^+ cation, and chlorine, bromine, and iodine can form singly and triply charged complex cations*; for example

$$I(pyridine)_2^+, \; ClF_2^+, \; and \; IF_4^+.$$

The $I(pyridine)_2^+$ cation is prepared by the reaction

$$AgNO_3 + I_2 + 2pyridine \; \rightarrow \; I(pyridine)_2^+ NO_3^- + AgI$$

Electrolysis of $I(pyridine)_2^+ NO_3^-$ in chloroform results in the liberation of iodine at the *cathode*, and therefore iodine must be present in solution as a cation.

Evidence for the other cationic species is sometimes structural (for example, solid IF_5 has been shown by X-ray diffraction to be $IF_4^+ IF_6^-$). It can also be indirect; thus liquid BrF_3 is quite a good electrical conductor and this is evidence that the self-ionization reaction

$$2BrF_3 \; \rightleftharpoons \; BrF_2^+ + BrF_4^-$$

occurs to some extent.

The Elements

Fluorine. Fluorine is prepared by the electrolysis of fused KHF_2 or a 1 : 2 mixture of KF/HF in a cell heated to 250°C, with a carbon anode.

At the cathode

$$2H^+ + 2e \; \rightarrow \; H_2$$

At the anode

$$2HF_2^- \; \rightarrow \; F_2 + 2HF + 2e$$

Fluorine is an extremely reactive gas. It reacts with nearly all elements at room temperature; however, some metals and their alloys become coated with a layer of coherent metal fluoride which prevents further attack.

Fluorine is a very powerful oxidizing agent, as indicated by its ε^0 value of -2.87. For this reason it cannot be prepared by electrolysis of aqueous fluorides, oxygen being liberated rather than fluorine.

Chlorine.   Chlorine is prepared from ionic chlorides by the oxidation of the chloride ion:

$$2Cl^- \rightarrow Cl_2 + 2e$$

This oxidation can be carried out either using chemical oxidizing agents, for example,

$$2MnO_4^- + 10Cl^- + 16H^+ \rightarrow 2Mn^{2+} + 8H_2O + 5Cl_2$$

or electrolytically using either aqueous or fused salt solutions. The electrolytic preparation is important industrially, chlorine being the by-product of the electrolytic preparation of, for example, sodium and sodium hydroxide from sodium chloride.

Chlorine is a green-yellow poisonous gas, bp $-35°C$. It can be liquified by cooling or by a pressure of a few atmospheres at room temperature. It is not as reactive as fluorine, but it is a powerful oxidizing agent which will explode when mixed with hydrogen in daylight

$$H_2 + Cl_2 \rightarrow 2HCl$$

This reaction is slow in the dark. Chlorine will react with most elements, but not with carbon, nitrogen, and oxygen. It is moderately soluble in water; the aqueous solution, known as "chlorine water," contains hydrated chlorine molecules, but there is some *hydrolysis* to give hypochlorous acid

$$Cl_2 + H_2O \rightleftharpoons HClO + H^+ + Cl^-$$

If the equilibrium is disturbed by the removal of either H^+ or Cl^-, an aqueous solution of hypochlorous acid is obtained. This equilibrium shift can be achieved by mixing aqueous chlorine with mercuric oxide

$$HgO + 2H^+ + 2Cl^- \rightarrow HgCl_2 + H_2O$$

Alternatively, alkali can be used to remove the H^+ ions produced. If excess alkali is added, a hypochlorite solution is produced by the dissociation of the weak acid, hypochlorous acid:

$$HClO + H_2O \;\rightleftharpoons\; H_3O^+ + ClO^-$$

Bromine.   Bromine can be prepared by oxidizing any ionic bromide:

$$2KBr + MnO_2 + 3H_2SO_4 \;\rightarrow\; Br_2 + 2KHSO_4 + MnSO_4 + 2H_2O$$

Bromine is distilled from the reaction mixture and condensed as a dark reddish-brown liquid, bp 59°C.

Bromine resembles chlorine in many of its properties, though it is rather less reactive and is a somewhat weaker oxidizing agent. It dissolves to some extent in water to give a brown solution which consists mainly of hydrated Br_2 molecules. There is appreciable hydrolysis producing hypobromous acid:

$$Br_2 + H_2O \;\rightleftharpoons\; HBrO + H^+ + Br^-$$

Iodine.   Like bromine and chlorine, iodine is prepared from ionic iodides by oxidation. Weaker oxidizing agents can be used to prepare iodine than the other two halogens (see ε^0s in Table 2-10), and even air oxidizes acid solutions of iodides:

$$2I^- + H_2O_2 + 2H^+ \;\rightarrow\; I_2 + 2H_2O$$
$$4I^- + O_2 + 4H^+ \;\rightarrow\; 2I_2 + 2H_2O$$

Iodine is often produced in the laboratory during volumetric titrations. All the reactions involved are special examples of the oxidation of iodide to iodine:

$$5I^- + IO_3^- + 6H^+ \;\rightarrow\; 3I_2 + 3H_2O$$
$$2I^- + Cu^{2+} \;\rightarrow\; \tfrac{1}{2}I_2 + CuI$$

Iodine is a lustrous, almost black, solid which melts and boils readily (mp 113°C, bp 184°C) to give a violet vapor.

Iodine is less reactive than the other halogens, but it combines with many metals and some nonmetals to give iodides. It is only very slightly soluble in water (0.3 g in one l.) and the iodine is only very slightly hydrolyzed to give hypoiodous acid:

$$I_2 + H_2O \;\rightleftharpoons\; HOI + H^+ + I^-$$

However, iodine is much more soluble in aqueous solutions of iodides, the triiodide complex ion being formed:

$$I_2 + I^- \rightleftharpoons I_3^-$$

It is also more soluble in alkaline solutions, where the iodine is hydrolyzed to give hypoiodite:

$$I_2 + 2OH^- \rightleftharpoons IO^- + I^- + H_2O$$

Solutions of hypoiodites are unstable and disproportionate quite rapidly to give iodate and iodide:

$$3IO^- \rightleftharpoons IO_3^- + 2I^-$$

Oxidation state of iodine atom   +1   +5   −1

The Hydrogen Halides

The hydrogen halides are

HF, hydrogen fluoride, hydrofluoric acid
HCl, hydrogen chloride, hydrochloric acid
HBr, hydrogen bromide, hydrobromic acid
HI, hydrogen iodide, hydriodic acid.

The anhydrous compounds are referred to by the first set of names listed above (for example, hydrogen fluoride) while the aqueous solutions are called by the second set of names (for example, hydrochloric acid).

Hydrogen fluoride, HF.   This is prepared by heating calcium fluoride (or any other ionic fluoride) with concentrated sulfuric acid:

$$CaF_2 + H_2SO_4 \rightarrow CaSO_4 + 2HF$$

Hydrogen chloride, HCl.   This chloride can be prepared by heating sodium chloride (or any other ionic chloride) with concentrated sulfuric acid:

$$NaCl + H_2SO_4 \rightarrow NaHSO_4 + HCl$$

In both of the above preparations the volatile acid is driven off by heating, so that the reactions go to completion.

Hydrogen bromide, HBr, *and hydrogen iodide*, HI.   These cannot be prepared in a similar way to HCl and HF by heating an ionic bromide or iodide with concentrated sulfuric acid. This is because they are oxidized to bromine or iodine by sulfuric acid:

$$2HBr + H_2SO_4 \rightarrow Br_2 + SO_2 + 2H_2O$$

Both HBr and HI can be prepared by the hydrolysis of a number of covalent bromides and iodides. The phosphorus compounds are the ones usually used, and they are often prepared *in situ*.

$$3Br_2 + 2P \rightarrow 2PBr_3$$
$$3I_2 + 2P \rightarrow 2PI_3$$
$$PBr_3 + 3H_2O \rightarrow 3HBr + H_3PO_3$$
$$PI_3 + 3H_2O \rightarrow 3HI + H_3PO_3$$

To prepare HBr, bromine is dropped on to moist violet phosphorus. To prepare HI, water is dropped on to a mixture of iodine and violet phosphorus.

Hydrogen fluoride is a volatile liquid (bp 19.5°C); the other three hydrogen halides are all gases (HCl: bp -84°C; HBr: bp -67°C; HI: bp -35°C). It has already been mentioned that the boiling point of hydrogen fluoride (compare water and ammonia) is anomalously high and that this is the result of the formation of hydrogen bonds leading to association of the molecules in the liquid.

All the hydrogen halides are extremely soluble in water, and the resulting solutions are acidic. All of them form constant-boiling mixtures with water.

Anhydrous hydrogen fluoride is a colorless liquid with a high dielectric constant (a consequence of hydrogen bonding) and is a poor electrical conductor. This electrical conduction is caused by slight self-ionization:

$$3HF \rightleftharpoons H_2F^+ + HF_2^-$$

Aqueous HF is, rather unexpectedly, only a weak acid in dilute solution. Two equilibria are important in aqueous solution:

$$HF + H_2O \rightleftharpoons H_3O^+ + F^-$$
$$HF + F^- \rightleftharpoons HF_2^-$$

In order words, there is competition between the two bases, water and fluoride, for the hydrogen fluoride.

Aqueous HF has the usual acidic properties. It attacks many metals to give fluorides with the liberation of hydrogen, dissolves hydroxides, and liberates carbon dioxide from carbonates. It is most unusual in dissolving silica, silicates, and glass (anhydrous HF does not attack these materials) to give silicon tetrafluoride and fluorosilicic acid, H_2SiF_6:

$$SiO_2 + 4HF \;\rightarrow\; 2H_2O + SiF_4$$

$$SiO_2 + 6HF \;\rightarrow\; 2H_3O^+ + SiF_6^{2-}$$

Aqueous HCl, HBr, and HI are all very strong monobasic acids which are completely dissociated even in concentrated solution. They have all the usual properties of acids and of the halide ions. As the molecular weight increases, they are increasingly easy to oxidize to the halogen.

The heats of formation of the hydrogen halides decrease with increasing molecular weight:

	HF	HCl	HBr	HI
$\Delta H_f(g)$, kcal/mole	-63	-22	-9	$+\bar{7}$
$\Delta H_f(aq)$	-79	-40	-29	$-1\bar{3}$

Anhydrous HI is seen to be a slightly endothermic substance. These heats of formation can be obtained from the bond energies listed in Table 2-13 by combining them with the values for the bond energies of the halogens and hydrogen, and with the enthalpy of formation of gaseous Br_2 and I_2 from the liquid and solid, respectively.

Table 2-13

	HF	HCl	HBr	HI
HX bond energies	-134	-103	-88	-71
$\frac{1}{2}\Delta H_{diss}(X_2)$	$+19$	$+29$	$+23$	$+18$
$\frac{1}{2}\Delta H_{diss}(H_2)$	$+52$	$+52$	$+52$	$+52$
$\Delta H_f(X_2, (g))$	0	0	$+4$	$+8$
$\Delta H_f(HX, (g))$	-63	-22	-9	$+7$

In aqueous solution, all of the halogen acids have more favorable ΔH_fs because of the favorable enthalpy of dissociation. It is seen from the figures that, as with the Group-VI hydrides, the trend in ΔH_f is primarily caused by the trend in bond strengths of the hydrogen halide molecules.

The Halogen Oxides, Oxyacids, and Oxyacid Anions

The halogens are erratic in the oxides and oxyacids that they form. Many of the compounds listed in Table 2-14 are rather unstable: only F_2O of all the listed oxides of fluorine and bromine can be isolated at room temperature. Some of the oxyacids can be obtained only in aqueous solution and not as pure compounds, and even some of the aqueous solutions (for example, those of HOBr and HOI) decompose rather rapidly. The reasons that some of these compounds can be obtained at room temperature but not others (including the obvious omissions in the above list, such as $HBrO_2$) are not understood. Many of the compounds that are known are only stable for kinetic reasons; for example, F_2O and all the chlorine oxides are endothermic compounds. It must be presumed that the reason some compounds cannot be prepared is that they have convenient decomposition paths with low activation energies.

Fluorine oxides. Oxygen difluoride, F_2O, is prepared by passing fluorine through dilute sodium hydroxide solution:

$$2F_2 + H_2O \rightarrow 2HF + F_2O$$

It is a pale yellow gas, bp $-145°C$. It is a strong oxidizing agent and also acts as a fluorinating agent:

$$F_2O + 2OH^- \rightarrow O_2 + 2F^- + H_2O$$

Table 2-14 Oxides and Oxyacids of the Halogens

Oxidation State of Halogen	Fluorine		Chlorine		Bromine		Iodine	
	Oxides	Oxyacids	Oxides	Oxyacids	Oxides	Oxyacids	Oxides	Oxyacids
+1	F_2O	—	Cl_2O	HClO	Br_2O	HBrO	—	HOI
+2	F_2O_2	—	—	—	—	—	—	—
+3	F_2O_3	—	—	$HClO_2$	—	—	—	—
+4	F_2O_4	—	ClO_2	—	BrO_2	—	I_2O_4	—
+5	—	—	—	$HClO_3$	—	$HBrO_3$	I_2O_5	HIO_3
+6	—	—	ClO_3	—	BrO_3	—	—	—
+7	—	—	Cl_2O_7	$HClO_4$	—	$HBrO_4$	I_2O_7	HIO_4 H_5IO_6 $H_4I_2O_9$

Dioxygen difluoride, F_2O_2, is an orange solid which decomposes into the elements at $-50°C$. It is used to prepare dioxygenyl compounds which contain the O_2^+ ion:

$$O_2F_2 + SbF_5 \rightarrow O_2^+SbF_6^- + \tfrac{1}{2}F_2$$

Dioxygen difluoride is prepared by passing an electric discharge through equimolar mixtures of oxygen and fluorine at liquid air temperatures:

$$F_2 + O_2 \xrightarrow[\text{discharge}]{\text{electric}} F_2O_2$$

There are no known oxyacids of fluorine.

Oxides of chlorine. Chlorine monoxide, Cl_2O, is prepared by the action of chlorine on mercuric oxide:

$$2HgO + 2Cl_2 \rightarrow HgOHgCl_2 + Cl_2O$$

The mercuric oxide, HgO, must be dry; if it is wet, hypochlorous acid, HClO, is formed.

Chlorine monoxide is a yellow-red gas, bp $2°C$, which explodes on warming:

$$2Cl_2O \rightarrow 2Cl_2 + O_2 \qquad \Delta H = -36 \text{ kcal}$$

Like all the other chlorine oxides, it is an endothermic compound. It is the anhydride of hypochlorous acid:

$$Cl_2O + H_2O \rightarrow 2HClO$$

The molecule is bent. The bonding in this molecule, and in F_2O (which has the same shape), resembles that in the water molecule.

Chlorine dioxide, ClO_2, is prepared by the action of concentrated sulfuric acid on potassium chlorate:

$$KClO_3 + H_2SO_4 \rightarrow HClO_3 + KHSO_4$$
Potassium   Chloric
chlorate   acid

$$3HClO_3 \xrightarrow{-H_2O} HClO_4 + 2ClO_2$$
Perchloric
acid

It is a yellow gas, bp 10°C, which explodes on warming:

$$2ClO_2 \rightarrow Cl_2 + 2O_2 \qquad \Delta H = -52 \text{ kcal}$$

The molecule contains an odd number of electrons; together with NO and NO_2 it is one of the rare " odd molecules " which are reasonably stable. Like NO, but unlike NO_2 and ClO_3, it shows no tendency to form a dimer. One consequence of the odd number of electrons is that the substance is paramagnetic. Chlorine dioxide disproportionates in alkaline solution to give a mixture of chlorite and chlorate:

$$2ClO_2 + 2OH^- \rightarrow ClO_3^- + ClO_2^- + H_2O$$

Oxidation state $\qquad +4 \qquad\qquad\qquad +5 \quad +3$
of chlorine atom

There is no oxyacid of oxidation state $+4$.

The molecule is nonlinear:

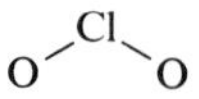

$$O \overset{\overset{\textstyle Cl}{\diagup \; \diagdown}}{} O$$

No simple explanation can be given for the bonding in this molecule.

Chlorine hexoxide, Cl_2O_6, is prepared by the action of ozone on chlorine dioxide:

$$2O_3 + 2ClO_2 \rightarrow Cl_2O_6 + 2O_2$$

It is a red liquid, mp 3.5°C, which is explosive and highly reactive. With aqueous alkali it gives a mixture of chlorate and perchlorate:

$$Cl_2O_6 + 2OH^- \rightarrow ClO_3^- + ClO_4^- + H_2O$$
$$\qquad\qquad\qquad\qquad\quad \text{Chlorate} \quad \text{Perchlorate}$$

Oxidation state $\; +6 \qquad\qquad\qquad +5 \quad +7$
of Cl atom

There is no oxyacid of chlorine having an oxidation state of $+6$.

Like N_2O_4, chlorine hexoxide undergoes dissociation:

$$Cl_2O_6 \rightleftharpoons 2ClO_3$$

Indeed, its vapor consists largely of *chlorine trioxide*, ClO_3, which is another paramagnetic odd molecule.

Chlorine heptoxide, Cl_2O_7, is prepared by the dehydration of perchloric acid with phosphorus pentoxide at low temperatures:

$$2HClO_4 \xrightarrow{-H_2O} Cl_2O_7$$

It is a colorless liquid, bp 83°C, which explodes when heated:

$$2Cl_2O_7 \rightarrow 2Cl_2 + 7O_2 \quad \Delta H = -126 \text{ kcal}$$

As the anhydride of perchloric acid, it reacts slowly with water to give this acid:

$$Cl_2O_7 + H_2O \rightarrow 2HClO_4$$

Oxides of Bromine. None of the bromine oxides can be isolated at room temperature, and their preparation and properties are not dealt with here.

Oxides of iodine. Iodine pentoxide, I_2O_5, is the only important oxide of iodine. It is prepared by heating iodic acid to about 220°C:

$$2HIO_3 \rightarrow I_2O_5 + H_2O$$

It is a white crystalline solid which reacts rapidly with water to give back iodic acid, and it is a powerful oxidizing agent.

Iodine tetroxide, I_2O_4, has been shown to be an ionic solid:

$$IO^+IO_3^-$$

The hypohalous acids, HOX: *hypochlorous acid*, HOCl; *hypobromous acid*, HOBr, *hypoiodous acid*, HOI. As was mentioned in the section dealing with the halogens, the hypohalous acids are present in equilibrium with the halogens in aqueous solution:

$$Cl_2 + H_2O \rightleftharpoons HOCl + H^+ + Cl^-$$

The equilibrium constants for the hydrolysis reaction decrease in the order $Cl_2 > Br_2 > I_2$. The equilibria can be driven to the right by treating the solutions with a suspension of mercuric oxide:

$$2Cl_2 + 2HgO + H_2O \rightarrow HgO \cdot HgCl_2 + 2HOCl$$

Hypohalite solutions can be obtained by treating the halogen with alkali:

$$Cl_2 + 2OH^- \rightarrow Cl^- + OCl^- + H_2O$$

The acids and their ions are not stable, and disproportionate at various rates:

$$3OX^- \rightarrow 2X^- + XO_3^-$$
$$X(+1) \quad X(-1) \quad X(+5)$$

The order of decreasing stability is $Cl > Br > I$; hypoiodous acid and hypoiodites have only brief existences under normal conditions.

The halous acids and halites, HXO_2 and XO_2^-.   Only chlorine forms an oxyacid of this type, chlorous acid, $HClO_2$; this is difficult to prepare and is very reactive.

Chlorites are prepared by dissolving ClO_2 in alkali:

$$2ClO_2 + 2OH^- \rightarrow ClO_2^- + ClO_3^- + H_2O$$

Chlorous acid can be obtained in aqueous solution by treating barium chlorite with sulfuric acid:

$$Ba(ClO_2)_2 + H_2SO_4 \rightarrow BaSO_4 + 2HClO_2$$

This is one of the general methods of preparing acids that cannot be distilled out of the reaction mixture. The acid decomposes quite rapidly but chlorites are moderately stable in alkaline solution.

The halic acids and halates, HXO_3 and XO_3^-.   All three halogens form acids and anions of this type. The halates are prepared by the disproportionation reaction of the hypohalous acids as described earlier, usually accelerated by warming the solutions.

Iodic acid, HIO_3 , can be isolated as a crystalline solid, but $HClO_3$ and $HBrO_3$ are known only in solution. A large number of crystalline salts of the halic acids are known, and bromates and iodates are frequently used in volumetric analysis:

$$IO_3^- + 5I^- + 6H^+ \rightarrow 3I_2 + 3H_2O$$
$$BrO_3^- + 6I^- + 6H^+ \rightarrow 3I_2 + 3H_2O + Br^-$$

The perhalate acids and perhalates, HXO_4 *and* XO_4^-. Chlorine, bromine, and iodine form compounds of this type, but the bromine compound has only recently been discovered.

Perchlorates are prepared by the anodic oxidation of chlorates at the anode:

$$ClO_3^- + 2OH^- \rightarrow ClO_4^- + H_2O + 2e$$

Pure perchloric acid, $HClO_4$, is a colorless liquid which can explode. It can be prepared from aqueous solutions by fractional distillation.

Periodic acids. There are several known oxyacids of iodine in the oxidation state $+7$:

$$HIO_3 \xrightarrow[\text{by } S_2O_8^{2-} \text{ or } OCl^-]{\text{oxidation}} H_5IO_6 \xrightarrow{80°} H_4I_2O_9 \xrightarrow[in\ vacuo]{100°} HIO_4$$

Iodic	Ortho-	Pyro-	Metaperiodic
acid	periodic	periodic	acid
$I(+5)$	acid	acid	$I(+7)$
	$I(+7)$	$I(+7)$	

If metaperiodic acid is heated more strongly, oxygen is liberated and one gets back iodic acid:

$$2HIO_4 \rightarrow 2HIO_3 + O_2$$

The structures of these oxyacids of iodine are

Iodic acid	Orthoperiodic acid	Pyroperiodic acid	Metaperiodic acid

It should be noticed that none of these "per" acids of chlorine or iodine is a true "per" acid, since they are not derivatives of hydrogen peroxide and do not contain the –O–O– group. Pyroperiodic acid is a condensed oxyacid derived from orthoperiodic acid by the elimination of three moles of water for every mole of acid produced. Meta and orthoperiodic acid differ in the coordination number of the iodine: four in the former acid and six in the latter acid.

All the halogen oxyacids and their anions are oxidizing agents:

$$Cl^- + 2OH^- \rightleftharpoons ClO^- + H_2O + 2e \qquad \varepsilon^0 = -0.89 \text{ volts}$$

$$Cl^- + 4OH^- \rightleftharpoons ClO_2^- + 2H_2O + 4e \qquad \varepsilon^0 = -0.78 \text{ volts}$$

$$Cl^- + 6OH^- \rightleftharpoons ClO_3^- + 3H_2O + 6e \qquad \varepsilon^0 = -0.63 \text{ volts}$$

$$Cl^- + 8OH^- \rightleftharpoons ClO_4^- + 4H_2O + 8e \qquad \varepsilon^0 = -0.56 \text{ volts}$$

The effectiveness of the oxyacids as oxidizing agents is sometimes reduced by kinetic effects. In particular, perchlorates are usually completely ineffective as oxidizing agents at room temperature, and perchlorate salts of many reducing metal ions have been prepared, for example, $Fe(ClO_4)_2$. In other words, reactions involving perchloric acid are often immeasurably slow.

The compounds most often used as oxidizing agents in practical chemistry are: hypochlorites, OCl^-, iodates, bromates, and chlorates and periodates. Hypochlorite solutions are useful oxidizing agents because they are easily prepared from chlorine and have reasonably large ε^0s.

The halates are useful because stable crystalline salts can be prepared. Periodates can also be prepared as stable crystalline salts and are particularly powerful oxidizing agents:

$$IO_3^- + H_2O \rightleftharpoons IO_4^- + 2H^+ + 2e \qquad \varepsilon^0 = -1.8 \text{ volts}$$

$$I^- + 8OH^- \rightleftharpoons IO_4^- + 4H_2O + 8e \qquad \varepsilon^0 = -0.39 \text{ volts}$$

They will oxidize Mn^{2+} to MnO_4^- and Cr^{3+} to CrO_4^{2-} in acid solution. The ε^0 values for the two different half-cell reactions of periodate given above indicate the importance of considering intermediate oxidation states in defining the strength of an oxidizing agent.

Group 0. The Noble Gases: Helium, Neon, Argon, Krypton, Xenon, and Radon

Until 1962, no stable compounds of this series of elements were known, and the gases were called *inert gases*, because it was believed that they could not form any chemical compounds at all. The American chemist Linus Pauling predicted in 1930 that xenon might form stable fluorides, but attempts to prepare them were not successful, probably because the techniques required to handle fluorine had not been fully developed. However, since 1962, a number of compounds of the three heaviest gases, krypton, xenon, and radon, have been prepared. It is now preferable to refer to these elements as the *noble* gases.

Some properties of the noble gases are listed in Table 2-15. All the Group-0 elements are gases at room temperature and pressure, and all of them except radon occur in significant quantities in the atmosphere:

	He	Ne	Ar	Kr	Xe	Rn
% abundance in atmosphere, by volume	5.2×10^{-4}	1.8×10^{-3}	0.93	1.1×10^{-3}	8.7×10^{-6}	—

Air contains nearly 1% argon by volume, and argon, neon, krypton,

Table 2-15   Properties of the Noble Gases

	Helium (He)	Neon (Ne)	Argon (Ar)	Krypton (Kr)	Xenon (Xe)	Radon (Rn)
Atomic number	2	10	18	36	54	86
Electronic configuration	$1s^2$	$[He]2s^22p^6$	$[Ne]3s^23p^6$	$[Ar]3d^{10}4s^24p^6$	$[Kr]4d^{10}5s^25p^6$	$[Xe]4f^{14}5d^{10}6s^26p^6$
Atomic radius, Å	1.2	1.6	1.9	2.0	2.2	—
First ionization potential, kcal/mole	567	497	363	323	279	249
Boiling point, °K	4.18	27.1	87.3	120.3	166.1	208.2

and xenon are all obtained industrially by the fractional distillation of liquid air. Helium, like hydrogen, is lost from the earth's atmosphere and is obtained from natural gas. All the isotopes of radon are radioactive, and the most stable isotope, $^{222}_{86}Rn$, has a half-life of only 3.8 days.

Helium has the lowest boiling point of any known substance. It is seen in Table 2-15 that the boiling points increase smoothly with increasing atomic weight. Van der Waals forces are the only forces which hold the noble gas atoms together in the liquid or solid phases, and these forces increase with increasing atomic weight, corresponding to the increasing polarizabilities of the atoms. All the noble gases are monatomic in the solid, liquid, and gaseous states.

Liquid ^4_2He between 2.18° and 4.18°K is called He(I). The liquid undergoes a transition at 2.18°K, and below this temperature the liquid is called He(II). He(II) has many interesting and not understood properties, such as zero viscosity and an extraordinarily high thermal conductivity.

Before 1962, the only compounds of the noble gases were paramagnetic species such as He_2^+ and HeH, which are unstable at room temperature and pressure. In other words these species are stable with respect to the reactions

$$HeH(g) \rightarrow He(g) + H(g)$$

and

$$He_2^+(g) \rightarrow He^+(g) + He(g)$$

which are endothermic processes, but are unstable with respect to the reactions

$$2\text{HeH}(g) \;\rightarrow\; 2\text{He}(g) + \text{H}_2(g)$$

and

$$\text{He}_2^+(g) + \text{e} \;\rightarrow\; 2\text{He}(g)$$

which are both endothermic reactions—because of the large heat of formation of H_2 from 2H or the large value of the ionization potential of helium.

A number of krypton, xenon, and radon compounds with halogens and oxygen have been prepared, but some of these compounds are only obtainable because they have considerable kinetic stability even though they are unstable thermodynamically. Krypton forms rather unstable compounds, most of which decompose under ordinary conditions. Xenon forms a large number of compounds. The chemistry of radon has not been much investigated because of the intense radioactivity of radon itself. From a chemical point of view, it is reasonable to suppose that radon compounds might be more stable thermodynamically than those of xenon.

Noble Gas Fluorides

If krypton or xenon is mixed with fluorine, and energy is supplied to the system (usually in the form of a silent electric discharge), a number of fluorides can be isolated. The precise products in the case of xenon depend on the molecular proportions of xenon and fluorine used:

$$\text{Kr} + \text{F}_2 \;\rightarrow\; \text{KrF}_2$$
$$\text{Xe} + n\text{F}_2 \;\rightarrow\; \text{XeF}_2, \text{XeF}_4, \text{XeF}_6$$

The krypton compound has a *positive* heat of formation and can only be obtained at low temperatures ($-60°\text{C}$), since it decomposes into the elements at room temperature:

$$\text{KrF}_2(g) \;\rightarrow\; \text{Kr}(g) + \text{F}_2(g) \qquad \Delta H = -14 \text{ kcal/mole}$$

The xenon fluorides have *negative* heats of formation and are crystalline solids at room temperature:

$$\text{XeF}_4(g) \;\rightarrow\; \text{Xe}(g) + 2\text{F}_2(g) \qquad \Delta H = +55 \text{ kcal/mole}$$
$$\text{XeF}_6(g) \;\rightarrow\; \text{Xe}(g) + 3\text{F}_2(g) \qquad \Delta H = +79 \text{ kcal/mole.}$$

From these heats of formation it is possible to calculate average Kr–F and Xe–F bond energies:

	Average bond energy, kcal/mole
KrF_2	12
XeF_2	33

It is clear that in Group 0 increasing atomic weight is accompanied by increasing bond strength; this is opposite to the trend usually observed. If this trend extends to the lighter Group-0 elements helium, neon, and argon, then it is clear that no fluorides of these elements would be thermodynamically stable at room temperature. The melting points of the three xenon fluorides and their latent heats of sublimation are

	Mp, °C	ΔH_{subl} kcal/mole
XeF_2	140	12.3
XeF_4	114	15.3
XeF_6	46	—
KrF_2	—	9.3

The melting points are of interest because they decrease with increasing molecular weight, whereas usually the opposite is found to be the case. In addition, the heats of sublimation are unusually high for covalent compounds. The explanation for both these results is to be found in the very ionic nature of the Xe–F and Kr–F bonds; this gives rise to lattice binding in the solids, which can be represented diagrammatically as follows:

$$F^{\delta-}—Xe^{\delta+}—F^{\delta-}$$
$$F^{\delta-}—Xe^{\delta+}—F^{\delta-}$$

Another xenon–fluorine species, XeF_5^+, is obtained in the reaction of PtF_6 with Xe and F_2, as the salt $XeF_5^+PtF_6^-$.

The structures of all these xenon–fluorine compounds have been shown to be those expected from simple theories of shapes of molecules, and in many cases they are isoelectronic or pseudoisoelectronic (contain the same number of valence electrons but different numbers of total electrons) with iodine compounds which have the same geometry.

XeF$_2$:   F$-$Xe$-$F   ICl$_2^-$:   [Cl$-$I$-$Cl]$^-$

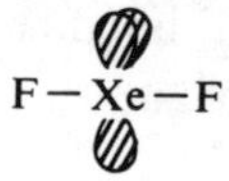

Xe and I sp^{3}d
hybridized

XeF$_4$:   ICl$_4^-$:

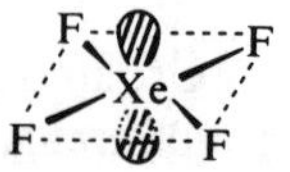

Xe and I sp^{3}d^2
hybridized

XeF$_5^+$:   IF$_5$:

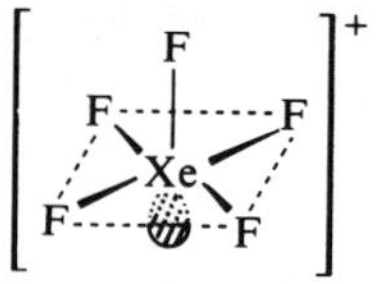

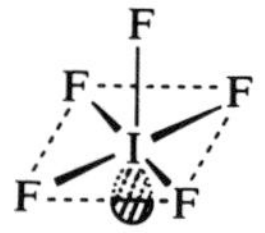

Xe and I sp^{3}d^2
hybridized

Reactions of xenon fluorides.

1. The xenon fluorides are powerful oxidizing agents:
(a) They react with hydrogen to give HF and xenon, with great
evolution of heat:

$$\text{XeF}_6(g) + 3\text{H}_2(g) \rightarrow \text{Xe}(g) + 6\text{HF}(g) \qquad \Delta H = -306 \text{ kcal/mole}$$

(b) They oxidize iodide to iodine

$$\text{XeF}_2 + 2\text{I}^- \rightarrow \text{Xe} + 2\text{F}^- + \text{I}_2$$

and these reactions have been used in the quantitative estimation
of xenon fluorides.
(c) They react with water:
  (i) XeF$_2$ oxidizes water in alkaline solution

$$\text{XeF}_2 + 2\text{OH}^- \rightarrow \text{Xe} + \tfrac{1}{2}\text{O}_2 + 2\text{F}^- + \text{H}_2\text{O}$$
$$\text{Xe} + 2\text{F}^- \rightarrow \text{XeF}_2 + 2e \qquad \varepsilon^0 = -2.2 \text{ volts}$$

  (ii) XeF$_4$ disproportionates in water

$$3\text{XeF}_4 + 6\text{H}_2\text{O} \rightarrow 2\text{XeO}_3 + \text{Xe} + 12\text{HF}$$
$$\text{Xe}(+4) \qquad\qquad \text{Xe}(+6) \quad \text{Xe}(0)$$

(iii) XeF_6 is hydrolyzed by water

$$XeF_6 + 3H_2O \;\rightarrow\; XeO_3 + 6HF$$

Mixed fluorine–oxygen compounds can also be obtained by partial hydrolysis or by the reactions

$$2XeF_6 + SiO_2 \longrightarrow 2XeOF_4 + SiF_4$$

$$XeF_4 + H_2O \xrightarrow{-80^\circ} XeOF_2 + 2HF$$

$XeOF_2$ decomposes below $0°C$, but xenon oxytetrafluoride, $XeOF_4$, is a volatile liquid, mp $-28°C$.

2. They form complexes:

(a) $XeF_6 + CsF \;\rightarrow\; CsXeF_7$

            $CsXeF_7 \xrightarrow{50^\circ} Cs_2XeF_8$

     $CsXeF_7$ and Cs_2XeF_8 are salts, the latter being stable up to $400°C$. These salts may contain the ions XeF_7^- and XeF_8^{2-}.

(b) $XeF_6 + BF_3 \;\rightarrow\; XeF_6 \cdot BF_3$

            $XeF_6 + AsF_5 \;\rightarrow\; XeF_6 \cdot AsF_5$

These solid adducts of XeF_6 with BF_3 and AsF_5 are probably the salts $XeF_5^+ BF_4^-$ and $XeF_5^+ AsF_6^-$. In addition it is possible to prepare a very concentrated solution of XeF_6 (up to nearly 20 M) in anhydrous HF, which is a good electrical conductor; however, the xenon species present in such a solution have not been determined.

Xenon dichloride, $XeCl_2$, is the only chloride compound which has been prepared; it is a crystalline solid that decomposes into the elements at $80°C$.

Noble Gas Oxygen Compounds

Xenon trioxide, XeO_3. This is prepared by the hydrolysis of either XeF_6 or XeF_4, as shown above. Xenon trioxide is a white, hygroscopic crystalline solid. It is an endothermic compound and decomposes explosively. It is soluble in water and is a powerful oxidizing agent:

In acid solution

$$Xe + 6H_2O \;\rightleftharpoons\; XeO_3 + 6H^+ + 6e \qquad \varepsilon^0 = -1.8 \text{ volts}$$

$$XeO_3 + 6I^- + 3H_2O \;\rightarrow\; Xe + 3I_2 + 6OH^-$$

Xenon trioxide is much more powerful than hydrogen peroxide as an oxidizing agent.

Solutions of XeO_3 in water are said to contain xenic acid, H_6XeO_6, but there is no evidence that the reaction

$$XeO_3 + 3H_2O \rightleftharpoons Xe(OH)_6$$

occurs, although salts of $HXeO_4^-$, such as $CsHXeO_4$, have been prepared.

Xenon trioxide disproportionates in strongly alkaline solution

$$4XeO_3 + 12OH^- \rightarrow Xe + 3XeO_6^{4-} + 6H_2O$$

to give xenon gas and solutions of perxenates, which contain the XeO_6^{4-} ion, in which xenon has the oxidation state $+8$. XeO_3 can also be oxidized to perxenates by ozone in alkaline solution:

$$XeO_3 + O_3 + 4OH^- \rightarrow XeO_6^{4-} + 2H_2O + O_2$$

Perxenate salts such as $Na_4Xe_6 8H_2O$ have been crystallized from solution. Perxenates are not true per compounds since they are not derived from hydrogen peroxide and do not contain the $-O-O-$ group. Perxenates are among the most powerful oxidizing agents known in solution.

In acid solution

$$XeO_3 + 3H_2O \rightarrow XeO_6^{4-} + 6H^+ + 2e \qquad \varepsilon^0 = -3.0 \text{ volts}$$

If sodium perxenate is treated with concentrated sulfuric acid, volatile XeO_4 is liberated:

$$Na_4XeO_6 + 2H_2SO_4 \rightarrow XeO_4 + 2Na_2SO_4 + 2H_2O$$

Xenon tetroxide, XeO_4. This is an endothermic and explosive compound:

$$XeO_4 \rightarrow Xe + 2O_2 \qquad \Delta H = -153 \text{ kcal/mole}$$

Krypton does not form such an extensive range of oxygen compounds, and only the barium salt, $BaKrO_4$, has been isolated. This salt is stable up to $50°C$.

XeO_3 is isoelectronic with the iodate ion, IO_3^-; XeO_4 is isoelectronic with the periodate ion, IO_4^-, while XeO_6^{4-} is isoelectronic with the orthoperiodate ion, IO_6^{5-}. In each case the xenon and iodine compounds have very similar structures:

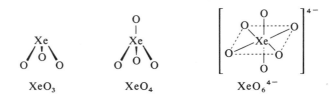

XeO₃   XeO₄   XeO₆⁴⁻

In these compounds there is evidence for double bonding between oxygen and xenon, just as there is between oxygen and iodine in the iodine compounds.

There is some evidence that radon forms oxygen compounds more readily than xenon, but little work has been done on the system.

Krypton, xenon, and radon are able to form compounds by using their empty d orbitals (in the case of xenon, its 5d orbitals) to unpair some of their valence electrons and hence form covalent bonds:

	5s	5p	5d
Xe $5s^2 5p^6$ (ground state)	↑↓	↑↓ ↑↓ ↑↓	☐☐☐☐☐
Xe $5s^2 5p^5 5d^1$ (excited state)	↑↓	↑↓ ↑↓ ↑	↑ ☐☐☐☐
Xe (in XeF₂)	↑↓	↑↓ ↑↓ ↑↓	↑↓ ☐☐☐

As has already been mentioned, Xe–F bonds are very polar. This can be understood on the basis of the valence-bond theory, because it is not possible to write nonionic resonance structures for these compounds. For instance, one can write down the resonance forms

$$F\text{---}Xe^+ \ldots F^- \quad \leftrightarrow \quad F^- \ldots Xe^+\text{---}F$$

but not nonionic forms such as

$$F\text{---}Xe\text{---}F$$

The simple application of valence bond theory above indicates that in XeF₂ there should be half a negative charge on each fluorine atom and a positive charge on the xenon atom:

$$F^{-1/2}\text{---}Xe^{+1}\text{---}F^{-1/2}$$

Calculations using molecular orbital theory indicate that this is substantially the correct interpretation. In XeF_4 and XeF_6, the bonds would be expected to be less polar, because otherwise there would be very large positive charges on the xenon atom ($+2$ in XeF_4 and $+3$ in XeF_6).

Problems

2-1. Demonstrate the nonoccurrence of compounds containing $H^+(g)$ by calculating the molar enthalpy of formation of $H^+(g) \cdots Cl^-(g)$ from the elements in their standard states, using the following data:

Heat of dissociation of H_2 :   104 kcal/mole of H_2
Heat of dissociation of Cl_2 :   57 kcal/mole of Cl_2
Electron affinity of chlorine: 87 kcal/g-atom
Ionization potential of hydrogen: 312 kcal/g-atom

Also calculate the enthalpy of formation of $H^+(aq) \cdots Cl^-(aq)$ from the elements in their standard states, using the data:

Heat of hydration of $H^+(g)$: -256 kcal/g-ion
Heat of hydration of $Cl^-(g)$: -90 kcal/g-ion

2-2. Use some of the data in (1), and in addition the fact that the heat of formation of $HCl(g)$ is -22 kcal/mole of HCl, to calculate a value for the bond strength of the H–Cl molecule.

2-3. Thallium forms four well-defined chlorides with the empirical formulas: $TlCl_3$, $TlCl_2$, Tl_2Cl_3, and $TlCl$. It has been shown that all of these compounds are diamagnetic and hence contain no unpaired electrons. This means that they must contain Tl^{3+} and/or Tl^+ ions. What are the oxidation states of thallium in the chlorides as written above? Formulate the four chlorides so that they are seen to be compounds containing Tl^{3+} and/or Tl^+ and Cl^-.

2-4. The complex ions $TlCl_4^-$, $TlCl_6^{3-}$, and $TlCl_2^-$ have been detected in a number of compounds. What are the oxidation states of thallium in these anions and what shapes whould you expect them to have? In which of the thallium chlorides would these complex anions be expected to occur?

2-5. What reaction would occur if the following were added to water? (a) Na, (b) B_2H_6, (c) F_2, (d) B^{3+}, (e) C^{4+}, (f) H^-, (g) Ag^{2+}, and (h) Fe^{3+}. In each case state the *type* of reaction.

2-6. Give plausible structures for compounds with the empirical formulas: $HgCl$, CH_2, BCl_2, BH_3, $AlBr_3$, PBr_7.

2-7. The oxidation potentials of the M(IV)/M(II) oxidation-reduction reactions of tin and lead are:

$$Sn^{2+}(aq) \ \rightleftharpoons \ Sn^{4+}(aq) + 2e \qquad \varepsilon^0 = -0.15 \text{ volts}$$

$$2H_2O + Pb^{2+}(aq) \ \rightleftharpoons \ PbO_2 + 4H^+ + 2e \qquad \varepsilon^0 = -1.46 \text{ volts}$$

What does this information tell one about the relative stabilities of the $+II$ and $+IV$ oxidation states of lead and tin? What properties of tin and lead could affect the relative stabilities of their two oxidation states? (The construction of a thermochemical cycle will assist in answering this question.)

2-8. Using heavy water (D_2O) as the source of deuterium, how could one conveniently prepare:

    (a) NaOD   (b) D_2SO_4 (c) LiD

    (d) $LiAlD_4$ (e) SiD_4 (f) DF

2-9. Why does thallium dissolve readily in dilute H_2SO_4, but not in dilute HCl?

2-10. Why does phosphorus form two fluorides, PF_3 and PF_5, while nitrogen forms NF_3 but NF_5 is not known?

2-11. Why does N_2O support combustion better than air, but not so well as pure oxygen?

2-12. In general, what are the trends in chemical behavior on

(a) passing across the periodic table from left to right;
(b) passing down the periodic table in a particular group?

2-13. "The chemistry of the lightest element of a group is not typical of that of the rest of the elements in the group."

(a) What evidence do you know in support of this statement, and what against?
(b) What are the causes of the differences and similarities you have listed?

Suggested Reading

Bagnall, K. W. "Polonium," *Endeavour*, May 1963, p. 61.

Brown, J., Jr. "Inclusion Compounds," *Sci. Am.*, July 1962, p. 82.

Charles, R. J. "The Nature of Glasses," *Sci. Am.*, Sept. 1967, p. 127.

Colburn, C. B. "The Fluorides of Nitrogen," *Endeavour*, Sept. 1965, p. 138.

Cottrell, A. H. "The Nature of Metals," *Sci. Am.*, Sept. 1967, p. 90.

Gilman, J. J. "The Nature of Ceramics," *Sci. Am.*, Sept. 1967, p. 113.

Gilman, J. J., and H. Eisch. "Lithium," *Sci. Am.*, Jan. 1963, p. 88.

Johnson, R. C. *Introductory Descriptive Chemistry*. Benjamin, New York, 1966.

Jolly, W. L. *The Chemistry of the Non-Metals*. Prentice-Hall, Inc., Engelwood Cliffs, N.J., 1966.

Massey, A. G. "Boron," *Sci. Am.*, Jan. 1964, p. 88.

McQuillan, M. K., and T. W. Farthing. "Beryllium," *Endeavour*, Jan. 1961. p. 11.

Mott, N. F. "The Solid State," *Sci. Am.*, Sept. 1967, p. 80.

Pfann, W. G. "Zone Refining," *Sci. Am.*, Dec. 1967, p. 62.

Runnels, L. K. "Ice," *Sci. Am.*, Dec. 1966, p. 118.

Sanderson, R. T. "Principles of Halogen Chemistry," *J. Chem. Ed.*, **41**, 361 (1964).

Selig, H., J. G. Malm, and H. H. Claassen. "The Chemistry of the Noble Gases," *Sci. Am.*, May 1964, p. 66.

Smith, G. S. "Materials," *Sci. Am.*, Sept. 1967, p. 69.

Stone, F. G. A. "Electron-Deficient Compounds," *Endeavour*, April 1961, p. 61.

Sullenger, D. B., and C. H. L. Kennard, "Boron Crystals," *Sci. Am.*, July 1966, p. 96.

Turner, J. J. "Oxygen Fluorides." *Endeavour*, Jan. 1968, p. 42.

Chapter 3   The Transition Elements

In the previous chapter we have been concerned with the chemistry of the nontransition elements, in which the s or p orbitals are normally incomplete and which commonly form bonds using s or p electrons. We have seen that in each group of the periodic table (in which the valence electron configuration is similar for each element) there are very noticeable chemical similarities between the elements. Changes in the valence electronic configuration result in the great differences in chemical properties found in passing *across* the periodic table from one group to another in the same period—for example, from carbon with the electronic configuration $[He]2s^22p^2$ to nitrogen with the configuration $[He]2s^22p^3$.

In contrast to the nontransition elements, the transition elements and the lanthanides and actinides (shown in Table 3-1) usually contain partly filled d or f orbitals. For reasons that will be mentioned later, this results in considerable chemical similarity *across* the periodic table as well as down a given group. There are, for instance, considerable chemical similarities between the elements Ti, V, Cr, Mn, Fe, Co, and Ni in the first transition series, and many of the lanthanide elements have almost identical chemical properties. This makes it possible to consider the transition elements, lanthanides, and actinides as single groups of elements. Some of the properties of the first-row transition elements are shown in Table 3-2.

The increase in atomic number (positive nuclear charge) across a period is counterbalanced by a corresponding increase in the number of electrons outside the nucleus. In the nontransition elements the

152

Table 3-1 The Transition, Lanthanide, and Actinide Elements

K	Ca	Sc	First-row transition elements:	Ti	V	Cr	Mn	Fe	Co	Ni	Cu	Zn	Ga	Ge
Rb	Sr	Y	Second-row transition elements:	Zr	Nb	Mo	Tc	Ru	Rh	Pd	Ag	Cd	In	Sn
Cs	Ba	La		Hf	Ta	W	Re	Os	Ir	Pt	Au	Hg	Tl	Pb
Fr	Ra	Ac												

The lanthanides

Ce	Pr	Nd	Pm	Sm	Eu	Gd	Tb	Dy	Ho	Er	Tm	Yb	Lu

The actinides

Th	Pa	U	Np	Pu	Am	Cm	Bk	Cf	Es	Fm	Md	No	Lw

Table 3-2 Properties of the First-Row Transition Elements

	Sc	Ti	V	Cr	Mn	Fe	Co	Ni	Cu	Zn
Atomic number	21	22	23	24	25	26	27	28	29	30
Electronic configuration	$[Ar]3d^14s^2$	$[Ar]3d^24s^2$	$[Ar]3d^34s^2$	$[Ar]3d^54s^1$	$[Ar]3d^54s^2$	$[Ar]3d^64s^2$	$[Ar]3d^74s^2$	$[Ar]3d^84s^2$	$[Ar]3d^{10}4s^1$	$[Ar]3d^{10}4s^2$
Mp, °C	1200	1725	1700	1920	1260	1535	1480	1455	1083	419
First ionization energy, $M(g) \rightarrow M^+(g) + e$ kcal/mole	151	178	176	176	194	206	205	199	201	244
Ionic radii, M^{2+} Å	—	0.72	0.65	0.89	0.82	0.77	0.72	0.68	0.72	0.74
M^{3+}	0.69	0.61	0.63	0.61	0.63	0.63	0.56	—	—	—
ε^0, volts $M(s) \rightleftharpoons M^{2+}(aq) + 2e$	—	+1.63	+1.18	+0.91	+1.18	+0.44	+0.28	+0.25	-0.34	+0.78
$M^{2+}(aq) \rightleftharpoons M^{3+}(aq) + e$	—	+0.37	+0.26	+0.41	-1.51	-0.77	-1.96	—	—	—
Heats of hydration of M^{2+} ion, kcal/mole	—	(426)	453	460	445	468	497	507	507	491

additional electrons are added to outer shells, but in the transition, lanthanide, and actinide elements the additional electrons enter inner shells. Electrons will always enter the empty or half-filled atomic orbital of lowest energy, so that the electronic configurations of elements are determined by the relative energies of different atomic orbitals. If we consider what happens when the nuclear charge is increased from 18 in argon to 31 in gallium, we find the following electron configurations.

	Ar	K	Ca	Sc	Ti	V	Cr	Mn
Atomic number	18	19	20	21	22	23	24	25
Configuration	[Ar]	[Ar]$4s^1$	[Ar]$4s^2$	[Ar]$3d^14s^2$	[Ar]$3d^24s^2$	[Ar]$3d^34s^2$	[Ar]$3d^54s^1$	[Ar]$3d^54s^2$

	Fe	Co	Ni	Cu	Zn	Ga
Atomic number	26	27	28	29	30	31
Configuration	[Ar]$3d^64s^2$	[Ar]$3d^74s^2$	[Ar]$3d^84s^2$	[Ar]$3d^{10}4s^1$	[Ar]$3d^{10}4s^24p^2$	[Ar]$3d^{10}4s^24p^1$

The 4s and 3d orbitals for most of these atoms are of very nearly the same energy (even though the 4s is of higher principal quantum number than the 3d), because the s orbital penetrates nearer to the nucleus than does the d orbital. For potassium and calcium, the 4s orbital is of lower energy, and the first two valence electrons enter this orbital. With scandium, the order of orbital energies is 4s < 3d < 4p, and, therefore, the extra electron enters the 3d orbital. For the rest of the first transition series, electrons are successively added to the 3d orbitals until they are filled, when the atoms have the electronic configuration $4s^23d^{10}$. It should be noticed that exceptions to this statement occur at chromium, which has the configuration $3d^54s^1$ rather than $3d^44s^2$, and at copper, which has the configuration $3d^{10}4s^1$ rather than $3d^94s^2$. This illustrates the very delicate balance between the relative energies of the 3d and 4s orbitals. The exceptional configurations of chromium and copper also illustrate the increased stability of exactly half-filled and filled subshells.

The relative energies of 3d and 4s orbitals are affected not only by nuclear charge but also by the oxidation state of the particular element under consideration. Although for the K^+ ion the lowest energy orbital is the 4s—and the electronic configuration of K is therefore [Ar]$4s^1$—with titanium the element and its ions have the following configurations:

Ti	Ti$^+$	Ti^{2+}	Ti^{3+}	Ti^{4+}
[Ar]$3d^24s^2$	[Ar]$3d^24s^1$	[Ar]$3d^2$	[Ar]$3d^1$	[Ar]

rather than

$$[Ar]3d^24s^2 \quad [Ar]3d^14s^2 \quad [Ar]4s^2 \quad [Ar]4s^1 \quad [Ar]$$

Therefore, for Ti^{3+}, the 3d orbitals are of lower energy than the 4s orbitals.

For the elements with atomic numbers greater than that of barium (atomic number 56), one has to consider the relative energies of the 4f, 5d, 6s, and 6p orbitals, and it turns out that none of these differs greatly in energy. Broadly speaking, the 6s orbitals are filled first, followed by the 4f, 5d, and 6p orbitals. The filling of the 4f orbitals corresponds to the 14 lanthanide elements, the 5d to the third transition series, and the 6p orbitals to the nontransition elements thallium through radon. Again we find unexpected electronic configurations among the elements and their ions: for instance gadolinium, with atomic number 64, has the configuration $[Xe]4f^75d^16s^2$ rather than $[Xe]4f^86s^2$, and gold (atomic number 79) has the configuration $[Xe]4f^{14}5d^{10}6s^1$ rather than $[Xe]4f^{14}5d^96s^2$. (Gold here resembles copper ($[Ar]3d^{10}4s^1$), with which it is said to be *pseudo-isoelectronic*.) Again we see the special stability of filled and half-filled shells having an effect on electronic configurations. The electrons entering the 4f orbitals in the lanthanides are entering orbitals with a principal quantum number *two* less than the quantum number of the s orbital which was of lower energy for barium. This is in contrast to the transition series of elements where electrons enter d orbitals with a principal quantum number *one* less than the principal quantum number of an s orbital which has already been filled.

We have already seen that changes in electron configuration from one atom to another do not have such marked effects on the chemistry of transition and lanthanide and actinide elements as they have on nontransition elements. Examples of this are the facts that all the lanthanides form reasonably stable M^{3+} ions in aqueous solution and that nearly all of the first-row transition elements form reasonably stable M^{2+} ions in aqueous solution. This behavior should be contrasted with, for instance, that of the elements sodium, magnesium, and aluminum among the nontransition elements, which form Na^+, Mg^{2+}, and Al^{3+} ions in solution but do *not* form ions of other oxidation states, for example, Na^{2+}, Mg^+, Al^+, and Al^{2+}. The reason for the lack of dramatic change in chemical properties as the number of valence electrons increases among the transition elements and the lanthanides and actinides is that increase in the number of valence electrons is not accompanied by large changes in ionization potential and sizes of atoms and ions. This is because the added valence electrons enter d and f shells, the d and f electrons screening each other poorly from the nuclear charge.

Oxidation States

One important characteristic of the transition elements is their ability to exist in a variety of oxidation states, each of reasonable thermodynamic stability (cf. Table 3-3). We have already seen that some nontransition elements, particularly the heavier ones in Groups III, IV, V, VI, VII, and 0, have the ability to exist in a variety of oxidation

Table 3-3 The Common Oxidation States of the First-Row Transition Elements. (The most important of these are shown in italic.)

| Oxidation State | Sc | Ti | V | Metal | | | Co | Ni | Cu | Zn |
				Cr	Mn	Fe				
M(I)									Cu(I)	
M(II)			V(II)	Cr(II)	*Mn*(II)	*Fe*(II)	*Co*(II)	*Ni*(II)	*Cu*(II)	*Zn*(II)
M(III)	*Sc*(III)	Ti(III)	V(III)	Cr(III)	Mn(III)	*Fe*(III)	Co(III)			
M(IV)		*Ti*(IV)	V(IV)		Mn(IV)					
M(V)			V(V)							
M(VI)				*Cr*(VI)	Mn(VI)					
M(VII)					*Mn*(VII)					

states, but this is only a limited ability—thallium for instance forms only Tl^{3+} and Tl^+ compounds, not Tl^{2+}. Since nearly all compounds of nontransition elements are diamagnetic and have *even* numbers of electrons, it follows that oxidation states of nontransition elements must usually differ by *two units*. For example,

$$Tl^{3+}, Tl^+$$
$$Pb^{4+}, Pb^{2+}$$

Xe(VIII)	Xe(VI)	Xe(IV)	Xe(II)
in XeO_4	in XeF_6	in XeF_4	in XeF_2

We shall see later that a great many transition-element compounds are *paramagnetic*, because the transition-metal atoms have a number of unpaired electrons; in addition, most transition elements can have a number of oxidation states differing by *one unit*. For example,

Mn(II)	Mn(III)	Mn(IV)
in $Mn^{2+}(aq)$	in $Mn^{3+}(aq)$	in MnO_2
Mn(V)	Mn(VI)	Mn(VII)
in MnO_4^{3-}	in MnO_4^{2-}	in MnO_4^-

The oxidation states of the first-row transition elements that have a reasonable stability are listed in Table 3-3. It should be noticed that, for the first-row transition elements scandium through manganese, the highest oxidation state attainable by the element corresponds to the removal of *all* the valence electrons outside the argon core. In old versions of the periodic table (see Table 3-4) the transition metals were placed in groups together with the nontransition elements. The reason for this was that there are some chemical resemblances between a nontransition and a transition metal with the same number of electrons in their valence shells. Examples of these similarities are shown below.

Group IV: TiO_2 (titanium dioxide) and SiO_2 (silicon dioxide)

Group V: V_2O_5 (vanadium pentoxide) and P_2O_5 (phosphorus pentoxide)

Group VI: CrO_4^{2-} (chromate anion) and SO_4^{2-} (sulfate anion)

Group VII: MnO_4^- (permanganate anion) and ClO_4^- (perchlorate anion)

However, although elements in both A and B subgroups may form compounds with the same formulas which have the central atom in the same oxidation state, the transition-metal compounds often differ in their properties from the nontransition-element compounds; the above pairs of compounds resemble each other in their oxidation power (although they often differ in rate of reaction) but differ in structure, color, solubilities, and so on.

Table 3-4   An Old Version of the Periodic Table

| Group I | | Group II | | Group III | | Group IV | | Group V | | Group VI | | Group VII | | Group VIII | | Group 0 |
A	B	A	B	A	B	A	B	A	B	A	B	A	B			
Li		Be		B		C		N		O		F				Ne
Na		Mg		Al		Si		P		S		Cl				Ar
K		Ca		Sc		Ti		V		Cr		Mn		Fe Co Ni		
	Cu		Zn		Ga		Ge		As		Se		Br			Kr
Rb		Sr		Y		Zr		Nb		Mo		Tc		Ru Rh Pd		
	Ag		Cd		In		Sn		Sb		Te		I			Xe

It must be stressed that although, for instance, the manganese atom has the oxidation state of $+7$ in the permanganate ion, MnO_4^-, the manganese atom is *not* present in MnO_4^- as Mn^{7+} but is covalently bonded to the oxygen atoms:

Some of the characteristics of transition metals and their compounds have already been mentioned: a general similarity in properties even though the electronic configuration changes (see the melting points of the elements, listed in Table 3-2); the paramagnetism of many transition metal compounds, resulting from the presence of unpaired electrons; and variable oxidation states, usually differing by only one unit. Another important characteristic is that a great many transition-metal compounds are quite strongly colored ($Ti^{3+}(aq)$ is purple; $V^{3+}(aq)$ is green; $Cr^{3+}(aq)$ is green; $MnO_4^-(aq)$ is purple; $Fe^{3+}(aq)$ is yellow-brown; $Co^{2+}(aq)$ is pink; $Ni^{2+}(aq)$ is blue-green; $Cu^{2+}(aq)$ is blue). Also, transition metals form a very large number of complexes (coordination compounds), and such complexes usually have one of three geometrical shapes: the octahedron, the tetrahedron, and the square-plane ($Co(NH_3)_6^{3+}$ is octahedral; $FeCl_4^-$ is tetrahedral; $Cu(NH_3)_4^{2+}$ is square-planar). Some of the transition metals, such as the heavy elements platinum and gold, cannot be obtained at all as hydrated cations (when the cation is complexed with water molecules) but can only be obtained as cations complexed with other ligands, such as ammonia or the chloride ion. For instance, $Pt^{2+}(aq)$ is unknown, but $Pt(NH_3)_4^{2+}$ and $PtCl_4^{2-}$, which contain platinum in the oxidation state $+2$, are well-known complex ions of platinum. Similarly for platinum in the oxidation state $+4$; $Pt^{4+}(aq)$ is unknown but ions such as $PtCl_6^{2-}$ and $Pt(NH_3)_4Cl_2^{2+}$ can be prepared in solution and form crystalline salts.

There are a number of types of compounds of transition metals which do not exist for nontransition elements. Examples are: carbonyls, which are compounds of a metal with carbon monoxide (for example, nickel carbonyl, $Ni(CO)_4$, and iron carbonyl, $Fe(CO)_5$); nitrosyls, which are complexes containing nitric oxide (for example, the nitroprusside ion, $Fe(CN)_5(NO)^{2-}$); and derivatives of unsaturated organic molecules such as the ethylene compound of platinum, $(PtCl_3C_2H_4)^-$.

We shall now consider some of the general characteristics of the transition metals.

Magnetism

The presence of partly filled d orbitals is responsible for the paramagnetism of many transition-metal complexes. Let us consider the ferrous ion, Fe^{2+}, as an example. This ion has the electronic configuration $[Ar]3d^6$. The uncomplexed ion has five 3d orbitals of the same energy. One would, therefore, expect such an ion to have four unpaired electrons. Similarly one would expect the ferric ion, Fe^{3+} with the electronic configuration $[Ar]3d^5$, to have five unpaired electrons:

Fe^{2+} Fe^{3+}

Both of these ions should be paramagnetic, but Fe^{3+} ions should be more strongly paramagnetic than Fe^{2+} ions.

In chemical systems, these ions are always complexed by ligands, and one effect of the formation of complexes is that in the complex ions the five 3d orbitals no longer have quite the same energy. The simplest types of complex to consider are octahedral complexes in which six identical ligands surround the metal ions, for example, $Fe(H_2O)_6^{2+}$, $Fe(H_2O)_6^{3+}$, $Fe(CN)_6^{4-}$, and $Fe(CN)_6^{3-}$:

$$\begin{bmatrix} & H_2O & \\ H_2O & \diagup \!\!\! \diagdown & OH_2 \\ & Fe & \\ H_2O & \diagup \!\!\! \diagdown & OH_2 \\ & H_2O & \end{bmatrix}^{2+} \quad \begin{bmatrix} & CN & \\ NC & \diagup \!\!\! \diagdown & CN \\ & Fe & \\ NC & \diagup \!\!\! \diagdown & CN \\ & CN & \end{bmatrix}^{3-}$$

In octahedral complexes the five 3d orbitals are split into two 3d orbitals of higher energy and three 3d orbitals of lower energy:

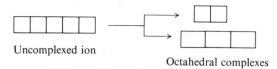

Uncomplexed ion

Octahedral complexes

The magnitude of the splitting varies from one complex to another. If the splitting is large, electrons will occupy the lower energy orbitals to the exclusion of the higher energy ones, but if the splitting is small, one has the same configuration as in the gaseous ion.

$Fe(CN)_6^{4-}$ and $Fe(CN)_6^{3-}$ are examples of complexes where the splitting is large; these ions have the configurations

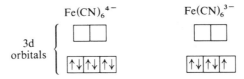

$Fe(CN)_6^{4-}$, therefore, has no unpaired electrons and is diamagnetic, and $Fe(CN)_6^{3-}$ has only one unpaired electron and is paramagnetic. The splitting of the 3d orbital energies is less in the aquo complexes $Fe(H_2O)_6^{2+}$ and $Fe(H_2O)_6^{3+}$, and these ions have the configurations

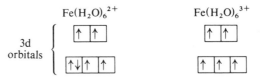

which are the same as for the gaseous ions. The magnetic character of transition-metal complexes, therefore, depends (a) on the number of d electrons, and (b) sometimes on the amount by which the energies of the 3d orbitals are split by the surrounding ligands in the complexes.

For quite a number of transition-metal ions in octahedral complexes, there is no change in the number of unpaired electrons with increase in d-orbital splitting. For example, an ion with two d electrons will have two unpaired electrons regardless of whether the d orbitals are split by a large or a small amount of energy:

The above splittings apply to octahedral complexes. The splitting is different in complexes where there is a tetrahedral or square-planar arrangement of ligands around the metal ion.

We have seen that there are similarities in the chemistry of transition elements in the same group, and to some extent between elements in the same period. This brief discussion of the paramagnetism of transition-metal ions leads to an important similarity found among transition-metal ions. This similarity is that those ions which have the same number of d electrons resemble each other in a number of properties such as magnetism, absorption of light, rates of substitution reactions, and so forth. For these properties the number of d electrons is more important than the nuclear charge of the atom, its oxidation state, or the ligands which surround the ion. For instance, the following ions all have six d electrons in their valence shells

$$Fe^{2+} \qquad Co^{3+} \qquad Ni^{4+}$$
$$Ru^{2+} \qquad Rh^{3+} \qquad Pd^{4+}$$
$$Os^{2+} \qquad Ir^{3+} \qquad Pt^{4+}$$

and many of the complexes of these elements in these oxidation states are remarkable for the slowness of their substitution reactions:

$$Co(NH_3)_5Cl^{2+} + H_2O \rightarrow Co(NH_3)_5(H_2O)^{3+} + Cl^-$$

This is a consequence of their d-electron configurations.

The magnetic properties will obviously be closely related to the number of d electrons in the ion and will be independent of the particular element being considered; one thus has to consider how magnetic properties change with an increasing number of d electrons rather than attempt to remember values for every element in all its oxidation states. For instance, all the ions listed above with six d electrons will either have no unpaired electrons and be diamagnetic or have four unpaired electrons and be paramagnetic in octahedral complexes; none of them can have, for example, two unpaired electrons.

Color

Many transition-metal complexes are colored (that is, they absorb light in the visible region of the spectrum), and their color can often be related to the d configuration of the ions. The detailed interpretation of the spectra is quite complicated. The absorption of light corresponds to the formation of an excited state, and often this excited state contains electrons in d orbitals of higher energy than in the ground state. For $Ti(H_2O)_6^{3+}$

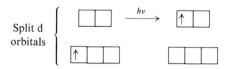

The energy involved in such transitions often corresponds to light in the visible region of the spectrum.

Ionic and Covalent Bonding in Complexes

Most complexes of transition metal-ions can be thought of as being held together primarily by electrostatic forces. With complexes formed between negative ions and positively charged metal ions, there is a strong electrostatic attraction between the negative charges on the ligands and the positively charged metal ion:

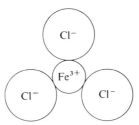

However, many complexes are formed between neutral molecules (such as water and ammonia) and transition-metal ions, and here the electrostatic attraction is between the negative end of the dipole to be found in the neutral molecule and the positive charge of the metal ion:

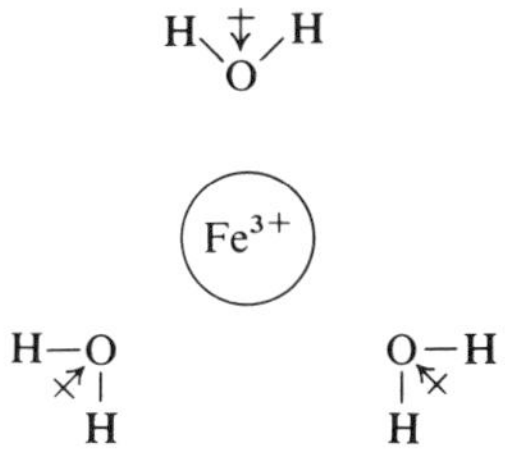

This electrostatic explanation for the forces which hold together complex ions is satisfactory for many complexes, but for others it is also necessary to consider covalent dative bonding between ligand molecules and transition-metal ions. This is illustrated by the data in Table 3-5, where the results of some experiments are given which measure the degree of covalent bonding in complexes.

In general, the importance of covalent bonding increases from the first to the third transition series and with increasing oxidation state of the transition-metal atom. The very high oxidation states ($+5$, $+6$, and $+7$) are never found in hydrated M^{5+}, M^{6+}, and M^{7+} ions but only in oxo ions such as VO_2^+, CrO_4^{2-}, and MnO_4^-. In all these

Table 3-5 Percentages of Ionic and Covalent Bonding

Complex Ion	Ionic Bonding, %	Covalent Bonding, %
NiF_6^{4-}	96	4
$CuCl_4^{2-}$	92	8
CoF_6^{4-}	96	4
$PdBr_4^{2-}$	60	40
PtI_6^{2-}	30	70

oxo ions there is considerable covalent bonding between oxygen and the transition metal, and it is better to think of them as containing dative bonds (in which each oxygen anion donates a pair of electrons into a sp³-hybrid orbital of the metal) rather than being held together by electrostatic forces:

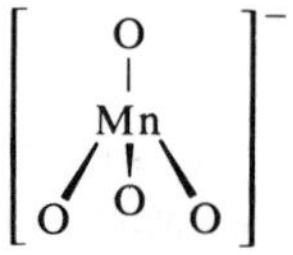

$$\left[\begin{array}{c} O \\ | \\ Mn \\ \diagup \ | \ \diagdown \\ O \quad O \quad O \end{array} \right]^{-}$$

Many of the characteristic compounds of the transition metals include bonds which involve the electrons in the partly filled d orbitals. The carbonyl compounds, for instance, which are compounds of carbon monoxide, contain an ordinary dative bond from carbon monoxide to the metal atoms

$$O \stackrel{..}{\equiv} C \rightarrow M$$

and, in addition, there is another dative bond from the metal atom to the carbon monoxide:

$$O = C \leftarrow M$$

This second dative bond is formed by overlap of a metal d orbital with an antibonding orbital of the carbon monoxide molecule:

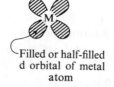

Filled or half-filled
d orbital of metal
atom

Empty antibonding π
orbital of carbon
monoxide

The net result is

$$O{=}C \rightleftharpoons M$$

This can occur with transition metals but not with nontransition metals; transition metals possess electrons in d orbitals of the right energy for bonding, while nontransition metals do not.

Other examples of compounds that are formed only by transition elements are certain derivatives of benzene, C_6H_6; an example is $Cr(C_6H_6)_2$:

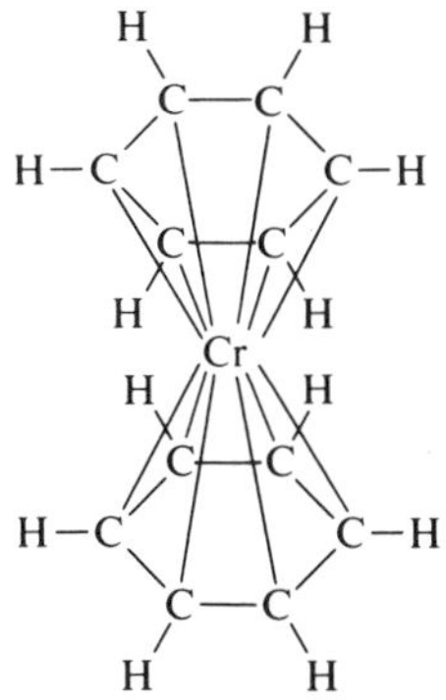

Such compounds in which a metal atom is situated between organic ring compounds are often termed "sandwich" compounds.

A brief survey of the chemistry of the first-row transition elements follows. It should be remembered that while the chemistry of the second- and third-row transition elements resembles that of the first-row elements, important differences do occur.

Scandium
[Ar]3d4s²

Scandium exists only in the +3 oxidation state. The ion Sc^{3+}, which has the electron configuration [Ar], occurs in aqueous solution and in a large number of compounds, such as the oxide Sc_2O_3; the trihalides, $ScCl_3$, for example; salts of oxyacids, such as $Sc_2(SO_4)_3$; and double salts, such as $K_2SO_4Sc_2(SO_4)_3$.

In general, scandium resembles the lanthanide elements in their chemistry. Sc(III) compounds are diamagnetic and usually colorless, as one would expect for an ion with no d electrons.

Titanium
[Ar]3d²4s²

The +4 oxidation state of titanium is the most stable (corresponding to the loss of all electrons outside the argon "core"); it is found in compounds such as TiO_2, $TiCl_4$, and TiF_4. Lower oxidation states of $+3$, $+2$, 0, and even -1 are known, but compounds containing these oxidation states are readily oxidized to Ti($+4$) compounds. Ti(IV) compounds are diamagnetic and usually colorless, and Ti(III) compounds are paramagnetic and purple in color. This is in agreement with the electron configurations of [Ar] for Ti^{4+} and $[Ar]d^1$ for Ti^{3+}.

$TiCl_4$ is a colorless liquid (bp 137°C) which fumes in moist air and is hydrolyzed by water to TiO_2:

$$TiCl_4 + 2H_2O \rightarrow TiO_2 + 4HCl$$

In the presence of concentrated hydrochloric acid, $TiCl_5^-$ and $TiCl_6^{2-}$ complex ions are formed

$$TiCl_4 + 2Cl^- \rightarrow TiCl_6^{2-}$$

and salts such as Cs_2TiCl_6 can be crystallized from solution. (Note the use of a large cation such as Cs^+ to obtain stable crystalline salts of a rather unstable anion such as $TiCl_6^{2-}$.)

Ti(III) compounds can be prepared by reducing Ti(IV) compounds, and in aqueous solution the purple $Ti(H_2O)_6^{3+}$ ion is present. Solutions of Ti(III) compounds are oxidized slowly by the air, but they are sometimes used in volumetric analysis, for instance in the determination of iron in the $+3$ oxidation state:

$$Fe^{3+}(aq) + Ti^{3+}(aq) \rightarrow Fe^{2+}(aq) + Ti^{4+}$$

None of the other oxidation states of titanium is stable in water. The dihalides TiX_2 and the oxide TiO can be prepared as solids by reducing the corresponding $+4$ oxidation-state compound with titanium metal at high temperatures:

$$TiO_2 + Ti \rightarrow 2TiO$$

Vanadium
$[Ar]3d^3 4s^2$

The common oxidation states are $+5$ (in which vanadium has used all its valence electrons), $+4$, $+3$, and $+2$, all of which can be obtained in aqueous solution. In addition, some compounds with vanadium in oxidation states lower than $+2$ have been prepared by use of suitable ligands such as carbon monoxide. Examples of the various states are shown below.

Oxidation state

V(V)	$VO_2^+(aq)$, V_2O_5, VF_5
V(IV)	$VO^{2+}(aq)$, VCl_4
V(III)	$V^{3+}(aq)$, VCl_4^-
V(II)	$V^{2+}(aq)$, $V(CN)_6^{4-}$
V(0)	$V(CO)_6$

The V^{5+} and V^{4+} ions as such do not exist in aqueous solutions since the equilibria

$$V^{5+} + 2H_2O \ \rightleftharpoons \ VO_2^+ + 4H^+$$

$$V^{4+} + H_2O \ \rightleftharpoons \ VO^{2+} + 2H^+$$

lie to the right in each case. In other words, the V^{5+} and V^{4+} ions are completely hydrolyzed in aqueous solution.

On the basis of their electronic configurations one would expect V(V) compounds to be diamagnetic and colorless, since vanadium in this oxidation state has lost all of its d electrons and has the electronic configuration [Ar]. On the other hand, V(IV), V(III), and V(II) compounds would be expected to be paramagnetic and colored, because they possess one, two, and three 3d electrons, respectively. These expectations are all realized in practice, though some V(V) compounds are colored.

Vanadium pentoxide, V_2O_5, will dissolve in acids to give the VO_2^+ ion, but it will also dissolve in alkali to give solutions of vanadates. The simplest vanadate has the formula VO_4^{3-}, but in less alkaline solutions highly condensed vanadates are obtained:

$$2VO_4^{3-} + 2H^+ \ \rightleftharpoons \ V_2O_7^{4-} + H_2O$$

$$3V_2O_7^{4-} + 6H^+ \ \rightleftharpoons \ 2V_3O_9^{3-} + 3H_2O$$

$$10V_3O_9^{3-} + 12H^+ \ \rightleftharpoons \ 3V_{10}O_{28}^{6-} + 6H_2O$$

In acid solution, VO_2^+ can be reduced successively to VO^{2+}, V^{3+}, and V^{2+}. In solution, these oxidation states are increasingly powerful reducing agents; V^{2+} is quite rapidly oxidized by air and will liberate hydrogen slowly from dilute acids, as is indicated by the ε^0 for the V^{2+}/V^{3+} couple:

$$V^{2+}(aq) \ \rightleftharpoons \ V^{3+}(aq) + e \qquad \varepsilon^0 = +0.26 \text{ volts}$$

$$V^{2+}(aq) + H_3O^+(aq) \ \rightarrow \ V^{3+}(aq) + \tfrac{1}{2}H_2 + H_2O$$

Chromium
[Ar]3d^{5}4s^1

The oxidation states $+6$ in CrO_4^{2-} (chromate), $+3$ in $Cr(H_2O)_6^{3+}$, and $+2$ in $Cr(H_2O)_6^{2+}$ can all be obtained in aqueous solution. Chromium has the "group" oxidation state in its $+6$ compounds, and has lost all its valence electrons; Cr(VI) compounds are therefore diamagnetic. The strong color of chromates, dichromates, and other Cr(VI) compounds is not caused by the presence of d electrons, since there are none. Cr(II) compounds in solution are very powerful reducing agents, as is indicated by the ε^0 for the Cr^{2+}/Cr^{3+} couple shown in Table 3-2. They are rapidly oxidized by air and they slowly reduce water to liberate hydrogen gas:

$$2Cr^{2+}(aq) + 2H_2O \rightarrow 2Cr^{3+}(aq) + 2OH^- + H_2$$

Chromium(III) compounds, which are usually green, are the characteristic compounds of chromium. Examples are the oxide Cr_2O_3 and the trihalides, CrX_3. Chromium(III) chloride forms three hydrates all with the formula $CrCl_3 \cdot 6H_2O$. The three forms contain different amounts of chloride coordinated to chromium: $Cr(H_2O)_6^{3+}3Cl^-$; $Cr(H_2O)_5Cl^{2+}2Cl^- \cdot H_2O$; $Cr(H_2O)_4Cl_2^+Cl^- \cdot 2H_2O$. Chromic oxide, CrO_3, readily dissolves in water to yield a solution of chromic acid, H_2CrO_4. The acid cannot be isolated as a pure compound, but there are two well-known series of salts derived from the acid: the chromates which contain the CrO_4^{2-} ion, and the dichromates which contain the $Cr_2O_7^{2-}$ ion. The dichromates should really be called pyrochromates, since the dichromate ion is a condensed ion derived from chromate:

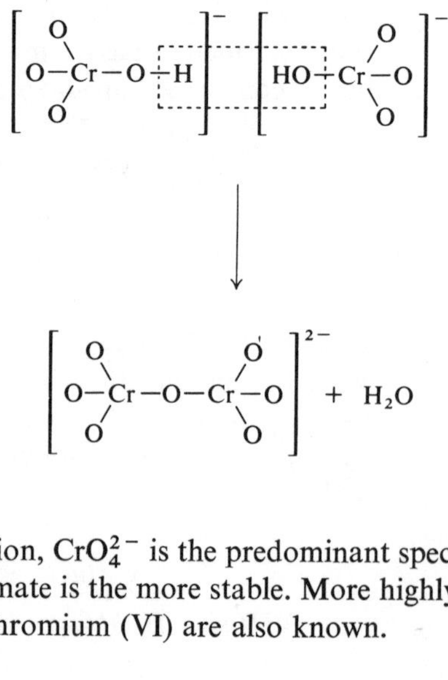

In alkaline solution, CrO_4^{2-} is the predominant species, while in acid solution, dichromate is the more stable. More highly condensed oxyacid anions of chromium (VI) are also known.

All chromium(VI) compounds are powerful oxidizing agents. Chromate and dichromate solutions are often used in volumetric analysis where the chromium(VI) is reduced to chromium(III):

$$2Cr^{3+} + 7H_2O \rightleftharpoons Cr_2O_7^{2-} + 14H^+ + 6e \qquad \varepsilon^0 = -1.3 \text{ volts}$$

$$Cr_2O_7^{2-} + 6Fe^{2+} + 14H^+ \rightarrow 2Cr^{3+} + 6Fe^{3+} + 7H_2O$$

In concentrated hydrochloric acid, chlorochromate(VI) anions with the formula CrO_3Cl^- are formed. If a mixture of a solid chromate, a chloride, and concentrated sulfuric acid is warmed, volatile chromyl chloride, CrO_2Cl_2, is liberated:

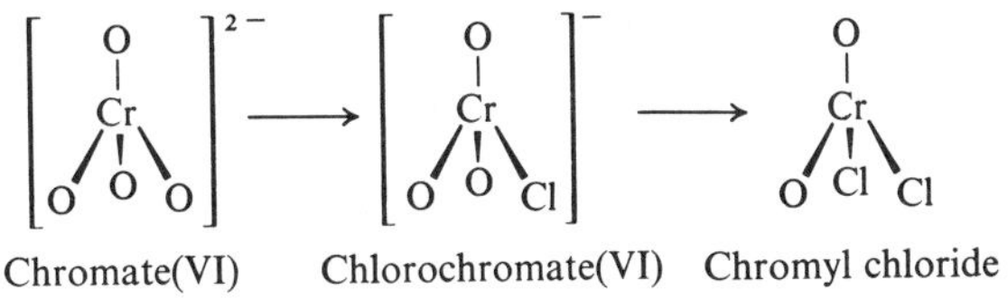

Chromate(VI)   Chlorochromate(VI)   Chromyl chloride

Chromyl chloride is hydrolyzed by water to give, successively, chlorochromic acid and chromic acid:

$$CrO_2Cl_2 + H_2O \rightleftharpoons CrO_3Cl^- + 2H^+ + Cl^-$$

$$CrO_3Cl^- + H_2O \rightleftharpoons CrO_4^{2-} + 2H^+ + Cl^-$$

Manganese, [Ar]3d^{5}4s^2

The most important oxidation states of manganese are +2, +3, and +7, though +1, +4, +5, and +6 compounds do exist. $Mn^{2+}(aq)$, unlike Ti^{2+}, V^{2+}, and Cr^{2+}, is not a powerful reducing agent, and this unusual stability of the Mn^{2+} ion is related to the fact that the Mn^{2+} ion has the electronic configuration [Ar]3d^5, with an exactly half-filled set of d orbitals. Many salts of the Mn^{2+} ion are known—for example, $MnSO_4$ and $MnCl_2$—and they are stable in acid solution. If alkali is added, $Mn(OH)_2$ is precipitated, and the precipitate is oxidized by air to the Mn(IV) compound, MnO_2:

$$Mn(OH)_2 + \tfrac{1}{2}O_2 \rightarrow MnO_2 + H_2O$$

Potassium permanganate, $KMnO_4$, contains the tetrahedral MnO_4^- ion, in which manganese has the oxidation state +7:

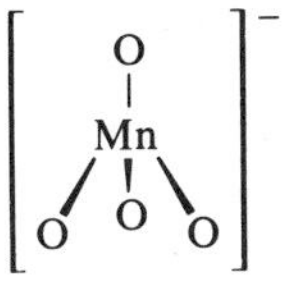

Potassium permanganate, an important oxidizing agent, is often used in volumetric analysis. It is a more powerful oxidizing agent in alkaline solution than in acid solution; in the former it undergoes a three-electron reduction to MnO_2, while in acid solution it undergoes a five-electron reduction to manganese(II):

In acid solution

$$Mn^{2+} + 4H_2O \rightleftharpoons MnO_4^- + 8H^+ + 5e \qquad \varepsilon^0 = -1.51 \text{ volts}$$

In alkaline solution

$$MnO_2 + 2H_2O \rightleftharpoons MnO_4^- + 4H^+ + 3e \qquad \varepsilon^0 = -1.70 \text{ volts}$$

Iron, [Ar]3d⁶4s²

The most important oxidation states of iron are $+2$ and $+3$. The $+2$ compounds are often called fer*rous* compounds, for example, $FeSO_4$, ferrous sulfate; and the $+3$ compounds are often called fer*ric* compounds, $FeCl_3$, ferric chloride, for example.

Ferrous sulfate, $FeSO_4 \cdot 7H_2O$, can be prepared by dissolving iron in dilute sulfuric acid:

$$Fe + 2H^+ + SO_4^{2-} \rightarrow Fe^{2+} + SO_4^{2-} + H_2$$

The hydrated ferrous ion, $Fe(H_2O)_6^{2+}$, is almost colorless, so that most ferrous salts are also almost colorless. They are readily oxidized by all common oxidizing agents to ferric compounds, which are usually much more strongly colored:

$$2Fe^{2+}(aq) + H_2O_2 + 2H^+ \rightarrow 2Fe^{3+} + 2H_2O$$

Anhydrous ferric chloride, $FeCl_3$, can be prepared by heating iron filings in a stream of chlorine gas

$$2Fe + 3Cl_2 \rightarrow Fe_2Cl_6$$

while anhydrous ferrous chloride is prepared by heating iron filings in a stream of dry hydrogen chloride:

$$Fe + 2HCl \rightarrow FeCl_2 + H_2$$

These reactions are of quite general application: heating a transition metal in chlorine gas usually gives the chloride of the metal in its highest oxidation state, while the use of hydrogen chloride leads to a lower oxidation-state chloride.

Anhydrous ferric chloride is volatile and readily sublimes. The vapor consists of Fe_2Cl_6 dimers, which have a structure similar to those of the dimeric aluminum trihalides (cf. p. 51):

$$
\begin{array}{ccc}
Cl & Cl & Cl \\
\diagdown & \diagup \diagdown & \diagup \\
& Fe \qquad Fe & \\
\diagup & \diagdown \diagup & \diagdown \\
Cl & Cl & Cl
\end{array}
$$

Heating leads to dissociation of the dimers into monomers, and stronger heating causes reversible loss of chlorine and the production of ferrous chloride:

$$Fe_2Cl_6 \;\rightleftharpoons\; 2FeCl_3 \;\rightleftharpoons\; 2FeCl_2 + Cl_2$$

Ferric chloride is very soluble in water, and the aqueous solution is acidic because of hydrolysis of the Fe^{3+} ion:

$$Fe(H_2O)_6^{3+} + H_2O \;\rightleftharpoons\; Fe(H_2O)_5OH^{2+} + H_3O^+$$

Aqueous solutions of ferric chloride also contain chloride complexes of iron(III). For example

$$Fe(H_2O)_6^{3+} + Cl^- \;\rightleftharpoons\; Fe(H_2O)_5Cl^{2+} + H_2O$$

The ferric ion is a moderately strong oxidizing agent (see ε^0 in Table 3-2), and if iodide is added to an aqueous solution, some oxidation of iodide occurs:

$$Fe(H_2O)_6^{3+} + I^-(aq) \;\rightleftharpoons\; Fe(H_2O)_6^{2+} + \tfrac{1}{2}I_2$$

Since this is an oxidation–reduction reaction, the extent of the reaction will depend on the ε^0 for the Fe(III)/Fe(II) half-cell reaction. The formation of complexes with ligands that stabilize the Fe(III) oxidation state (decrease the ε^0), such as fluoride and cyanide complexes (for example, FeF_6^{3-} and $Fe(CN)_6^{3-}$), leads to reduced oxidation of iodide to iodine.

Oxidation states other than $+2$ and $+3$ do exist for iron; however, the lower oxidation-state compounds are readily oxidized while the higher oxidation-state compounds are powerful oxidizing agents. Examples of iron in low oxidation state are

$$Fe(CO)_4^{2-} \qquad \text{Oxidation state } -2$$
$$Fe(CO)_5 \qquad \text{Oxidation state } \;\;\; 0$$

and examples of high oxidation states are

$$FeO_4^-\quad\text{Oxidation state }+4$$
$$FeO_4^{3-}\quad\text{Oxidation state }+5$$
$$FeO_4^{2-}\quad\text{Oxidation state }+6$$

Cobalt, [Ar]3d⁷4s²   The common oxidation states of cobalt, like those of iron, are $+2$ and $+3$. Unless the cobalt atom is complexed with ammonia or some other nitrogen-containing ligand, the Co(II) oxidation state is the more stable. Cobalt dissolves quite readily in dilute mineral acids to give Co^{2+} salts

$$Co + 2H^+(aq) \rightarrow Co^{2+}(aq) + H_2$$

as is indicated by the Co/Co^{2+} electrode potential given in Table 3-2. The $Co(H_2O)_6^{2+}$ ion is pink and so most hydrated cobalt(II) compounds are also pink. Formation of complexes sometimes changes the color of the ion

$$\underset{\text{pink}}{Co(H_2O)_6^{2+}} + 4Cl^- \rightarrow \underset{\text{blue}}{CoCl_4^{2-}} + 6H_2O$$

and both four-coordinated tetrahedral complexes ($CoCl_4^{2-}$, for example) and six-coordinated octahedral complexes ($Co(H_2O)_6^{2+}$, for example) are known. $Co(NH_3)_6^{3+}$ and $Co(CN)_6^{3-}$ are examples of stable complexes of Co^{3+}. Both ions can be prepared by atmospheric oxidation of the corresponding Co^{2+} complexes. Co(III) complexes have the electronic configuration $[Ar]3d^6$, and in octahedral environments they could be either diamagnetic or paramagnetic with four unpaired electrons:

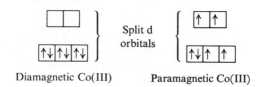

Diamagnetic Co(III)   Paramagnetic Co(III)

Which is the case depends on the separation of the energy levels of the two sets of 3d orbitals. In fact, Co(III) compounds are nearly always diamagnetic; $Co(NH_3)_6^{3+}$ and $Co(CN)_6^{3-}$ are both examples of diamagnetic Co(III) complexes. If the 3d orbitals were of equal energy, then Co(III) compounds would necessarily be paramagnetic:

It has already been mentioned (p. 162) that Co(III) complexes undergo unusually slow substitution reactions, and this is also a consequence of the diamagnetic d^6 configuration.

Nickel
[Ar]3d⁸4s²

Nickel has only one common oxidation state, Ni(II). Nickel dissolves in dilute aqueous acids, as is indicated by the sign of the ε^0 for the electrode reaction

$$\text{Ni} \rightleftharpoons \text{Ni}^{2+}(aq) + 2e \qquad \varepsilon^0 = +0.25 \text{ volts}$$

Nickel resembles iron in not being attacked by concentrated nitric acid—because of the formation of a protective layer on the metal. The $\text{Ni}(\text{H}_2\text{O})_6^{2+}$ ion is green.

Nickel forms a great number of complexes, which can be four-coordinated with either a tetrahedral or a square-planar arrangement of ligands about the nickel atom, or six-coordinated with an octahedral arrangement of ligands about the nickel atom:

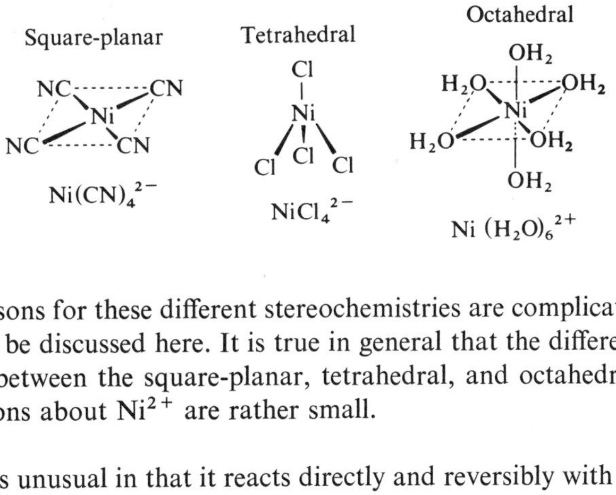

The reasons for these different stereochemistries are complicated and will not be discussed here. It is true in general that the differences in energy between the square-planar, tetrahedral, and octahedral configurations about Ni^{2+} are rather small.

Nickel is unusual in that it reacts directly and reversibly with carbon monoxide to give nickel tetracarbonyl, which contains nickel in the zero oxidation state:

$$\text{Ni(s)} + 4\text{CO} \rightleftharpoons \text{Ni(CO)}_4$$

This reaction is used to obtain extremely pure nickel metal.

Copper,
[Ar]3d¹⁰4s¹

The common oxidation states of copper are $+1$ and $+2$. Copper (II) compounds are often referred to as cup*ric* compounds, while copper (I) compounds are termed cup*rous* compounds. Copper(I) compounds disproportionate in aqueous solution unless they are either complexed with ligands that stabilize this oxidation state, for example, $Cu(CN)_4^{3-}$, or are insoluble, for example, $CuCl$.

Copper is the only first-row transition element that will not dissolve in dilute acids to liberate hydrogen, the Cu/Cu^{2+} electrode potential (Table 3-2) being negative. It *will* dissolve in nitric acid (which is an oxidizing agent as well as an acid) to give nitrogen products that depend on the acid concentration.

In dilute nitric acid

$$3Cu + 8HNO_3 \;\rightarrow\; 3Cu(NO_3)_2 + 4H_2O + 2NO$$

In concentrated nitric acid

$$Cu + 4HNO_3 \;\rightarrow\; Cu(NO_3)_2 + 2H_2O + 2NO_2$$

The Cu^+ ion has the electronic configuration $[Ar]3d^{10}$ and therefore contains no unpaired electrons. Copper(I) compounds are therefore diamagnetic and usually colorless. The Cu^{2+} ion has the electronic configuration $[Ar]3d^9$ and must contain one unpaired electron. Copper(II) compounds are therefore paramagnetic and are blue or green; the precise color depends on the environment of the copper atom:

$$\underset{\text{blue}}{Cu(H_2O)_4^{2+}} + 4Cl^- \;\rightarrow\; \underset{\text{green}}{CuCl_4^{2-}} + 4H_2O$$

Both copper(I) and copper(II) atoms are usually four-coordinated; copper(I) complexes are usually tetrahedral while copper(II) complexes are usually square-planar:

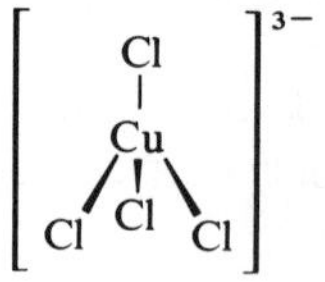

$CuCl_4{}^{3-}$ 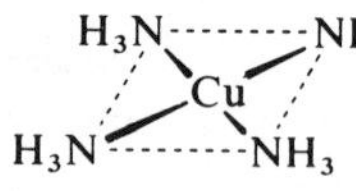 $Cu(NH_3)_4{}^{2+}$

The oxidation potential for the Cu(II)/Cu(I) electrode reaction

$$Cu^+ \;\rightleftharpoons\; Cu^{2+} + e \qquad \varepsilon^0 = -0.153 \text{ volts}$$

would lead one to suppose that copper(II) should not readily oxidize compounds to give copper(I), especially in view of the fact that the potential for the Cu(II)/Cu electrode reaction

$$Cu \rightleftharpoons Cu^{2+} + 2e \qquad \varepsilon^0 = -0.34$$

is larger. However, the cupric ion *is* reduced to the cuprous ion by a number of weak reducing agents, such as iodide and cyanide:

$$Cu^{2+} + 2I^- \rightarrow CuI + \tfrac{1}{2}I_2$$

$$Cu^{2+} + 2CN^- \rightarrow CuCN + \tfrac{1}{2}(CN)_2$$

This occurs mainly because the cuprous compounds so formed are extremely insoluble so that the equilibrium is displaced to the right.

Zinc, [Ar]3d^{10}4s^2

Zinc is not usually considered to be a transition metal, since neither the metal atom in isolation nor the zinc atom in any compound has an incomplete set of 3d electrons. For convenience, it will be dealt with as the last member of the first transition series rather than as a non-transition element. In its properties it has resemblances to both series of elements.

The only oxidation state of zinc of any importance is the $+2$ state. The Zn^{2+} ion has the electronic configuration [Ar]3d^{10}, which is *not* that of a noble gas. (The next noble gas, krypton, has the electronic configuration [Ar]3d^{10}4s^{2}4p^6.)

Zinc is a reactive metal, as is indicated by the ε^0 for the electrode reaction

$$Zn(s) \rightleftharpoons Zn^{2+}(aq) + 2e \qquad \varepsilon^0 = +0.78 \text{ volts}$$

It burns in air on heating, to give the oxide, ZnO. The oxide reacts with water to give the rather insoluble hydroxide, $Zn(OH)_2$. The hydroxide is amphoteric, dissolving in acids

$$Zn(OH)_2 + 2H^+(aq) \rightleftharpoons Zn^{2+}(aq) + 2H_2O$$

to give the hydrated Zn^{2+} cation, and in alkali to give zincate anions,

$$Zn(OH)_2 + 2OH^- \rightleftharpoons Zn(OH)_4^{2-}$$

This behavior is in marked contrast to that of the hydroxides of the nontransition elements of Group IIA, magnesium through barium. Zinc also differs from these elements in showing a greater tendency to form complexes with a variety of ligands: $ZnCl_4^{2-}$, $ZnBr_4^{2-}$, ZnI_4^{2-},

$Zn(CN)_4^{2-}$, and $Zn(NH_3)_6^{2+}$ are all known in solution and can be crystallized as solids with large cations.

Mercury
[Xe] $4f^{14}5d^{10}6s^2$

Mercury is the heaviest member of the zinc, cadmium, and mercury group of elements, and it differs rather more in properties from the lighter members of its group than do other transition elements. The most important difference between mercury and zinc is that mercury forms "mercurous" compounds, which contain the Hg_2^{2+} cation, $[Hg\text{–}Hg]^{2+}$, in which mercury is in the oxidation state $+1$. Mercurous ions exist in equilibrium with mercury and mercuric ions

$$Hg_2^{2+} \quad \rightleftharpoons \quad Hg + Hg^{2+}$$

and the equilibrium constant for this disproportionation reaction has the value

$$K = \frac{[Hg^{2+}]}{[Hg_2^{2+}]} = 6 \times 10^{-3}$$

This means that Hg_2^{2+} is only just stable with respect to disproportionation; the addition of reagents to mercurous solution which lead to stabilization of Hg^{2+} or precipitation of insoluble Hg^{2+} compounds leads to disproportionation:

$$Hg_2^{2+} + 2OH^- \quad \rightarrow \quad Hg(l) + HgO + H_2O$$
$$Hg_2^{2+} + S^{2-} \quad \rightarrow \quad Hg(l) + HgS$$
$$Hg_2^{2+} + 2CN^- \quad \rightarrow \quad Hg(l) + Hg(CN)_2(aq)$$

The mercurous ion, Hg_2^{2+}, contains a mercury–mercury covalent bond; the mercury atoms have each lost one electron by ionization and have used the remaining valence electron to form the covalent bond. The tendency to form metal–metal bonds is found in general to increase with increasing atomic weight for transition elements, and a number of examples are known with elements such as gold, platinum, rhenium, and tungsten.

Problems and Suggested Reading relating to the material of this chapter will be found at the end of Chapter 4.

Chapter 4　　　The Lanthanides and Actinides

The lanthanide elements, which are listed in Table 4-1, resemble one another very closely in properties, so much so that there is considerable difficulty in separating them from one another. The same is true of the actinides, which are listed in Table 4-2.

The Lanthanides　　The classical method of separating the various members of the lanthanide series, employed in the nineteenth century, was the fractional crystallization of double salts such as the ammonium or manganese nitrates $Ln(NO_3)_3 2NH_4NO_3 \cdot 4H_2O$ and $2Ln(NO_3)_3 3Mn(NO_3)_2 \cdot 24 H_2O$. Each lanthanide forms such salts, and there is some variation

Table 4-1 The Lanthanides

Element	Symbol	Atomic Number	Electron Configuration	M^{3+} Ionic Radii, Å	Oxidation Potential $(M(s) \rightleftharpoons M^{3+}(aq) + 3e)$, volts	Color of M^{3+} Ions	Known Oxidation States
Lanthanum	La	57	$[Xe]5d^1 6s^2$	1.061	2.54	Colorless	3
Cerium	Ce	58	$[Xe]4f^2 5d^0 6s^2$	1.034	2.48	Colorless	3, 4
Praseodymium	Pr	59	$[Xe]4f^3 5d^0 6s^2$	1.013	2.47	Green	3, 4
Neodymium	Nd	60	$[Xe]4f^4 5d^0 6s^2$	0.995	2.44	Red	3
Promethium	Pm	61	$[Xe]4f^5 5d^0 6s^2$	0.979	2.42	Pink	3
Samarium	Sm	62	$[Xe]4f^6 5d^0 6s^2$	0.964	2.41	Yellow	2, 3
Europium	Eu	63	$[Xe]4f^7 5d^0 6s^2$	0.950	2.41	Pink	2, 3
Gadolinium	Gd	64	$[Xe]4f^7 5d^1 6s^2$	0.938	2.40	Colorless	3
Terbium	Tb	65	$[Xe]4f^9 5d^0 6s^2$	0.923	2.39	Pink	3
Dysprosium	Dy	66	$[Xe]4f^{10} 5d^0 6s^2$	0.908	2.35	Yellow	3
Holmium	Ho	67	$[Xe]4f^{11} 5d^0 6s^2$	0.894	2.32	Yellow	3
Erbium	Er	68	$[Xe]4f^{12} 5d^0 6s^2$	0.881	2.30	Red	3
Thulium	Tm	69	$[Xe]4f^{13} 5d^0 6s^2$	0.869	2.28	Green	3
Ytterbium	Yb	70	$[Xe]4f^{14} 5d^0 6s^2$	0.858	2.27	Colorless	2, 3
Lutetium	Lu	71	$[Xe]4f^{14} 5d^1 6s^2$	0.848	2.25	Colorless	3

177

Table 4-2   The Actinides

Name	Symbol	Atomic Number	Electron Configuration	M^{4+} Radius, Å
Actinium	Ac	89	$[Rn]6d^17s^2$	—
Thorium	Th	90	$[Rn]6d^27s^2$	0.99
Protactinium	Pa	91	$[Rn]5f^26d^17s^2$	0.96
Uranium	U	92	$[Rn]5f^36d^17s^2$	0.93
Neptunium	Np	93	$[Rn]5f^46d^17s^2$	0.92
Plutonium	Pa	94	$[Rn]5f^66d^07s^2$	0.90
Americium	Am	95	$[Rn]5f^76d^07s^2$	0.89
Cerium	Cm	96	$[Rn]5f^76d^17s^2$	0.88
Berkelium	Bk	97	$[Rn]5f^86d^17s^2$	—
Californium	Cf	98	$[Rn]5f^{10}6d^07s^2$	—
Einsteinium	Es	99	$[Rn]5f^{11}6d^07s^2$	—
Fermium	Fm	100	$[Rn]5f^{12}6d^07s^2$	—
Mendelevium	Md	101	$[Rn]5f^{13}6d^07s^2$	—
Nobelium	No	102	$[Rn]5f^{14}6d^07d^2$	—
Lawrencium	Lw	103	$[Rn]5f^{14}6d^17s^2$	—

of solubility. However, these methods are very time consuming and have now been superseded by separation using cation-exchange resins*, or solvent extraction of lanthanide complexes into an organic solvent.

Some properties of the lanthanides are given in Table 4-1. These elements do not exhibit such a wide range of oxidation states as do the transition elements. Those lanthanides that form cations other than M^{3+} in aqueous solution can easily be separated from those that do not, since the compounds of M(IV) have very different properties from those of M(III) lanthanides. As a result, cerium and praseodymium (which can be oxidized to Ce^{4+} and Pr^{4+}) and samarium europium, and ytterbium (which can all be reduced to M^{2+} ions in solution) can be easily separated from the other lanthanides and from each other.

All the isotopes of *promethium* are radioactive and they occur in nature in undetectably small amounts. ^{147}Pm is the longest-lived isotope of promethium and has a half-life of only 2.6 years. It has become available from fission products of nuclear reactors in quite large amounts, and work with this isotope has confirmed the expec-

---

* A *cation-exchange resin* is a resinous (i.e. amorphous, plastic) substance at the surface of which cations can be interchanged with one another without there being any significant change in the over-all composition of the solid.

tation that the chemistry of promethium is that of a typical lanthanide.

Scandium and yttrium, which are not strictly lanthanides because they do not possess partly filled f orbitals, resemble the lanthanides in many of their properties and, in particular, form only M^{3+} ions.

Many of the lanthanide M^{3+} ions are paramagnetic because they possess unpaired f electrons and are colored. The color is often associated with excitation of f electrons.

The lanthanide metals are very reactive, as is indicated by the ε^0 values given in Table 4-1. It should be noticed that the lanthanides have similar ε^0s to those of sodium ($\varepsilon^0 = +2.71$ volts) and magnesium ($\varepsilon^0 = +2.37$ volts), and they all react slowly with water in the cold, liberating hydrogen:

$$M(s) + 3H_2O \quad \rightarrow \quad M(OH)_3 + \tfrac{3}{2}H_2$$

They also burn readily in air to give oxides. All but cerium yield a sesquioxide, M_2O_3; cerium produces CeO_2. The metals react with hydrogen to produce hydrides, but the resulting hydrides are non-stoichiometric, usually being intermediate in composition between MH_2 and MH_3. The bonding in these hydrides seems to be intermediate between that of the saline hydrides and the interstitial hydrides (see p. 36).

The ε^0 values listed in Table 4-1 vary smoothly from lanthanum ($\varepsilon^0 = +2.54$ volts) to lutetium ($\varepsilon^0 = +2.25$ volts). This very gradual change of properties with atomic number is the typical behavior of the lanthanides, and it corresponds to a slight decrease in basic character with increasing atomic number.

The radii of the M^{3+} ions, listed in Table 4-1, show a steady decrease with increasing atomic weight; the over-all reduction from lanthanum to lutetium is 0.213 Å. This decrease in ionic radius, known as the *lanthanide contraction*, is caused by the poor screening of one f electron by other f electrons. As the nuclear charge increases, the effective nuclear charge experienced by the f electrons also increases.

The lanthanide contraction has important consequences for the properties of the elements of the third transition series which follow the lanthanide elements in the sixth period of the periodic table. The increased effective nuclear charge is responsible, for instance, for the fact that mercury has a larger first-ionization energy than cadmium or even zinc, the elements above mercury in the group. It is also responsible for the fact that the radii of the third-row transition-metal ions are only a little larger than those of the corresponding second-row transition-metal ions; some values are

$$Zr^{4+}, 0.80 \quad Nb^{5+}, 0.70 \quad Mo^{4+}, 0.68$$

$$Hf^{4+}, 0.81 \quad Ta^{5+}, 0.73 \quad W^{4+}, 0.68$$

This has some important consequences for the chemistry of the third transition series of elements. A similar, but smaller and less regular, contraction is also observed across each of the transition series. In the transition series of elements the contraction is smaller, because the d electrons are better at screening other d electrons from the nuclear charge than are f electrons.

The Actinides

The actinide elements and their electronic configurations are listed in Table 4-2. It can be seen from the electronic configurations of the atoms in their ground states that in the atoms the energies of the 5f and 6d orbitals are nearly identical. (For some of the elements the electronic configuration is not known with certainty.) The actinide series of elements is similar to the lanthanides in that over the series as a whole the 5f orbitals are filled.

All of the actinides are radioactive, but the isotopes of the elements differ greatly in their half-lives. In general, half-lives decrease with increasing mass and only the four lightest actinide elements occur in significant amounts in nature. Some typical half-lives for isotopes of the actinides are shown in Table 4-3. Because the uranium and thorium

Table 4-3   Half-Lives of Actinides

Isotope	Half-Life
^{227}Ac	22 years
^{232}Th	$1.4 + 10^{10}$ years
^{231}Pa	3.4×10^4 years
^{235}U	7.1×10^8 years
^{238}U	4.5×10^9 years
^{253}Fm	3 days

isotopes have such long half-lives, they are only weakly radioactive and are safe to work with in the laboratory. Other, short-lived isotopes (and particularly those of the heavier actinides) are much more intensely radioactive and can be handled safely only if special precautions are taken.

The radioactive decay of uranium and thorium isotopes found in nature leads eventually to the formation of three different stable lead isotopes. The radioactive decays proceed by a series of intermediate unstable isotopes and are responsible for the natural occurrence of many elements in small abundance. The over-all processes occurring in the uranium, thorium, and actinum series are shown below.

The uranium decay series $^{238}_{92}U \xrightarrow{8\alpha, 6\beta} {}^{206}_{82}Pb$

The thorium decay series $^{232}_{90}Th \xrightarrow{6\alpha, 4\beta} {}^{208}_{82}Pb$

The actinium decay series $^{235}_{92}U \xrightarrow[1\beta]{2\alpha} {}^{227}_{89}Ac \xrightarrow[3\beta]{5\alpha} {}^{207}_{82}Pb$

The symbols above the arrows indicate the number of alpha and beta particles emitted. One of these three series, the thorium series, is given in full in Table 4-4 to illustrate the complexity of radioactive decay series. It will be noticed that in the thorium series, isotopes of actinium, radium, radon, polonium, and bismuth are produced with a variety of half-lifes ranging from 3×10^{-7} seconds to 6.7 years, and that the end product of this series is the lead isotope of mass 208. The other two decay series produce different intermediate isotopes, and the end product in each case is a different lead isotope.

The elements heavier than uranium have all been produced synthetically, either in nuclear reactors or particle accelerators.

When the chemistry has been investigated, it is clear that the actinides are more complicated than the lanthanides, as might be expected from the near equality of the energy of the 5f and 6d orbitals. For the first four actinides, the most stable oxidation state increases with increasing atomic number from 3 to 6. The high oxidation states of $+5$ and $+6$ never occur as M^{5+} and M^{6+} ions, but as oxo ions,

$$M^{5+} + 2H_2O \rightarrow MO_2^+ + 4H^+$$

$$M^{6+} + 2H_2O \rightarrow MO_2^{2+} + 4H^+$$

and the M^{4+} cations are extensively hydrolyzed in solution.

$$M^{4+} + H_2O \rightleftharpoons MOH^{3+} + H^+$$

Table 4-4   The Thorium Radioactive Decay Series

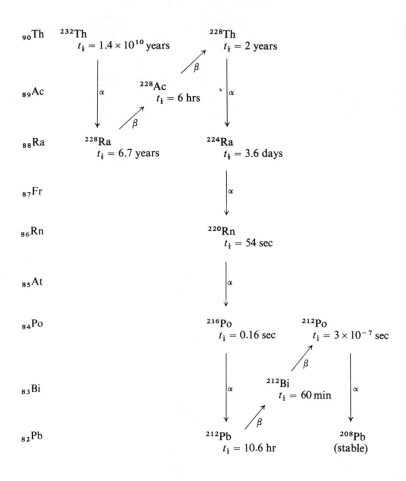

Several of the oxidation states that occur are unstable under most conditions with respect to disproportionation:

$$2UO_2^+ + 4H^+ \rightarrow U^{4+} + UO_2^{2+} + 2H_2O$$

U(V)   U(IV)   U(VI)

$$3AmO_2^+ + 4H^+ \rightarrow 2AmO_2^{2+} + Am^{3+} + 2H_2O$$

Am(V)   Am(VI)   Am(III)

The radii of some of the actinide M^{4+} ions are given in Table 4-2. It will be seen that the same type of reduction in ionic radii with increasing atomic number as was previously noted for the lanthanides is found to occur with the actinides.

The ions derived from the actinides are highly charged and are comparatively large. As a result, unusually high coordination numbers of 8, 10, and even 12 have been observed in some complexes.

Coordination number 8: $U(NCS)_8^{4-}$; AmF_8^{4-}
Coordination number 12: $Th(NO_3)_6^{2-}$

Problems

4-1. Would you expect $TiCl_4$, $TiCl_3$, $TiCl_2$, and Ti to be
(a) oxidized,
(b) reduced,
(c) hydrolyzed,
(d) hydrated
by water? Give brief reasons for your answers.

4-2. Mercurous sulfide has never been prepared. What products will be formed if H_2S gas is bubbled through an aqueous solution of mercurous nitrate?

4-3. The atomic radii of vanadium, niobium, and tantalum are:

V, 1.34 Å;   Nb, 1.46 Å;   Ta, 1.46 Å.

Write the electronic configuration of the three atoms. Why is there an increase in radius from vanadium to niobium but no increase from niobium to tantalum?

4-4. In general, what are the differences between transition and non-transition elements? To what can these differences be attributed? Illustrate your answer by referring in detail to the chemistry of one transition and one nontransition element.

4-5. Which of the following transition metal ions would be expected to be paramagnetic
(a) in the gas phase,
(b) in octahedral complexes where the amount by which the d-orbital energies are split is large:

Ti^{2+}, Ti^{3+}, Ti^{4+}, Mn^{2+}, Mn^{3+}, Mn^{4+}, M^{5+}, Mn^{6+}, Mn^{7+}, Zn^+, Zn^{2+}.

4-6. What reactions would occur if the following were added to water?

V^{+5}, Mn^{+7}, U^{+6}, Ce, Cu, Fe

4-7. Three hydrates of chromium(III) chloride with the formula $CrCl_3$ have been reported. However it might be possible to obtain *six* different compounds with this formula. Write down the structures of these six species.

4-8. Give examples of (a) a molecule and (b) an ion with the following geometries:

A–A;   A–X;   X–A–X (linear); $X-A\diagdown_X$ (nonlinear).

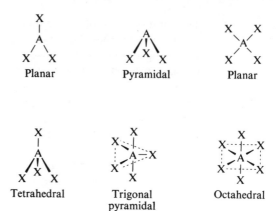

Planar   Pyramidal   Planar

Tetrahedral   Trigonal   Octahedral
                     pyramidal

Suggested   Basolo, F., and R. C. Johnson. *Coordination Chemistry*. Benjamin, New
Reading   York, 1964.

Johnson, R. C. "A Simple Approach to Crystal Field Theory," *J. Chem. Ed.*, **42**, 147 (1965).

Malatesta, L. "Zerovalent Compounds of Metals," *Endeavour*, Jan. 1969, p. 30.

Moeller, T. *The Chemistry of the Lanthanides*. Reinhold, New York, 1963.

Nechamkin, H. *Problems in Inorganic Chemistry*. Van Nostrand, New York, 1963.

Chapter 5   Compounds of Carbon

The element carbon is unique in forming a vast number of compounds. Well over a million carbon compounds have already been identified, and there is no reason to believe that there is any limit to the number that can be prepared. There are more known compounds of carbon than of all of the other elements put together. Partly because of this, the study of carbon compounds is a separate branch of chemistry—known as *organic* chemistry because of the important role played by carbon compounds in connection with living organisms. The present chapter gives a brief introduction to this branch of chemistry. In the next chapter we shall consider some compounds of biological interest and learn something of the relationships between molecular structure and physiological activity.

In this chapter we shall be concerned particularly with classes of organic compounds and with some of the characteristic reactions of the compounds in each class.

The Paraffin Hydrocarbons, or Alkanes

We begin with a group of compounds, known as *hydrocarbons*, which contain carbon and hydrogen only. There are several kinds of hydrocarbons, including the paraffins (or alkanes), the olefins (or alkenes), and the aromatic hydrocarbons. The paraffins are referred to as saturated hydrocarbons, which means that they are saturated with hydrogen; that is to say, their molecules contain a certain number of carbon atoms and as many hydrogen atoms as is possible in view of the valences of the two elements (4 and 1, respectively). If there is one carbon atom, for example, there are four hydrogen atoms, the molecule being

185

$$
\begin{array}{c}
\text{H} \\
| \\
\text{H}-\text{C}-\text{H} \\
| \\
\text{H}
\end{array}
$$

This is the molecule of methane, the simplest of the alkanes. There are four equivalent carbon–hydrogen bonds in this molecule, the four hydrogen atoms lying at the corners of a regular tetrahedron. The shape of the molecule is represented in Figure 5-1. The four hydrogen

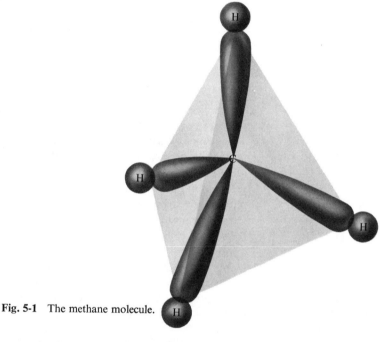

Fig. 5-1   The methane molecule.

atoms in the molecule are, therefore, equivalent to one another. The student should try to get used to the idea of the shapes of organic molecules, especially since the conventional two-dimensional representations are somewhat misleading.

Next in order of complexity is ethane, C_2H_6, which has the conventional two-dimensional structure

$$
\begin{array}{c}
\text{H} \quad \text{H} \\
| \quad | \\
\text{H}-\text{C}-\text{C}-\text{H} \\
| \quad | \\
\text{H} \quad \text{H}
\end{array}
$$

The actual shape of the molecule is represented in Figure 5-2. The bonds issuing from each carbon atom point toward the corners of a

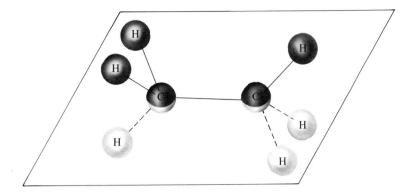

Fig. 5-2   The ethane molecule.

regular tetrahedron, the angle between any two bonds being the tetrahedral angle, 109° 28'. It is sometimes useful to regard ethane as a derivative of methane, formed by the imaginary process in which one of the hydrogen atoms of methane is replaced by a $-CH_3$ fragment:

$$\underset{\substack{|\\H}}{\overset{\substack{H\\|}}{H-C-H}} \quad + \quad \underset{\substack{|\\H}}{\overset{\substack{H\\|}}{-C-H}} \quad \longrightarrow \quad \underset{\substack{|\,|\\H\ H}}{\overset{\substack{H\ H\\|\,|}}{H-C-C-H}} \; + \; H$$

A fragment of a molecule, such as $-CH_3$, is known as a *radical*, and the $-CH_3$ radical is called the *methyl* radical. The general term for a radical formed from an alkane is *alkyl radical*; if a hydrogen atom is removed from ethane, C_2H_6, the resulting radical

$$\underset{\substack{|\,|\\H\ H}}{\overset{\substack{H\ H\\|\,|}}{H-C-C-}}$$

is known as the ethyl radical. The radicals are, in fact, given names that allow them to be easily related to the alkanes from which they are formed. Several alkyl radicals have actually been formed in the free state, in which case they are known as *free radicals*. Free radicals are usually very unstable and combine rapidly to form stable molecules.

Propane, C_3H_8, can be derived conceptually by causing a methyl radical to replace one of the hydrogen atoms of ethane:

$$\underset{\substack{|\,|\\H\ H}}{\overset{\substack{H\ H\\|\,|}}{H-C-C-H}} \quad + \quad \underset{\substack{|\\H}}{\overset{\substack{H\\|}}{-C-H}} \quad \longrightarrow \quad \underset{\substack{|\,|\,|\\H\ H\ H}}{\overset{\substack{H\ H\ H\\|\,|\,|}}{H-C-C-C-H}} \; + \; H$$

The shape of the propane molecule is shown in Figure 5-3. It is to be seen that the eight hydrogen atoms are not equivalent to one another, but fall into two groups:

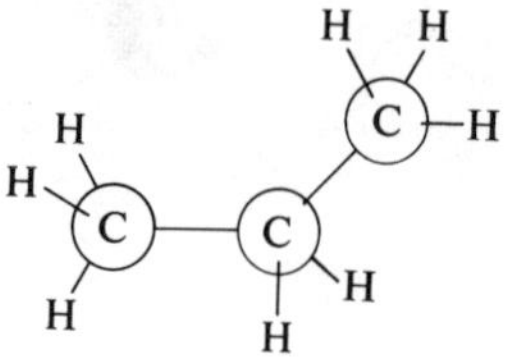

Fig. 5-3   The propane molecule.

1. the six hydrogen atoms that are bonded to the exterior carbon atoms;
2. the two hydrogen atoms that are bonded to the interior carbon atom.

This grouping has an important consequence that becomes apparent as we continue the conceptual process of generating alkanes by replacing a hydrogen atom by a methyl group. If any one of the six equivalent hydrogen atoms on the exterior carbon atoms in propane is replaced by CH_3, the result is the molecule called normal butane, or *n*-butane, the structure of which is

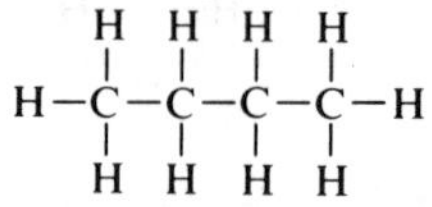

n-Butane

Replacement of one of the two hydrogen atoms bonded to the interior carbon atom of propane, on the other hand, yields the molecule known as isobutane:

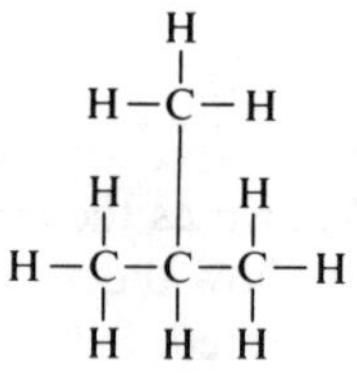

Isobutane

The shapes of these two molecules are represented in Figure 5-4.

The molecules of *n*-butane and isobutane have the same molecular formula, namely C_4H_{10}, but they are distinctly different compounds with somewhat different physical and chemical properties. Normal butane, for example, melts at $-135°C$, while isobutane melts at $-145°C$. Molecules having the same molecular formulas but differing in structural formulas are known as *isomers*, and the phenomenon is

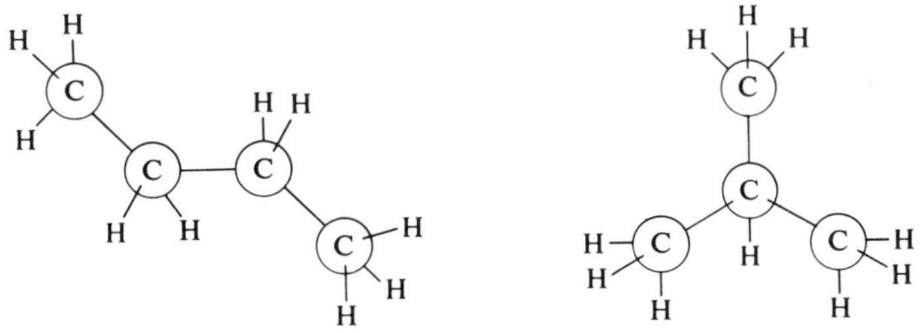

Fig. 5-4   The butane and isobutane molecules.

known as *isomerism*. There are various kinds of isomers. The molecules of *n*-butane and isobutane are examples of *structural* or *positional isomers*; they are molecules that differ in the *sequence* in which the atoms are bonded to each other. Hydrocarbons like *n*-butane, in which the carbon atoms in the conventional representation are in a straight line, are known as *straight-chain hydrocarbons*. It is important to realize, however, that the carbon atoms are not really in a straight line; the angle between the bonds is in fact close to 109°28′, as shown in Figure 5-4. In the straight-chain hydrocarbons no carbon atom is bonded to more than two carbon atoms. Isobutane is an example of a *branched-chain hydrocarbon*, one of its carbon atoms being bonded to *three* other carbon atoms.

There are two different groups of hydrogen atoms in the *n*-butane molecule, and replacement of each type by a methyl group leads to two different molecules, known as normal pentane (*n*-pentane) and isopentane; the conceptual processes are

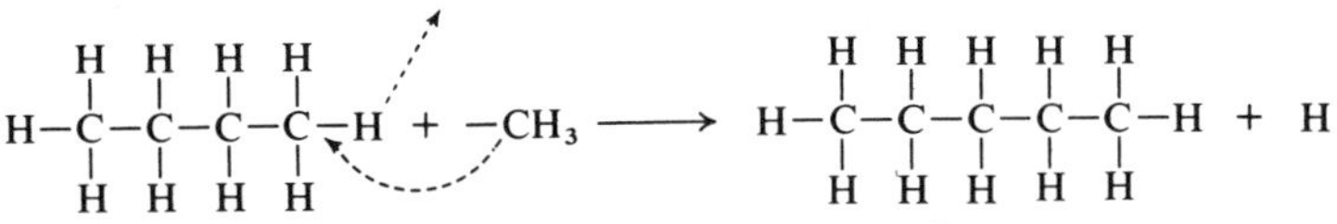

n-Butane   *n*-Pentane

and

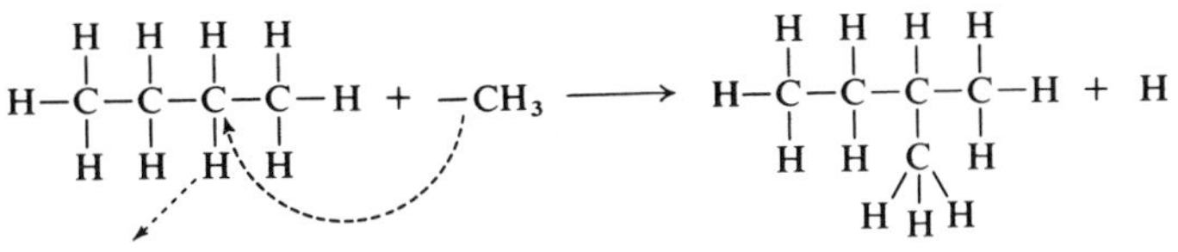

n-Butane   Isopentane

Note that replacement of a hydrogen atom on the right-hand carbon atom by CH_3 leads to *n*-pentane, and that replacement at the second-from-the-right carbon atom leads to isopentane. A third pentane isomer, neopentane, is formed by substitution of one of the central hydrogen atoms in isobutane.

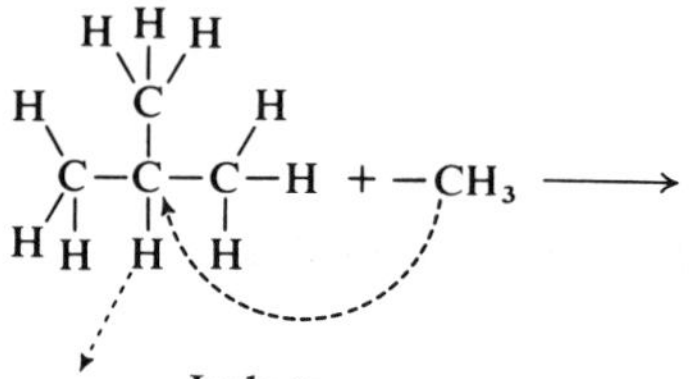

Isobutane 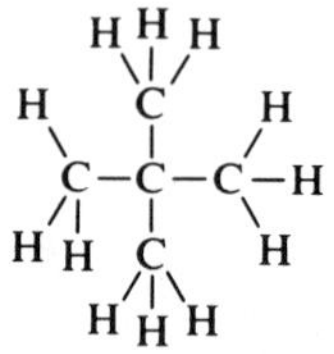   Neopentane

The student is encouraged to verify that these three molecules, of *n*-pentane, isopentane, and neopentane, are different from one another, and that there are no other pentane isomers. The melting points of the three compounds are, respectively, $-130°C$, $-160°C$, and $-20°C$; they are, therefore, very significantly different from each other. There are also small differences in chemical properties; in particular, the substances undergo reactions at significantly different *rates*.

The student will find it a useful exercise to verify that there are five positional isomers of hexane, C_6H_{12}, and nine of heptane, C_7H_{16}. He may prefer to take our word for it that there are 18 isomers of octane, C_8H_{18}, and 75 of decane, $C_{10}H_{22}$. The number of positional isomers increases rapidly as the number of carbon atoms increases.

There is another class of hydrocarbons in which the carbon atoms form a ring; these are known as *cycloparaffins* or *cycloalkanes*. The simplest member of the series, cyclopropane, C_3H_6, is conventionally represented as

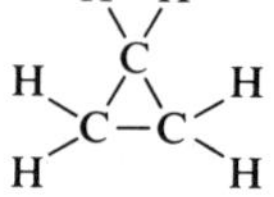

Its actual shape is represented in Figure 5-5. The carbon atoms in cyclopropane are at the corners of an equilateral triangle; three of the hydrogen atoms are on one side of the plane of the carbon atoms,

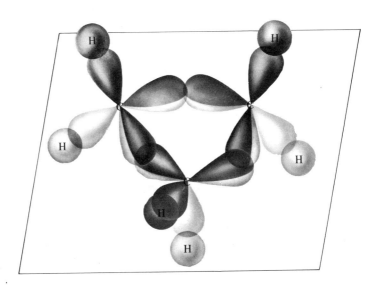

Fig. 5-5 The cyclopropane molecule. Note the existence of bent bonds, arising from the sideways overlap of sp³ orbitals.

and three are on the other side. The angle between two neighboring C–C bonds, 60°, is considerably less than the normal tetrahedral angle, 109° 28′, and the bonds are, therefore, strained out of their normal directions; in fact, as shown in Figure 5-5, the bonds are bent, there being some sideways overlapping of orbitals. In cyclobutane, C_4H_8, the carbon skeleton forms a slightly puckered square, the angles being not far from 90°; again there is a certain amount of strain. In the higher cyclic hydrocarbons, on the other hand, the rings are puckered in such a way that the angles between neighboring C–C bonds are close to the normal tetrahedral angle. Figure 5-6 shows two different ways in which this can be done for the cyclo-hexane molecule. These two molecules are said to exist in different *conformations*. There is an important difference between conformations and isomers. In order for a molecule to be converted into one of its isomers it is necessary for a chemical bond to be broken. The conversion of a molecule from one conformation into another, on the other hand, can be achieved without the breaking of chemical bonds. During recent years it has been realized that the study of molecular conformations is of great importance, because chemical and biological properties are markedly dependent on molecular conformations.

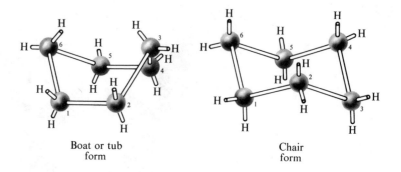

Boat or tub   Chair
form   form

Fig. 5-6   The two conformations of the cyclohexane molecule.

Properties of Alkanes

The word *paraffin* comes from Latin words meaning "against affinity," and the alkanes are indeed quite unreactive substances, at any rate at ordinary temperatures. When heated, all of them undergo decomposition; ethane, for example, at temperatures of 500°C and higher, readily decomposes, producing largely ethylene, C_2H_4, and hydrogen:

$$C_2H_6 \rightarrow C_2H_4 + H_2$$

The mechanism of this reaction is somewhat complex. At higher temperatures, and under the action of light of suitable wavelengths, the paraffins will also react with halogens and other substances. At room temperature, however, they undergo few reactions.

The alkanes are only very slightly soluble in water. Because of the very low polarity of the carbon–hydrogen bonds there is little attraction between an alkane molecule and a water molecule. We have seen that in liquid water there is fairly strong attraction between neighboring water molecules, because of hydrogen bonding which is caused largely by dipole–dipole forces. If hydrocarbon molecules were to dissolve in water, many of these hydrogen bonds would be broken, and would be replaced by the much weaker water–hydrocarbon attractions. As a result, a more stable arrangement results if the water molecules all remain together and the hydrocarbon molecules all remain together, rather than if a solution is formed. This tendency for nonpolar groups, such as hydrocarbon residues, to cluster together in water is sometimes spoken of as *hydrophobic bonding*. It is not a true bonding, but is produced indirectly by the attraction that water molecules have for one another.

The alkanes burn readily in air and particularly in oxygen to yield carbon dioxide and water. The reaction in the case of methane, for example, is

$$CH_4 + 2O_2 \rightarrow CO_2 + 2H_2O$$

and with ethane

$$C_2H_6 + 7\!/\!2O_2 \rightarrow 2CO_2 + 3H_2O$$

All such reactions are accompanied by the evolution of considerable amounts of heat, so that many alkanes are valuable as fuels. Natural gas, commonly used as a domestic fuel, is predominantly methane. Propane, C_3H_8, is also frequently used as a fuel. Automobile and aircraft engines burn gasolines that are mixtures of many higher hydrocarbons, including, in particular, the many isomers of octane, C_8H_{18}.

The Olefin Hydrocarbons, or Alkenes

The olefins, or alkenes, are hydrocarbons that contain fewer hydrogen atoms than do the corresponding alkanes; therefore, they are known as unsaturated hydrocarbons. They contain one or more carbon–carbon double bonds:

$$\text{>}C\!=\!C\text{<}$$

The monoalkenes, or monoolefins, contain one such double bond, the dialkenes two, and so on. The alkenes are named in such a way as to indicate their relationship to the corresponding alkanes. Thus the simplest alkene, C_2H_4, of structure

$$\begin{array}{c}
H \qquad\qquad H \\
\text{\textbackslash}\quad\;\;/ \\
C\!=\!C \\
/\quad\;\;\text{\textbackslash} \\
H \qquad\qquad H
\end{array}$$

is given the name *ethylene*, or *ethene*, to show its relationship to ethane. Similarly, the monoalkene corresponding to propane is known as *propylene* or *propene*, its structure being

$$\begin{array}{c}
H \quad H \\
\text{\textbackslash}\;\;/ \\
C \\
/\quad\text{\textbackslash} \\
H \qquad\; H \\
\text{\textbackslash}\qquad/ \\
C\!=\!C \\
/\qquad\text{\textbackslash} \\
H \qquad H
\end{array}$$

In general, the suffix *ene* replaces the suffix *ane* in the corresponding alkane. According to strict modern usage, the names ethene and propene should be employed for the two alkenes mentioned above, but the older names ethylene and propylene are still in very common use.

The simplest dialkene is butadiene, which is related to normal butane; its structure is

$$
\begin{array}{c}
\mathrm{H} \\
\mathrm{H-C} \\
\quad \diagdown \mathrm{C-C} \diagup \quad \mathrm{H} \\
\mathrm{H} \diagup \qquad \diagdown \mathrm{C} \\
\qquad\qquad \mathrm{H} \diagdown \mathrm{H} \\
\qquad\quad \mathrm{H}
\end{array}
$$

This compound is a good example of one in which the orbitals are not localized. The middle carbon–carbon bond, for example, is not a pure single bond, but has some double-bond character.

As with alkanes, the higher alkenes can occur in a number of isomeric forms, the number increasing strongly with the size of the molecule. To understand what different isomers are possible, we must consider the shapes of molecules containing carbon–carbon double bonds. In such molecules there is sp^2 hybridization, leading to a planar structure, the angles between the bonds being $120°$. The double bond is composed of a σ bond, formed by the overlapping of two sp^2 hybrids, and a π bond, formed by the lateral overlapping of two p orbitals which are at right angles to the plane of the sp^2 hybrids. The whole arrangement is shown in Figure 5-7. This sideways overlapping of the p orbitals makes it difficult for the double bond to be twisted.

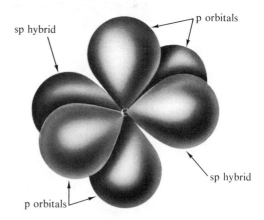

Fig. 5-7 The two orbitals formed by *sp* hybridization together with the two *p* orbitals.

One important consequence of the configuration about the σ–π double bond is the existence of what are known as geometrical isomers. A simple example of this type of isomerism is in 2-butene. This molecule can be regarded as formed from *n*-butane by the removal of a hydrogen atom from each of the middle two carbon atoms, with the formation of a double bond:

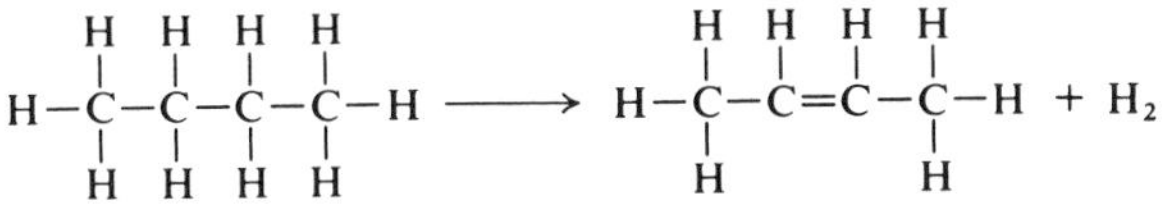

Butane   2-Butene

If we consider the spatial arrangement of the bonds about the double bond we see that the molecule can exist in two forms:

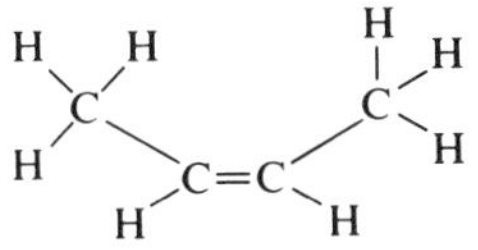

cis-2-Butene 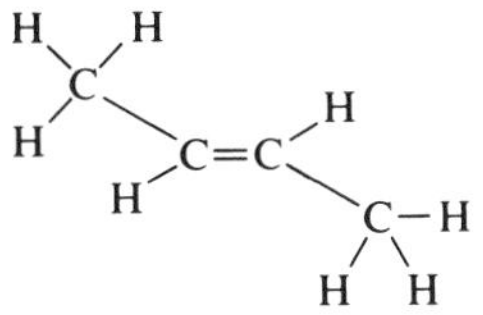   trans-2-Butene

In *cis*-2-butene the two methyl groups are on the same side of the double bond, while in *trans*-2-butene the methyl groups are on opposite sides. These two isomers have slightly different melting and boiling points; their chemical properties are qualitatively the same, but there are slight quantitative differences. For example, their heats of formation are slightly different (-1.67 and -2.67 kcal/mole, respectively; the *trans* form is slightly more stable), and they undergo reaction at slightly different rates. This type of isomerism, when there are *cis* and *trans* forms, is referred to as *cis–trans* isomerism, or *geometrical* isomerism.

There are two other isomers of butene. One of these, known as 1-butene, may be regarded as being formed from *n*-butane by the removal of hydrogen atoms from the end carbon atom and its neighbor:

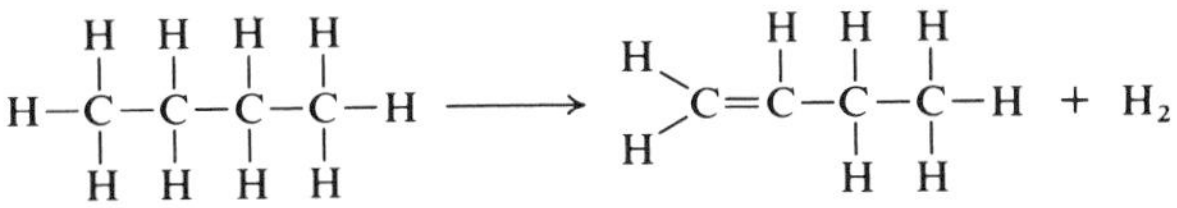

There is also an isomer, known as isobutylene or methyl propene, which can be regarded as formed from isobutane:

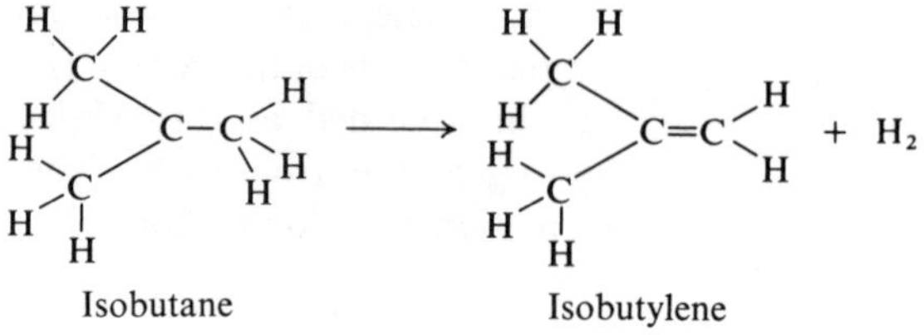

Isobutane   Isobutylene

The student can easily verify that there are no isomers of butene other than these four, namely *cis* and *trans*-2-butene, 1-butene, and isobutene. A useful exercise at this stage is to write down the structures of all the isomers of pentene, C_5H_{10}.

Reactions of Alkenes

The most important reactions of alkenes involve the addition of molecules to the double bond. Bromine, for example, reacts rapidly with alkenes, by reactions such as

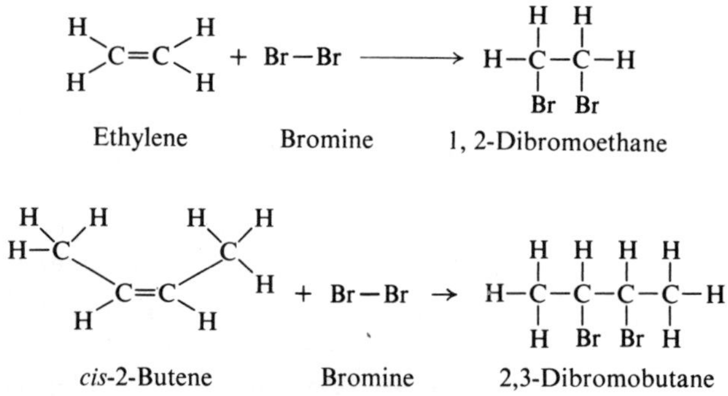

Ethylene   Bromine   1, 2-Dibromoethane

cis-2-Butene   Bromine   2,3-Dibromobutane

These reactions occur if the alkene is introduced into a solution of bromine in water at room temperature. The occurrence of these reactions is the basis of a simple test which distinguishes alkenes from alkanes; the latter only reacts with bromine at high temperatures or under the influence of intense illumination.

Molecular hydrogen also adds on to the double bonds in alkenes, but not as readily as do the halogens. These reactions are usually carried out by the use of hydrogen at high pressure and in the presence of a catalyst, such as finely divided platinum or palladium. Examples of such reactions, and of the addition of HBr, are

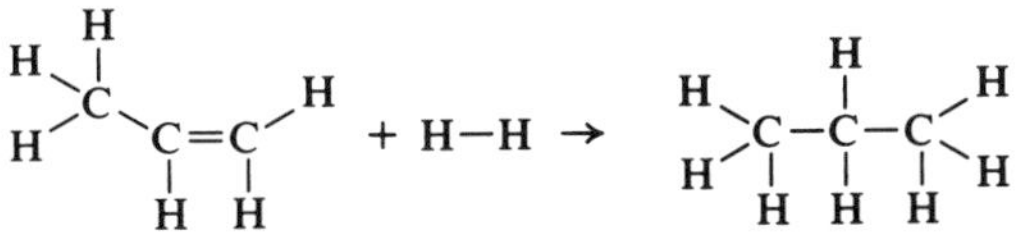

$$\underset{\text{Propylene}}{\overset{\displaystyle H}{\underset{\displaystyle H}{H}}\text{C=C}\begin{matrix}H\\H\end{matrix}} + \underset{\text{Hydrogen}}{H-H} \rightarrow \underset{\text{Propane}}{\overset{\displaystyle H}{H}\text{C}-\text{C}-\text{C}\begin{matrix}H\\H\end{matrix}}$$

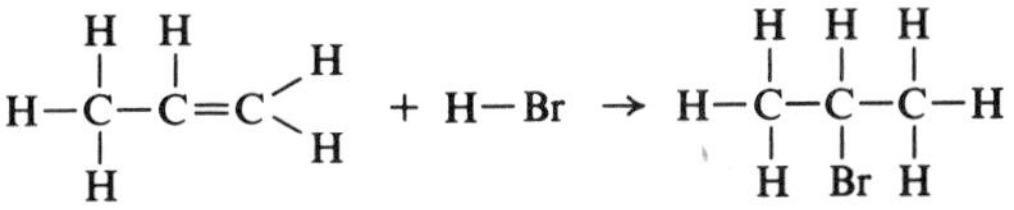

$$\underset{\text{Propylene}}{H-\text{C}-\text{C=C}\begin{matrix}H\\H\end{matrix}} + \underset{\substack{\text{Hydrogen}\\\text{bromide}}}{H-Br} \rightarrow \underset{\substack{\text{2-Bromopropane}\\\text{(or isopropyl bromide)}}}{H-\text{C}-\text{C}-\text{C}-H}$$

In principle, hydrogen bromide could add on to propylene in two different ways, to give either 2-bromopropane (whose structure is given above) or 1-bromopropane (*n*-propyl bromide), whose structure is

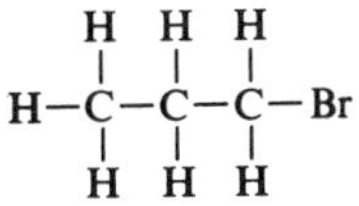

$$H-\text{C}-\text{C}-\text{C}-Br$$

The main product is 2-bromopropane, and it has been found that reactions of this kind follow a predictable course, which is summarized in a rule due to Markovnikov. According to Markovnikov's rule, *the hydrogen atom of the acid adds to the carbon atom that has attached to it the greater number of hydrogen atoms*; the halogen adds to the carbon atom having the smaller number of hydrogen atoms. Markovnikov's rule also applies to hydration reactions, such as

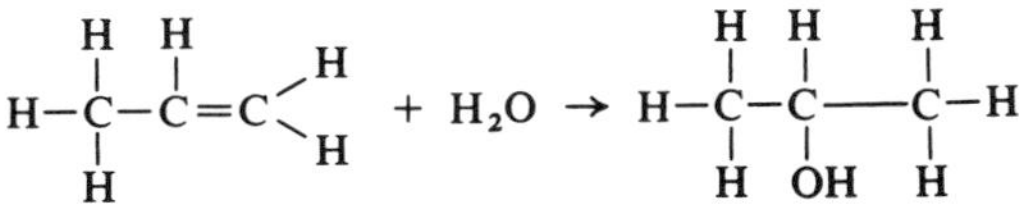

$$\underset{\text{Propylene}}{H-\text{C}-\text{C=C}\begin{matrix}H\\H\end{matrix}} + H_2O \rightarrow \underset{\substack{\text{2-Propanol}\\\text{(or isopropyl alcohol)}}}{H-\text{C}-\text{C}-\text{C}-H}$$

There is much evidence that the addition of acids to double bonds proceeds by a mechanism involving the initial transfer of a proton from the acid to the alkene; the ion formed in this process is known as a *carbonium ion*. An example is

$$
\underset{\text{Propylene}}{\overset{\begin{array}{cc}H & H\\ | & |\end{array}}{H-\overset{|}{\underset{|}{C}}-\overset{}{C}=C<\overset{H}{\underset{H}{}}}} \;+\; \underset{\substack{\text{Hydrogen}\\\text{bromide}}}{H-Br} \;\longrightarrow\; \underset{\substack{\text{Carbonium}\\\text{ion}}}{H-\overset{|}{\underset{|}{C}}-\overset{|}{C}{}^{+}} \;+\; \underset{\substack{\text{Bromide}\\\text{ion}}}{Br^{-}} \tag{1}
$$

In a second step the bromide ion adds on to the carbonium ion, becoming attached at the carbon atom that bears the positive charge:

$$
\underset{\substack{\text{Carbonium}\\\text{ion}}}{H-C-C^{+}} \;+\; Br^{-} \;\longrightarrow\; \underset{\text{2-Bromopropane}}{H-C-C-Br} \tag{2}
$$

In the first stage, reaction (1), the proton could have been attached as shown, or at the central carbon atom:

$$
\underset{\text{Propylene}}{H-C-C=C<\overset{H}{\underset{H}{}}} \;+\; \underset{\substack{\text{Hydrogen}\\\text{bromide}}}{H-Br} \;\longrightarrow\; \underset{\substack{\text{Carbonium}\\\text{ion}}}{H-C-C-C^{+}} \;+\; Br^{-} \tag{1'}
$$

There is considerable evidence that the type of carbonium ion formed in reaction (1), having the positive charge on a carbon atom that is attached to two other carbon atoms, is more stable than that formed in reaction (1′); in the latter reaction the positive charge is on a carbon atom attached to only one carbon atom. Carbonium ions are very reactive and occur only as intermediates in reactions; they have incomplete outer shells, containing six electrons which are in sp^2-hybrid orbitals. The carbonium ion formed in reaction (1), of the type

$$
R-\overset{\displaystyle H}{\underset{}{C^{+}}}-R
$$

is known as a *secondary* carbonium ion, while that formed in (1′), of the type

$$
R-\overset{\displaystyle H}{\underset{}{C^{+}}}-H
$$

is a *primary* carbonium ion. There can also exist *tertiary* carbonium ions, of the type

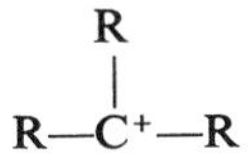

$$\begin{array}{c} R \\ | \\ R-C^+-R \end{array}$$

The order of stability of carbonium ions is

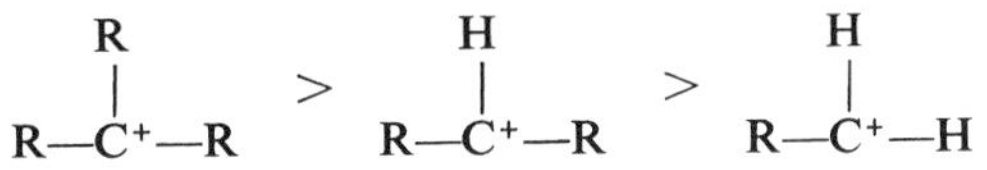

$$\begin{array}{ccccc} R & & H & & H \\ | & & | & & | \\ R-C^+-R & > & R-C^+-R & > & R-C^+-H \\ \text{Tertiary} & & \text{Secondary} & & \text{Primary} \end{array}$$

This order of stability leads to the result that the product formed in the reaction between a hydrogen halide and an alkene is that in which the hydrogen atom adds to the carbon atom with the greatest number of hydrogen atoms attached to it. Markovnikov's rule can therefore be rationalized on the basis of the relative stabilities of carbonium ions.

Alkenes also react readily with a number of oxidizing agents, such as an aqueous acidic solution of potassium permanganate. An example of such a reaction is

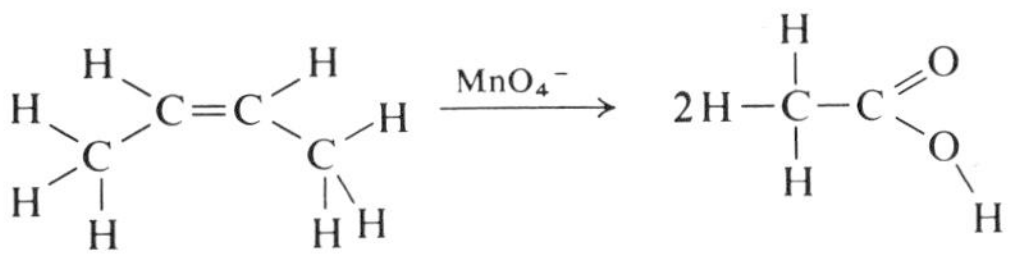

cis-2-Butene   Acetic acid

The alkene is cleaved into two oxidized fragments. This type of reaction is the basis of a qualitative test for the double bond; the purple color of the permanganate disappears as the alkene is oxidized.

The Acetylene Hydrocarbons, or Alkynes

The acetylenes, or alkynes, are hydrocarbons which contain one or more carbon–carbon triple bonds. The simplest of them is acetylene, C_2H_2, the structure of which is

$$H-C\equiv C-H$$

This type of molecule involves sp hybridization, which leads to two orbitals in the same straight line; the angle between the C—H and C≡C bonds is thus 180°, and the whole molecule is linear. The second and third bonds are formed by lateral overlapping of p orbitals.

All of the other alkynes may be regarded as derived from acetylene by replacement of one or both hydrogen atoms by an alkyl group. If, for example, one hydrogen atom is replaced by a methyl group, the result is methylacetylene:

$$\begin{array}{c} H \\ | \\ H-C-C\equiv C-H \\ | \\ H \end{array}$$

Since the alkynes are unsaturated hydrocarbons, they resemble the alkenes in reacting readily with various substances that add to the triple bond. The alkynes have positive heats of formation; that is to say, their formation from graphite and hydrogen is an endothermic process. Compounds of this type are commonly referred to as *endothermic compounds*. Endothermic compounds usually show a tendency to decompose spontaneously even at ordinary temperatures. The reason is that their decomposition is an *exothermic* process; heat evolved when some of the substance decomposes causes a rise in temperature which aids the decomposition of the surrounding molecules. The alkynes very often decompose spontaneously with explosive violence. Mixtures of alkynes and oxygen are also highly explosive.

Functional Groups

So far in this chapter we have considered only compounds containing carbon and hydrogen, but we have encountered a considerable number of different molecules. When other elements, such as oxygen, nitrogen, and the halogens, are involved as well, the number of possible compounds becomes very vast—indeed it is limitless. The study of organic chemistry would be prohibitively difficult if it were not for the fact that the compounds can be grouped into a few classes, the members of each of which exhibit behavior very similar to one another. The basis for this classification is the *functional group*, which is a group of atoms that occurs in a series of molecules and causes the molecules to react in a similar way. A study of the functional groups and their characteristics therefore leads to a considerable understanding of the properties of organic compounds. There are a number of different functional groups, but only a few of them are of frequent occurrence. It is to these that attention will be devoted here.

Some of the more important functional groups are listed in Table 5-1; their names and structures are given, as well as the general name of the compounds in which each occurs. Examples of these various

Table 5-1 Functional Groups

Functional Groups	Structure	Name of Compound in Which the Functional Group is Present
Halogen atom (e.g., chlorine)	—X (e.g., —Cl)	Halide (e.g., chloride)
Hydroxyl group	—O—H	Alcohol
Carbonyl group	$>C=O$	Aldehyde or ketone
Carboxyl group	$-C\diagup^{O}_{O-H}$	Carboxylic acid
Ether group	—O—	Ether
Ester group	$-C\diagup^{O}_{O-}$	Ester
Amino group	$-N\diagup^{H}_{H}$	Amine
Carbonyl amino group	$-C\diagup^{O}_{N\diagup^{H}_{H}}$	Amide

types of compounds, and some of the reactions they undergo, will be mentioned later.

The important simplifying feature of organic compounds is that the majority of the chemical reactions that occur involve changes in the functional groups only, with no change in the rest of the molecule. This is sometimes referred to as the *principle of skeletal integrity*, the carbon "skeleton" of the molecule remaining unchanged as the functional groups undergo reaction.

A large number of substances react with the various functional groups, but most of the reactions of the groups fall into one of the following three classes.

1. *Displacement reactions*, in which one functional group is replaced by another.

2. *Addition and elimination reactions*. In the addition reactions there is direct addition of a molecule to the functional group. The elimination reactions are the reverse of this; there is a loss or elimination of a molecule.

3. *Oxidation and reduction reactions*, in which the functional group is either oxidized or reduced.

Various examples of these different kinds of reactions are considered later in this chapter.

Nomenclature

Before we proceed to discuss some of the different kinds of organic compounds, it is convenient to digress and consider the principles by which the compounds are named. Because of the large number of organic compounds, nomenclature presents a considerable problem. There exist systematic methods, agreed to by the International Union of Pure and Applied Chemistry, for naming organic compounds, and some of the rules will be mentioned here. Unfortunately, some of the rules are rather cumbersome, and some organic chemists prefer to use simpler, less systematic names. To add to the difficulty, many familiar organic compounds have "popular" or "common" names—received before there was any system—which are still generally used; these names sometimes relate to the biological origin of the substance but sometimes are of no known significance. Fortunately, we need only the simplest of the formal rules to deal with the compounds we shall discuss, but we shall also need to know some of the common names.

The systematic naming of organic compounds is based on the largest straight-chain hydrocarbon from which the molecule can be regarded as derived. The branched hydrocarbons, for example, are regarded as alkyl derivatives of this straight-chain hydrocarbon, derived from it by replacing one hydrogen atom by an alkyl group. Consider, for example, the alkane of structure

$$
\begin{array}{c}
\text{H} \\
| \\
\text{H}\quad\text{H}\ \ \text{H}-\text{C}-\text{H}\ \ \text{H}\ \ \text{H} \\
|\quad\ |\quad\quad\ |\quad\quad |\ \ | \\
\text{H}-\text{C}-\text{C}---\text{C}---\text{C}-\text{C}-\text{H} \\
|\quad\ |\quad\quad\ |\quad\quad |\ \ | \\
\text{H}\quad\text{H}\quad\quad\text{H}\quad\quad\text{H}\ \ \text{H}
\end{array}
$$

The longest "straight" hydrocarbon chain has five carbon atoms, and the molecule has a methyl group substituted on the third carbon atom from either end. The straight-chain hydrocarbon having five carbon atoms is called pentane, and the molecule is called 3-methylpentane. Similarly the molecule

$$
\begin{array}{c}
\text{H}\ \text{H}\ \text{H} \\
\backslash\ |\ / \\
\text{H}\quad\quad\text{C}\quad\quad\text{H}\ \ \text{H} \\
|\quad\quad\ |\quad\quad |\ \ | \\
\text{H}-\text{C}---\text{C}---\text{C}-\text{C}-\text{H} \\
|\quad\quad\ |\quad\quad |\ \ | \\
\text{H}\quad\quad\text{H}\quad\quad\text{H}\ \text{H}
\end{array}
$$

is called 2-methylbutane. It would not be unreasonable to call it 3-methylbutane, since the methyl group is on the third carbon atom from the right-hand end. The convention, however, is to count from the end of the molecule that is closest to the branches; the numbers used are therefore as small as possible.

To name compounds in this way the names of the straight-chain hydrocarbons are needed, as well as the names of certain alkyl radicals. Some of these are given in Table 5-2.

Table 5-2 The Names of Straight-Chain Alkanes and Some Simple Alkyl Radicals

Names of Alkane	No. of Carbon Atoms	Name of Radical	Structure
Methane	1	Methyl	$H-\overset{\displaystyle H}{\underset{\displaystyle H}{C}}-$
Ethane	2		
Propane	3		
Butane	4	Ethyl	$H-\overset{\displaystyle H}{\underset{\displaystyle H}{C}}-\overset{\displaystyle H}{\underset{\displaystyle H}{C}}-$
Pentane	5		
Hexane	6		
Heptane	7	n-Propyl	$H-\overset{\displaystyle H}{\underset{\displaystyle H}{C}}-\overset{\displaystyle H}{\underset{\displaystyle H}{C}}-\overset{\displaystyle H}{\underset{\displaystyle H}{C}}-$
Octane	8		
Nonane	9		
Decane	10		
(After the C_4 hydrocarbon, the name consists of the suffix *ane* combined with a prefix that is derived from the Greek name for the number of carbon atoms in the chain.)		Isopropyl	
		n-Butyl	$CH_3CH_2CH_2CH_2-$
		sec-Butyl	$CH_3\underset{\mid}{C}HCH_2CH_3$
		Isobutyl	$\underset{H_3C}{\overset{H_3C}{>}}CHCH_2-$
		t-Butyl	$H_3C-\overset{\displaystyle CH_3}{\underset{\displaystyle CH_3}{C}}-$

The naming of the alkenes and alkynes is done in a similar way, the position of the double or single bond being indicated by the number of the carbon atoms. For example, the compound of structure

$$
\begin{array}{c}
\quad\quad\quad\overset{\displaystyle H\ H\ H}{\underset{}{\diagdown\ |\ \diagup}} \\
\overset{H\ \ H}{\underset{|\quad|}{}}\quad\overset{C}{\underset{|}{}}\quad\overset{H\ \ H}{\underset{|\quad|}{}} \\
\underset{|}{\overset{|}{C}}=\underset{}{\overset{}{C}}\text{---}\underset{|}{\overset{}{C}}\text{---}\underset{|}{\overset{}{C}}\text{-}\underset{|}{\overset{}{C}}\text{-H} \\
H\quad\quad\quad H\quad\ \ H\ H
\end{array}
$$

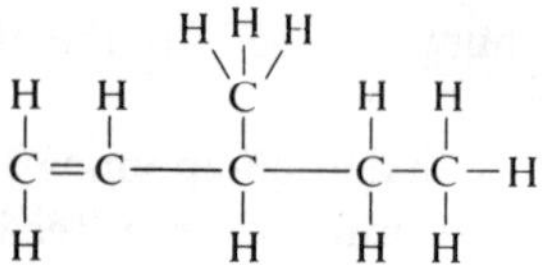

is called 3-methyl-1-pentene. The longest chain contains five carbon atoms, so that the molecule is a substituted pentene. It is a substituted 1-pentene, because the double bond involves the first carbon atom. The methyl group is on the third carbon atom so that the compound is a 3-methyl-1-pentene. Similarly,

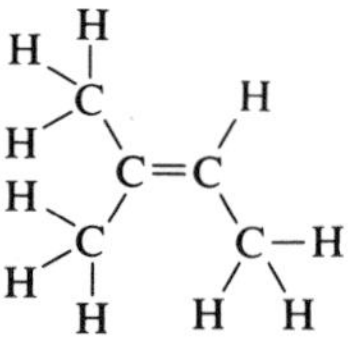

would be called 2-methyl-2-butene. The alkynes are named in an exactly similar way; the compound of structure

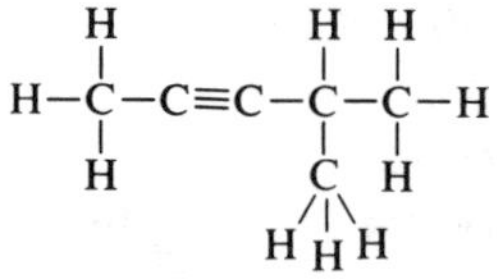

is called 4-methyl-2-pentyne.

The naming of compounds containing functional groups, such as the alcohol and acid groups, follows the same general principles. The alcohol of structure

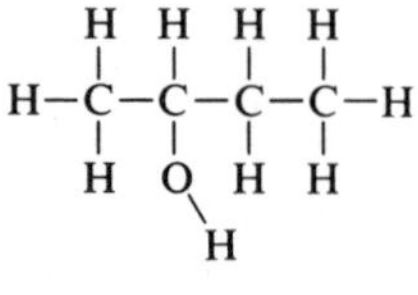

is called 2-butanol; the suffix *ol* indicates that it is an alcohol. It is not called 3-butanol, the convention being to count from the end that gives the smallest number. The compound of structure

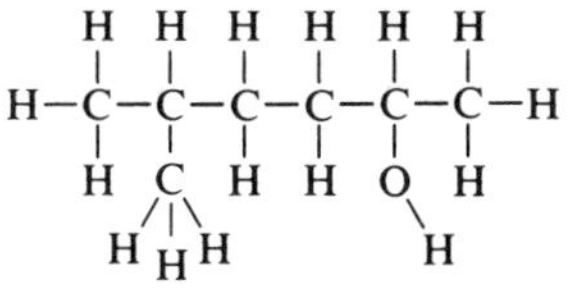

$$
\begin{array}{ccccccc}
 & H & H & H & H & H & H \\
 & | & | & | & | & | & | \\
H- & C & C & C & C & C & C-H \\
 & | & | & | & | & | & | \\
 & H & C & H & H & O & H \\
 & & /|\backslash & & & \backslash \\
 & & H\,H\,H & & & & H
\end{array}
$$

is called 5-methyl-2-hexanol; the methyl group is on the fifth carbon atom and the alcohol group is on the second.

The ketones are given names that end in *one* and indicate the positions of the carbonyl group and side chains by means of numbers. The compound of structure

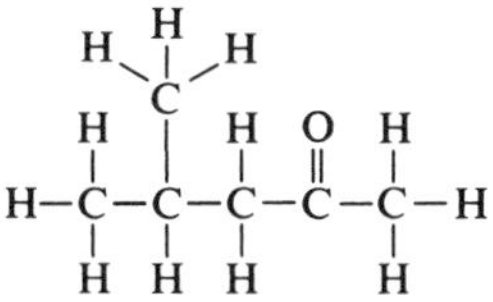

$$
\begin{array}{ccccc}
 & & H\; \overset{H}{\underset{C}{|}}\; H & & \\
 & H & H & O & H \\
 & | & | & \| & | \\
H- & C-C-C-C-C-H \\
 & | & | & | & | \\
 & H & H & H & H
\end{array}
$$

is called 4-methyl-2-pentanone. It is also common, however, to name the simpler ketones in terms of the groups attached to the carbonyl group. Thus

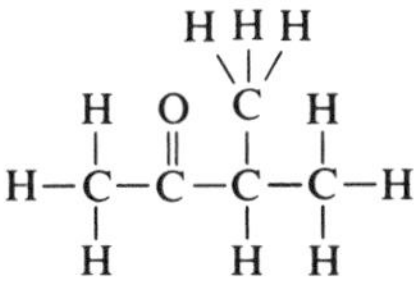

$$
\begin{array}{cccc}
 & & H\,H\,H & \\
 & & \backslash|/ & \\
H & O & C & H \\
| & \| & | & | \\
H-C-C-C-C-H \\
| & & | & | \\
H & & H & H
\end{array}
$$

can be called methyl isopropyl ketone as well as 3-methyl-2-butanone. The simplest ketone

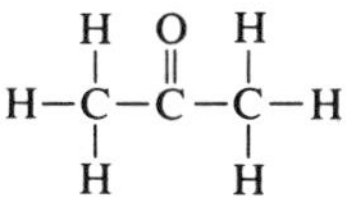

$$
\begin{array}{ccc}
H & O & H \\
| & \| & | \\
H-C-C-C-H \\
| & & | \\
H & & H
\end{array}
$$

is usually called acetone; it can also be called dimethyl ketone and 2-propanone.

Compounds containing other functional groups are named similarly; some examples will appear later.

The Halides

There are a number of organic compounds that contain carbon, hydrogen, and a halogen, such as chlorine. For example, starting with methane, CH_4, we can successively replace a hydrogen atom by a chlorine atom and obtain the following series of compounds:

$$
\begin{array}{cccc}
& H & & H & & H & & Cl \\
& | & & | & & | & & | \\
H-C-Cl & & H-C-Cl & & Cl-C-Cl & & Cl-C-Cl \\
& | & & | & & | & & | \\
& H & & Cl & & Cl & & Cl \\
\text{Methyl} & & \text{Methylene} & & \text{Chloroform} & & \text{Carbon} \\
\text{chloride} & & \text{dichloride} & & & & \text{tetrachloride}
\end{array}
$$

The first two of these compounds have systematic names; the CH_3 group is the methyl group, so that CH_3Cl is called methyl chloride; the CH_2 group is the methylene group, so that CH_2Cl_2 is called methylene chloride or methylene dichloride. The name chloroform, a nonsystematic name, was given many years ago to this substance, which is widely used as an anesthetic. The name carbon tetrachloride is again a systematic name; this compound is widely used as a commercial solvent and for cleaning purposes.

A similar series of compounds is formed by replacing the hydrogen atoms in methane by fluorine, bromine, and iodine. Similar substitutions can be made with the other hydrocarbons, both saturated and unsaturated, so that a very wide variety of organic halogen derivatives can be formed.

The Alcohols

The alcohols contain the *hydroxyl* group, —O—H, attached to a hydrocarbon radical. The simplest alcohol, of structure

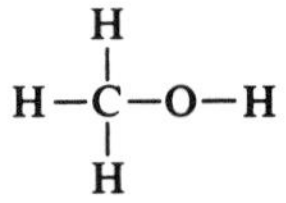

$$
\begin{array}{c}
H \\
| \\
H-C-O-H \\
| \\
H
\end{array}
$$

is called methanol or methyl alcohol. As indicated in the last section, the alcohols are named from the corresponding long-chain hydrocarbon (methane in this case), the final *e* of the name of the hydrocarbon being replaced by *ol*. Methyl alcohol, a common industrial solvent, is very poisonous.

The next number of the alcohol series is ethanol, or ethyl alcohol:

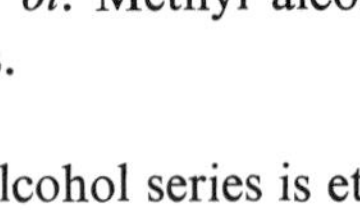

$$
\begin{array}{c}
H \quad H \\
| \quad | \\
H-C-C-O-H \\
| \quad | \\
H \quad H
\end{array}
$$

This is the alcohol that is found in ordinary alcoholic beverages. It is striking that the additional CH_2 group leads to such a large change in physiological properties. Ethanol is also used extensively as a solvent in chemical and industrial processes.

There are two isomeric propanols, namely

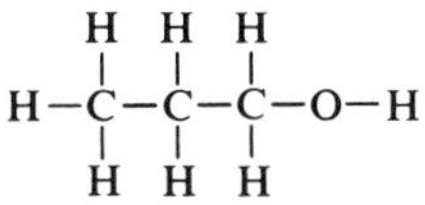

1-Propanol or
n-propyl alcohol

and

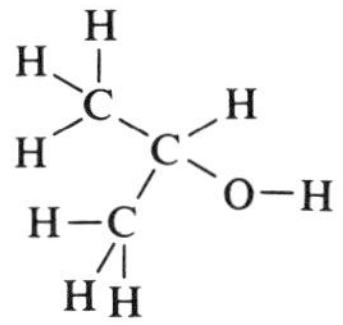

2-Propanol or isopropyl
alcohol

The first of these is called a *primary* alcohol. Isopropyl alcohol is called a *secondary* alcohol, since the carbon atom attached to the oxygen atom is also attached to *two* carbon atoms. An alcohol in which the carbon atom attached to the oxygen atom is also attached to *three* carbon atoms is called a *tertiary* alcohol; the simplest example is

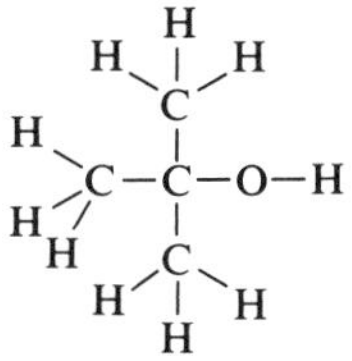

which is known as tertiary butyl alcohol, tertiary butanol, or 2-methyl-2-propanol. The student is urged at this stage to determine the number of butanols, of molecular formula C_4H_9OH.

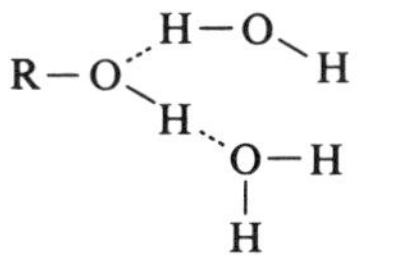

Methanol, ethanol, and the propanols are colorless nonviscous liquids that are completely miscible with water. As the carbon chain lengthens, however, the solubility in water decreases. The alcoholic group becomes attached to water molecules by hydrogen bonding of the type but the hydrocarbon chain shows no such affinity for water. (As noted earlier, the hydrocarbons are insoluble in water.) Therefore, the greater the proportion of hydrocarbon chain in the alcohol, the less is the tendency of the molecule to become attached to water molecules.

The boiling points of the alcohols are considerably higher than those of the corresponding alkanes. Ethanol, for example, boils at 78°C and ethane boils at -89°C, while propane, the molecular weight of which is close to that of ethanol, boils at -42°C. The higher boiling points of the alcohols are a consequence of the existence of hydrogen bonding between alcohol molecules in the liquid state. There is association between the hydrogen atom of one hydroxyl group and the oxygen atom of another:

$$\overset{\displaystyle R}{\underset{\displaystyle O-H}{\diagdown}} \cdots \overset{\displaystyle R}{\underset{\displaystyle O-H}{\diagdown}}$$

The bonding is mainly electrostatic in nature, the alcoholic hydrogen atom being somewhat positively charged and the oxygen atom somewhat negatively charged.

Another consequence of the dipolar character of the O—H bond is that the alcohols show both acidic and basic properties, that is, they are amphoteric substances. Alcohols accept protons from very strong acids to give ROH_2^+, analogous to H_3O^+, but the tendency to do so is very small. Alcohols will also react with alkalis to give alkoxides, RONa:

$$ROH + NaOH \rightleftharpoons RONa + H_2O$$

The alkoxides actually consist of the ions RO^- and Na^+. The tendency for alkoxide formation is also very small. Alcohols thus accept and donate protons only with difficulty; they are very weak in both basic and acidic properties.

The hydroxyl group can be *displaced* by a number of reagents. Alcohols react, for example, with hydrogen bromide with the formation of ethyl bromide:

$$CH_3CH_2OH + HBr \rightarrow CH_3CH_2Br + H_2O$$

The rate of this displacement reaction is proportional to the concentrations of H^+, Br^-, and the alcohol:

$$v = k[H^+][Br^-][CH_3CH_2OH]$$

A mechanism consistent with this behavior is that there is an initial rapid equilibrium involving alcohol and the hydrogen ion

$$C_2H_5OH + H^+ \rightleftharpoons C_2H_5OH_2^+ \quad \text{(fast)} \tag{3}$$

so that the concentration of $C_2H_5OH_2^+$ is proportional to

$$[C_2H_5OH][H^+]$$

The slow and rate-determining step in the reaction is then

$$C_2H_5OH_2^+ + Br^- \rightarrow C_2H_5Br + H_2O \quad \text{(slow)} \tag{4}$$

The over-all rate of reaction is, therefore

$$v = k_2[C_2H_5OH_2^+][Br^-]$$

where k_2 is the rate constant for reaction (4). Since $[C_2H_5OH_2^+]$ is proportional to $[C_2H_5OH]$ and to $[H^+]$, the over-all rate is proportional to $[C_2H_5OH][H^+][Br^-]$, as found experimentally. A variety of evidence has confirmed that this is indeed the reaction mechanism.

The reverse of this type of reaction also takes place; thus, processes such as

$$C_2H_5Br + OH^- \rightarrow C_2H_5OH + Br^-$$

are convenient for converting alkyl halides into alcohols.

Alcohols also undergo *elimination* reactions, the species eliminated being water. Thus ethyl alcohol in the presence of concentrated sulfuric acid splits off water with the formation of ethylene:

$$CH_3CH_2OH \xrightarrow{H_2SO_4} CH_2{=}CH_2 + H_2O$$

Such reactions represent convenient ways of forming alkenes. The elimination of water also occurs when hot ethanol vapor is brought in contact with certain solid catalysts, such as alumina, Al_2O_3. On the surfaces of metals, such as copper, on the other hand, the decomposition is mainly into acetaldehyde and hydrogen:

$$CH_3CH_2OH \longrightarrow CH_3C{\overset{\displaystyle H}{\underset{\displaystyle O}{\diagdown}}} + H_2$$

This is an interesting example of catalyst *specificity*, different catalysts bringing about different modes of decomposition.

Alcohols readily undergo *oxidation*. Ethyl alcohol, for example, is readily oxidized by potassium dichromate in aqueous acidic solution, initially producing acetaldehyde:

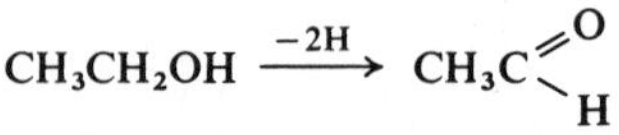

$$CH_3CH_2OH \xrightarrow{-2H} CH_3C\underset{H}{\overset{O}{\diagup}}$$

This is a *dehydrogenation* reaction, which is a special case of an oxidation. The aldehydes are also oxidized further; acetaldehyde gives rise to acetic acid:

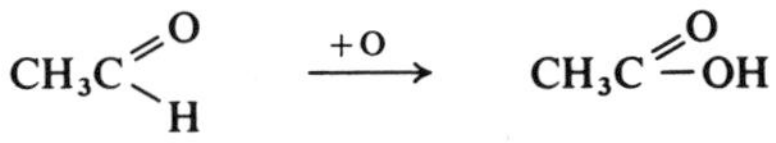

$$CH_3C\underset{H}{\overset{O}{\diagup}} \xrightarrow{+O} CH_3C\overset{O}{\diagup}-OH$$

If it is desired to prepare acetaldehyde by the oxidation of ethyl alcohol, it is necessary to distil it out of the system to prevent its further oxidation.

The *secondary alcohols*, which are of the general type

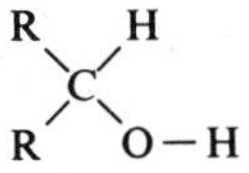

$$\underset{R}{\overset{R}{\diagdown}}C\underset{O-H}{\overset{H}{\diagup}}$$

are oxidized to ketones by dichromate ions in acid solution. Isopropyl alcohol, for example, is oxidized to acetone:

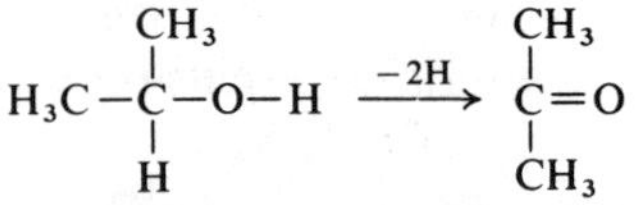

$$H_3C-\underset{\underset{H}{|}}{\overset{\overset{CH_3}{|}}{C}}-O-H \xrightarrow{-2H} \underset{\underset{CH_3}{|}}{\overset{\overset{CH_3}{|}}{C}}=O$$

Carbonyl Compounds

The carbonyl group, $>C=O$, occurs in aldehydes and ketones and also in other compounds. The large number of reactions undergone by the carbonyl group makes these compounds of great importance in chemical research and technology.

The difference between aldehydes and ketones is that in the former there is always a hydrogen atom attached to the carbonyl group; that is, the aldehydes contain the structure

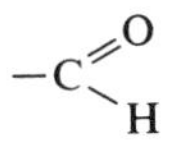

$$-C\diagdown^{O}_{H}$$

The simplest of the aldehydes is formaldehyde

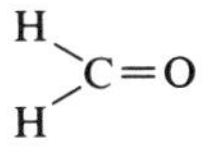

$$\begin{matrix} H \diagdown \\ \\ H \diagup \end{matrix} C=O$$

so called because of its relationship to formic acid (cf. p. 214). The next members of the series are

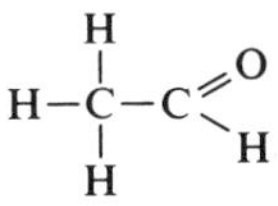

$$H-\overset{\displaystyle H}{\underset{\displaystyle H}{C}}-C\diagup^{O}_{H} \qquad \text{and} \qquad H-\overset{\displaystyle H}{\underset{\displaystyle H}{C}}-\overset{\displaystyle H}{\underset{\displaystyle H}{C}}-C\diagup^{O}_{H}$$

Acetaldehyde   Propionaldehyde

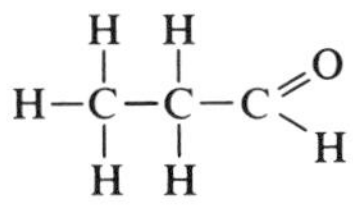

The name *aldehyde* is derived from the fact that these substances can be prepared by *al*cohol *dehydr*ogenation at high temperatures; thus ethyl alcohol loses hydrogen at certain metal surfaces, such as that of copper.

$$CH_3CH_2OH \rightarrow CH_3CHO + H_2$$

Aldehydes are named by adding the suffix *al* to the name of the longest straight-chain alkyl group; for example

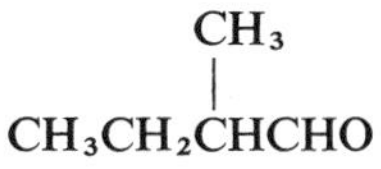

$$\overset{\displaystyle CH_3}{\underset{\displaystyle |}{}}$$
$$CH_3CH_2CHCHO$$
2-Methylbutanal

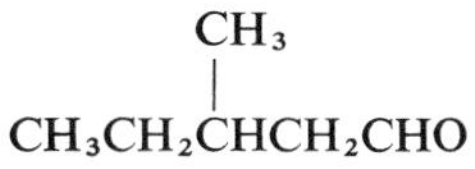

$$\overset{\displaystyle CH_3}{\underset{\displaystyle |}{}}$$
$$CH_3CH_2CHCH_2CHO$$
3-Methylpentanal

The numbering of the carbon atoms always begins at the aldehyde group.

The simplest ketone is dimethyl ketone, usually known as acetone:

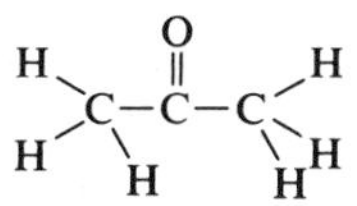

$$\begin{matrix} H \diagdown & O & \diagup H \\ & \parallel & \\ H \diagup C-C-C \diagdown & & \diagdown H \\ H & H & H \end{matrix}$$

Another ketone is methyl ethyl ketone:

$$\underset{\underset{H}{H}}{\overset{H}{\diagdown}}C-\overset{\overset{O}{\|}}{C}-\overset{\overset{H}{|}}{\underset{\underset{H}{|}}{C}}-\overset{\overset{H}{|}}{\underset{\underset{H}{|}}{C}}-H$$

The ketones may be named using the two alkyl groups attached to the carbonyl carbon atom, as in the two examples above. In more complicated cases, the carbonyl group and substituents are indicated by numbers, the suffix *one* being used to indicate a ketone. Examples are

$$\overset{\overset{CH_3}{|}}{CH_3CHCH_2CCH_3}$$

4-Methyl-2-pentanone

$$\overset{\overset{OH}{|}}{CH_2}-\overset{\overset{CH_3}{|}}{CH}-CH_2\overset{\overset{O}{\|}}{C}-CH_2CH_3$$

6-Hydroxy-5-methyl-3-hexanone

Aldehydes and ketones undergo addition and oxidation reactions. An addition reaction characteristic of the carbonyl group is addition of the bisulfite ion:

$$\underset{R}{\overset{R}{\diagdown}}C=O \ + \ HSO_3^- \ \longrightarrow \ \underset{R}{\overset{R}{\diagdown}}\underset{SO_3^-}{\overset{OH}{\diagup}}C$$

This bisulfite addition product is an ion that can be precipitated as a sodium salt. This reaction is convenient for separating aldehydes and ketones from other organic substances.

Hydroxylamine, NH_2OH, and hydrazine, NH_2NH_2, also add to the carbonyl bond, and these reactions are also useful for demonstrating the presence of carbonyl groups. In both cases, the initial addition products lose water to give the final compounds. Hydroxylamine reacts with aldehydes and ketones as follows:

$$\underset{R}{\overset{R}{\diagdown}}C=O \ + \ H_2NOH \ \longrightarrow \ \underset{R}{\overset{R}{\diagdown}}\underset{NHOH}{\overset{OH}{\diagup}}C \ \longrightarrow \ \underset{R}{\overset{R}{\diagdown}}C=NOH$$

An oxime

The product is referred to as an aldoxime if the starting compound is an aldehyde, and a ketoxime if it is a ketone. Oximes are often crystalline compounds having characteristic melting points, so that their formation is useful in identifying aldehydes and ketones. The reactions with hydrazine are

$$\underset{R}{\overset{R}{>}}C=O \ + \ NH_2NH_2 \quad \longrightarrow \quad \underset{R}{\overset{R}{>}}\underset{NHNH_2}{\overset{OH}{C}} \quad \longrightarrow \quad \underset{R}{\overset{R}{>}}C=NNH_2$$

A hydrazone

The hydrazones also are often crystalline with characteristic melting points, so that these reactions are again very widely used for identifying carbonyl compounds.

Another very useful addition reaction of carbonyl compounds involves a compound known as a *Grignard reagent*. These substances have the general structure RMgX, where R is an alkyl group and X is a halogen atom. They are made by the reaction of an alkyl halide with metallic magnesium in dry ether:

$$RX + Mg \ \rightarrow \ RMgX$$

Grignard reagents react with carbonyl compounds in the following way:

$$\underset{R}{\overset{R}{>}}C=O \ + \ R'MgX \quad \longrightarrow \quad \underset{R}{\overset{R}{>}}\underset{OMgX}{\overset{R'}{C}}$$

Water is then added to hydrolyze the addition product to an alcohol:

$$\underset{R}{\overset{R}{>}}\underset{OMgX}{\overset{R'}{C}} \ + \ H_2O \quad \longrightarrow \quad \underset{R}{\overset{R}{>}}\underset{OH}{\overset{R'}{C}} \ + \ \underset{OH}{\overset{X}{Mg}}$$

The reaction of a Grignard reagent with a ketone leads to a tertiary alcohol, while that with an aldehyde gives a secondary alcohol. Since the Grignard reaction introduces any desired alkyl group into a molecule, it is frequently used in the synthesis of new compounds.

Both aldehydes and ketones can be oxidized. However, ketones are not easily oxidized; strong oxidizing agents must be used, and the carbon skeleton is destroyed. Aldehydes, on the other hand, are very easily oxidized to carboxylic acids:

$$R-C{\overset{O}{\underset{H}{<}}} \quad \overset{+O}{\longrightarrow} \quad R-C{\overset{O}{\underset{O-H}{<}}}$$

This reaction is brought about by ordinary oxidizing agents, such as acidified dichromate solution. Both aldehydes and ketones can be reduced to alcohols in several ways; this can be done by molecular hydrogen on platinum and other surfaces, and by sodium in alcoholic solution; for example

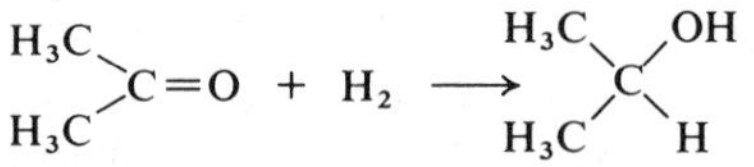

$$H_3C \atop H_3C \, \rangle C=O \; + \; H_2 \; \longrightarrow \; H_3C \atop H_3C \, \rangle C \langle {OH \atop H}$$

Acetone	Isopropyl alcohol

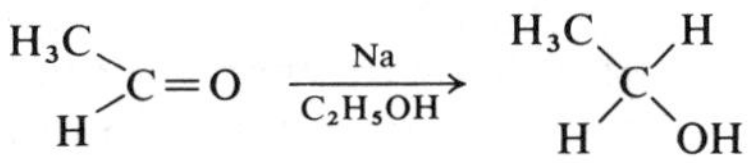

$$H_3C \atop H \, \rangle C=O \; \xrightarrow[C_2H_5OH]{Na} \; H_3C \atop H \, \rangle C \langle {H \atop OH}$$

Acetaldehyde	Ethanol

Reduction of the aldehyde yields a primary alcohol, that of a ketone yields a secondary alcohol.

Carboxylic Acids   Carboxylic acids also contain the carbonyl group, $\rangle C=O$ and have a hydroxyl group attached to it; they have the general structure

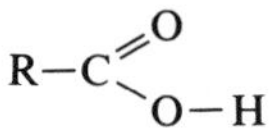

$$R-C{\diagup\!\!O \atop \diagdown O-H}$$

The simplest carboxylic acid is formic acid:

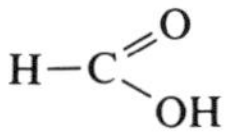

$$H-C{\diagup\!\!O \atop \diagdown OH}$$

The name of this substance is derived from the Latin (*formica*) for an ant; the acid at one time was prepared by the distillation of ants. The next member of the series is the commonest carboxylic acid, acetic acid:

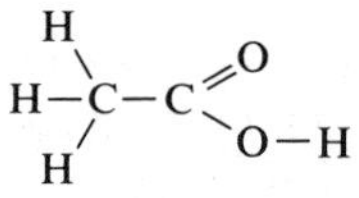

$$H-C{\!\!H \atop H}-C{\diagup\!\!O \atop \diagdown O-H}$$

This acid is the final product of fermentation reactions and is the sour constituent of vinegar (Latin *acetum*).

The lower carboxylic acids are completely miscible in water, but the solubility steadily diminishes as the length of the side chain increases. The reason for this is the same as with the alcohols (cf.

p. 207); the carboxyl group, $-C\overset{\displaystyle /\!\!\!O}{\underset{\displaystyle \backslash OH}{}}$ hydrogen-bonds to water,

but the alkyl chain has no affinity for water.

Except for some special types of compounds, the carboxylic acids are rather weak acids. Acetic acid, for example, has a dissociation constant of 1.8×10^{-5} at 25°C; in an 0.1 M solution it is only about 1% dissociated into H^+ and CH_3COO^-. The carboxylic acids form the usual salts, such as sodium acetate.

One important reaction of the carboxylic acids, their reaction with alcohols to form esters, is considered later (p. 216).

The Ethers

The ethers have an oxygen atom bonded to two carbon atoms, so that their general structure is

$$R—O—R'$$

where R and R' are alkyl groups. Alcohol molecules may be regarded as water molecules in which one hydrogen atom has been replaced by an alkyl group; in the same way an ether molecule may be regarded as a water molecule in which both hydrogen atoms have been replaced.

The simplest ether is dimethyl ether:

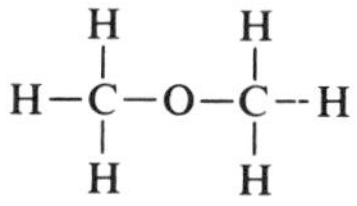

$$
\begin{array}{ccc}
\text{H} & & \text{H} \\
| & & | \\
\text{H}-\text{C}-\text{O}-\text{C}-\text{H} \\
| & & | \\
\text{H} & & \text{H}
\end{array}
$$

The commonest is diethyl ether:

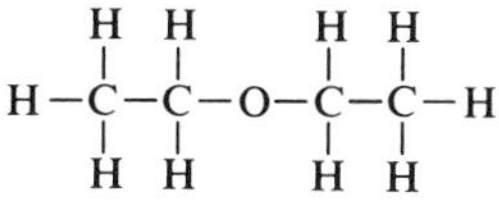

$$
\begin{array}{cccc}
\text{H} & \text{H} & \text{H} & \text{H} \\
| & | & | & | \\
\text{H}-\text{C}-\text{C}-\text{O}-\text{C}-\text{C}-\text{H} \\
| & | & | & | \\
\text{H} & \text{H} & \text{H} & \text{H}
\end{array}
$$

This is the substance that is used as an anesthetic.

The ethers are practically insoluble in water; the absence of a hydrogen atom attached to the oxygen atom greatly reduces the tendency for hydrogen bonding. The ethers are much more volatile than are the alcohols with approximately the same molecular weights; the reason is, again, the absence of hydrogen bonding between neighboring ether molecules in the liquid state.

The Esters

The esters contain the group

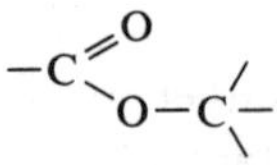

$$-C\overset{\displaystyle O}{\underset{\displaystyle O-C-}{}}$$

and are formed by the reaction between an alcohol and an acid. Acetic acid reacts with ethyl alcohol, for example, with the formation of ethyl acetate:

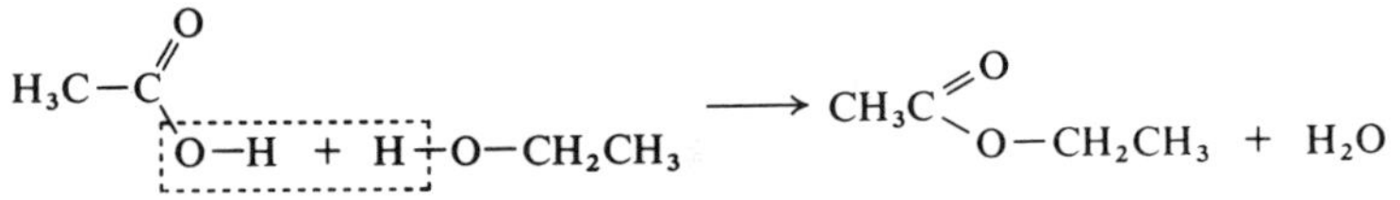

$$H_3C-C\overset{O}{\underset{O-H \ + \ H+O-CH_2CH_3}{}} \longrightarrow CH_3C\overset{O}{\underset{O-CH_2CH_3}{}} + H_2O$$

This reaction involves the splitting off of a water molecule between the two molecules, and a reaction of this type is known as *condensation* reaction. The reverse type of reaction, in which a water molecule causes a splitting of a substance into two fragments, is known as a *hydrolytic* reaction, or *hydrolysis*. Ethyl acetate, for example, can be hydrolyzed into acetic acid and ethyl alcohol, particularly in the presence of basic catalysts such as hydroxide ions. The reaction that occurs is exactly the reverse of the reaction written above, but the acetic acid reacts with the base to form a salt such as sodium acetate.

Esters are named in terms of the acid and alcohol from which they are formed. The first part of the name is the name of the alkyl radical corresponding to the alcohol from which the ester is formed. The second part of the name uses the suffix *ate* with a prefix derived from the name of the acid. Thus the ester

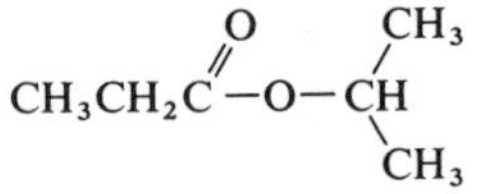

$$CH_3CH_2C\overset{O}{\underset{}{}}-O-CH\overset{CH_3}{\underset{CH_3}{}}$$

which is a combination of propionic acid, CH_3CH_2COOH, and isopropyl alcohol, is called isopropyl propionate.

The esters are only very slightly soluble in water.

Amines

The primary amines contain the amino group

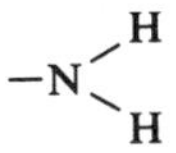

$$-N \overset{\displaystyle H}{\underset{\displaystyle H}{\diagdown}}$$

The simplest of them is methylamine:

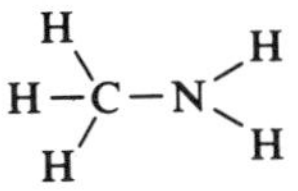

$$H - \overset{\displaystyle H}{\underset{\displaystyle H}{\overset{\displaystyle |}{C}}} - N \overset{\displaystyle H}{\underset{\displaystyle H}{\diagup}}$$

The amines are named simply by combining the name of the alkyl radical with the suffix "amine." The primary amines can be regarded as derivatives of ammonia in which one of the hydrogen atoms is replaced by an alkyl group. Like ammonia, they are bases. Thus in acid solution the amine molecules accept a proton to form species that may be regarded as the ammonium ion, NH_4^+, in which one of the hydrogen atoms has been replaced by an alkyl group; for example

$$CH_3NH_2 + H^+ \rightleftharpoons CH_3NH_3^+$$

Methylamine and its homologs are somewhat stronger bases than ammonia.

There also exist *secondary amines*, which may be regarded as derived from ammonia by the replacement of two hydrogen atoms by an alkyl group. The simplest example is dimethylamine:

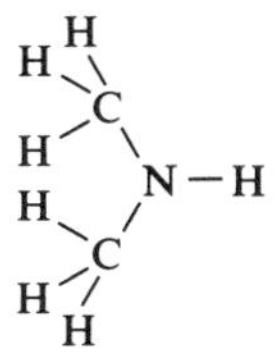

$$\begin{array}{c} H \\ H \diagdown \\ H \diagdown C \\ H \diagdown \diagup \diagdown N - H \\ H \diagdown C \diagup \\ H \diagup \\ H \end{array}$$

Such compounds are somewhat stronger bases than the corresponding primary amines; they accept a proton to form the doubly substituted ammonium ion:

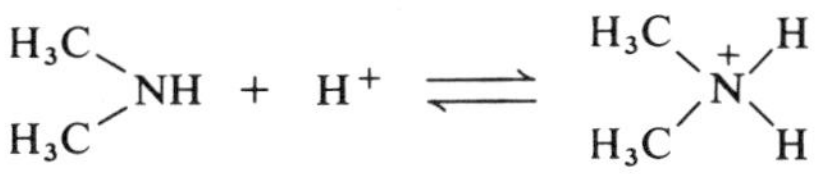

$$\begin{array}{c} H_3C \\ \diagdown \\ NH \\ \diagup \\ H_3C \end{array} + \ H^+ \ \rightleftharpoons \ \begin{array}{c} H_3C \quad + \quad H \\ \diagdown N \diagup \\ \diagup \quad \diagdown \\ H_3C \quad\quad H \end{array}$$

The *tertiary amines*, in which the three hydrogen atoms of ammonia have been replaced by alkyl groups, are bases of similar strengths to the secondary amines. An example is trimethylamine, which accepts a proton to form the triply substituted ammonium ion:

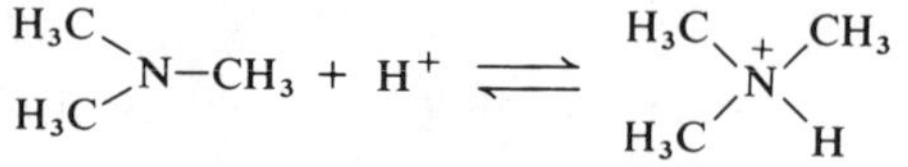

$$H_3C \diagdown \atop H_3C \diagup N-CH_3 \ + \ H^+ \ \rightleftharpoons \ H_3C \diagdown \overset{+}{N} \diagup CH_3 \atop H_3C \diagup \ \diagdown H$$

There also exist salts that are ammonium salts in which all four hydrogen atoms have been replaced by alkyl groups. Thus, if in ammonium iodide (which exists as ammonium and iodide ions, NH_4^+ and I^-) the four hydrogen atoms are replaced by methyl radicals, the result is tetramethyl ammonium iodide:

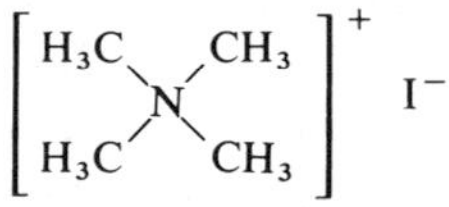

$$\left[H_3C \diagdown \atop H_3C \diagup N \diagdown CH_3 \atop \diagup CH_3 \right]^+ \quad I^-$$

Compounds of this type are known as *quaternary ammonium salts*. They show the typical properties of salts; they form conducting solutions which exhibit the properties of the ions they contain.

The Carbonyl Amino, or Amide, Group

The amides contain the grouping

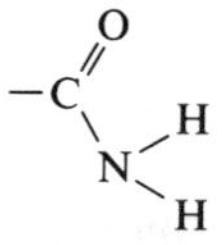

$$-C \overset{O}{\diagdown} \atop \diagdown N \diagdown {H \atop H}$$

A simple example is acetamide:

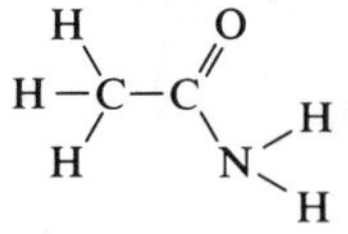

$$H-\overset{\overset{\displaystyle H}{|}}{\underset{\underset{\displaystyle H}{|}}{C}}-C \overset{O}{\diagup} \atop \diagdown N \diagdown {H \atop H}$$

This compound may be regarded as a derivative of acetic acid and ammonia, formed by a condensation reaction:

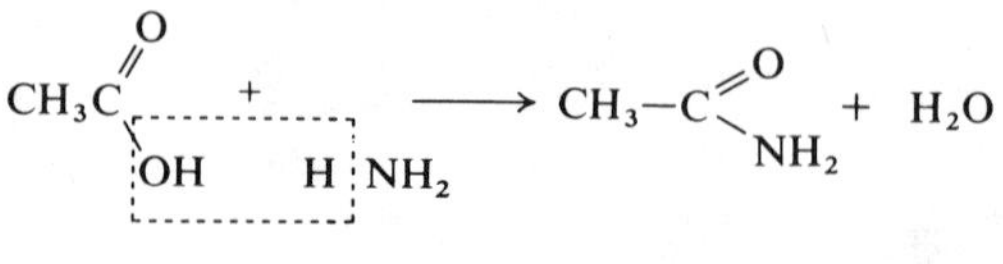

$$CH_3C \overset{O}{\diagup} \atop \diagdown \underline{OH} \quad \underline{H \ NH_2} \ \longrightarrow \ CH_3-C \overset{O}{\diagup} \atop \diagdown NH_2 \ + \ H_2O$$

The amides are quite readily hydrolyzed into the acid and ammonia, by the reverse of this process. They are easily prepared by heating ammonium salts, such as ammonium acetate which produces acetamide:

$$CH_3C\overset{O}{\underset{ONH_4}{\diagdown}} \longrightarrow CH_3C\overset{O}{\underset{NH_2}{\diagdown}} + H_2O$$

Aromatic Compounds

The organic compounds that we have considered so far in this chapter may be described as *aliphatic* compounds; they are related to the alkanes. There is also a vast number of organic molecules whose structures are based on that of the molecule benzene, C_6H_6, which may conventionally be written as

$$\begin{array}{c}
H \\
| \\
H\diagdown \overset{\displaystyle C}{\underset{\displaystyle C}{\quad}} \diagup H \\
\end{array}$$

In the molecule of benzene the orbitals are, in fact, nonlocalized. It is not correct to regard the molecule as having alternating single and double bonds; each carbon–carbon bond is in reality a bond of 3/2 order. As shown in Figure 5-8, there are p orbitals issuing from

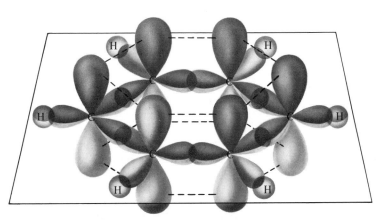

Fig. 5-8 A molecule of benzene showing the arrangement of orbitals.

each carbon atom, at right angles to the plane of the ring, and these orbitals overlap laterally right around the molecule.

The nonlocalized orbitals that exist in benzene and its derivatives confer unique characteristic properties on these compounds, so that the study of aromatic compounds has a number of special and important aspects. In particular, the aromatic ring is much more stable and less reactive than it would be if it did contain three double bonds. We saw earlier in this chapter (p.196) that a characteristic property of the alkenes is that they readily add on a halogen, such as bromine. Such reactions do not occur, however, with the aromatic ring. Instead, the characteristic reaction of benzene and its derivatives is substitution involving the displacement of a hydrogen atom. Thus, bromine in the presence of a catalyst such as iron(III) (or ferric) bromide, $FeBr_3$, brings about substitution into the benzene ring:

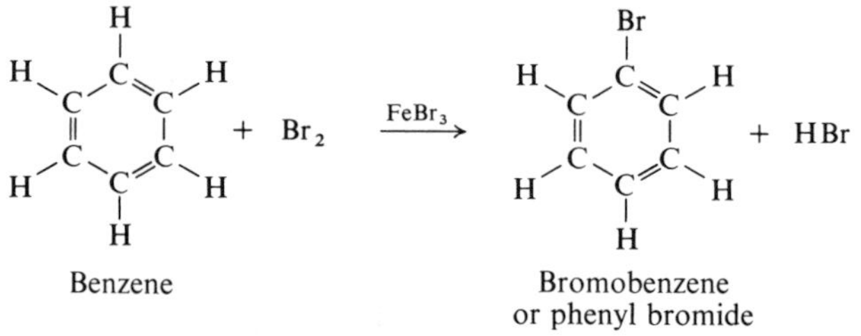

Benzene   Bromobenzene
                           or phenyl bromide

Another important type of substitution reaction is brought about when an aromatic compound is treated with nitric acid in concentrated sulfuric acid solution. The product of reaction is a nitro-compound; benzene itself, for example, gives rise to nitrobenzene:

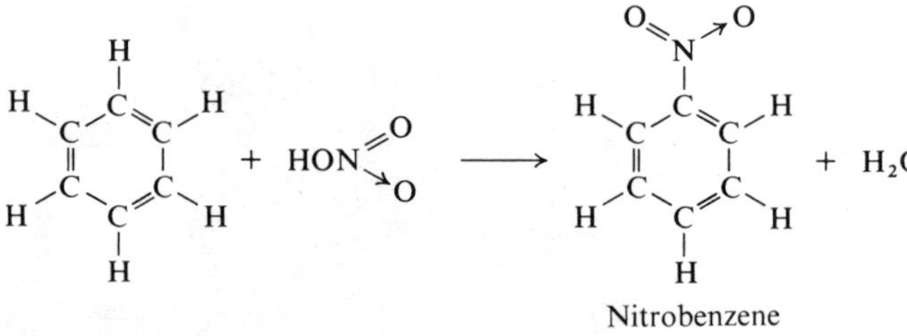

Nitrobenzene

In these and other substitution reactions, the aromatic character of the ring remains intact—because of the high stability of the aromatic ring resulting from the presence of delocalized orbitals.

A vast number of derivatives of benzene are known, and there is no limit to the number that could be prepared. The functional groups discussed earlier in this chapter are frequently found in aromatic compounds, and they exhibit more or less the same properties in aromatic as in aliphatic compounds. If a hydrogen atom in benzene is replaced by a hydroxyl group, the result is phenol:

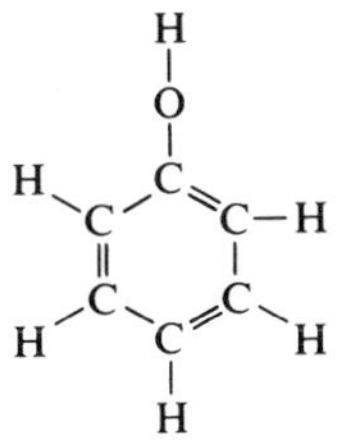

The properties of phenol and of analogous compounds are quite similar to those of the alcohols. Replacement of a hydrogen atom in benzene by the carboxyl group gives rise to benzoic acid:

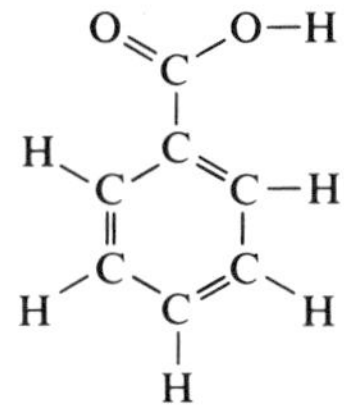

This is a typical organic acid, the acidic properties being similar to that of acetic acid. Reagents that attack the aromatic ring in compounds like phenol and benzoic acid, however, do so in a way that is more typical of benzene than of aliphatic compounds. Phenol and benzoic acid can, for example, be brominated and nitrated, with substitution of Br or NO_2 into the aromatic ring.

Isomerism

Compounds that have the same numbers of the different kinds of atoms are said to be *isomers*; the phenomenon is known as *isomerism*. We have already met, in this chapter, *positional* isomerism and *geometrical* or *cis–trans* isomerism. In this section, we shall discuss briefly some other examples and other types of isomerism.

A simple example of isomerism is to be found in the two compounds propylene and cyclopropane:

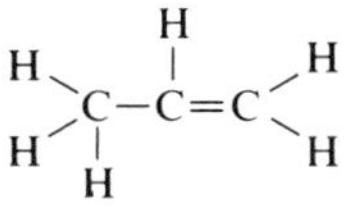

Propylene 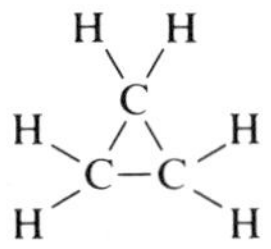   Cyclopropane

Both compounds have the molecular formula C_3H_6, but one contains a double bond and the other does not. When functional groups are different in the two molecules, as in this example, the isomers are referred to as *functional isomers*. Another example is to be found in dimethyl ether and ethyl alcohol:

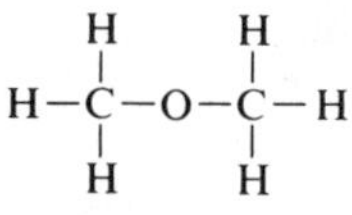

Dimethyl ether 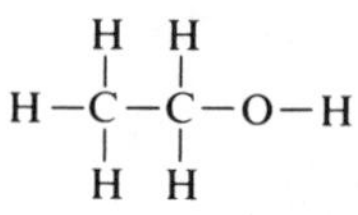   Ethyl alcohol

Both have the molecular formula C_2H_6O, but one is an ether and the other an alcohol.

A second type of isomerism is known as *positional isomerism*; in this case, the functional groups are the same, but they are placed in different positions in the molecules. Examples are

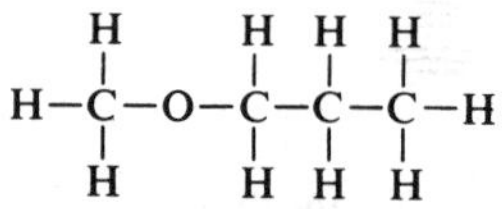

Methyl *n*-propyl ether   Diethyl ether

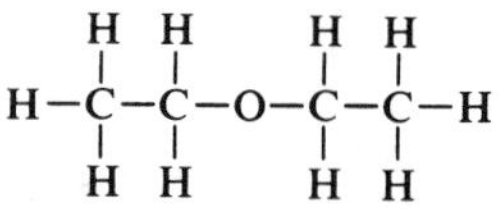

Both have the molecular formula $C_4H_{10}O$; both are ethers; but the ether group, –O–, is placed in different positions on the carbon skeleton.

Geometrical isomerism, or *cis–trans isomerism*, which we met on p. 195, occurs when the isomers differ with respect to the position of groups attached to a pair of doubly bonded carbon atoms. Other examples of geometrical isomers are

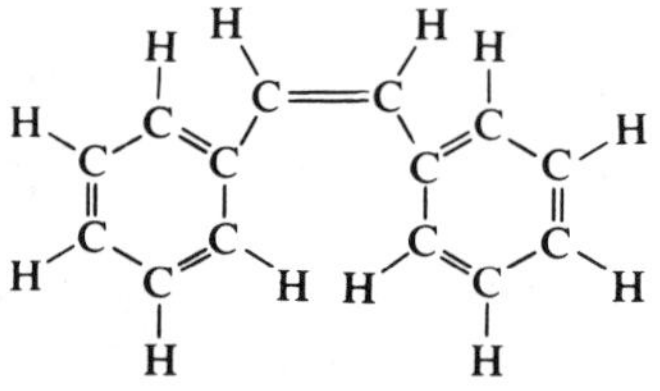

cis-Stilbene 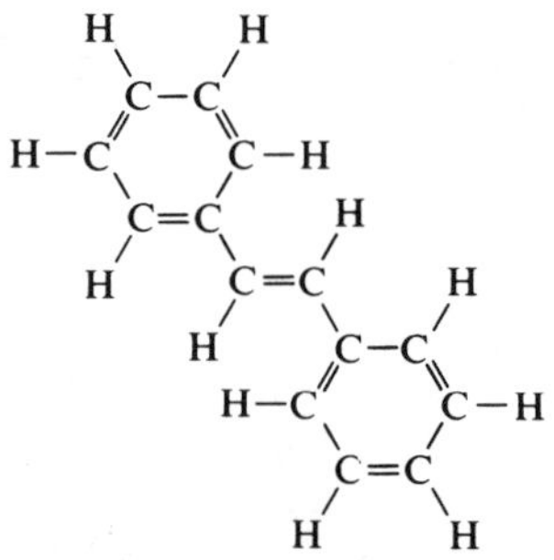   *trans*-Stilbene

A fourth class of isomerism arises if a molecule has no plane or point of symmetry. This occurs in particular if the molecule contains a carbon atom which is attached to four different groups; such an atom is known as an *asymmetric carbon atom*, but of course it is the molecule, not the atom, that is asymmetric. As shown in Figure 5-9, the molecule can then exist in two forms which are nonsuperimposable, but each of which is the mirror image of the other.

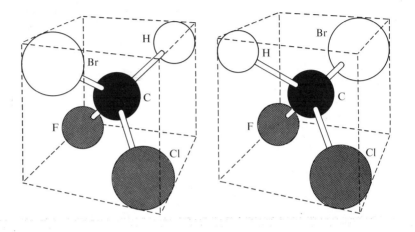

Fig. 5-9 The two molecules that can be formed when a carbon atom is attached to four different atoms or groups.

Lactic acid is an example of this; in this molecule the four groups attached to a carbon atom are H, OH, CH_3, and COOH, the two structures being shown in Figure 5-10. Two molecules related to each other in this way are called enantiomorphs (from the Greek *enantios*, opposite; *morph*, form). Enantiomorphs have identical physical properties except that they rotate the plane of polarized light in opposite directions. Compounds that rotate the plane of polarized light are said to be *optically active*, and enantiomorphs are also called *optical* isomers.

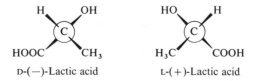

Fig. 5-10 The two enantiomeric forms of lactic acid.

Molecules having an asymmetric carbon atom are not the only ones to exhibit optical isomerism. A molecule having a coiled or helical structure can also exist in two forms, one resembling a right-handed screw, the other a left-handed screw. These two forms of the same helix rotate the place of polarized light in opposite directions and are enantiomorphs.

For many years it was not known which of a pair of enantiomorphs rotated the plane of polarized light to the right, and which to the left. This problem was solved in 1951 by a crystal-structure determination of glyceraldehyde using X-ray methods. It was found in this way that the enantiomorph of glyceraldehyde that rotates the plane of polarized light in a positive (clockwise) direction has the structure shown in Figure 5-11. This particular enantiomorph is

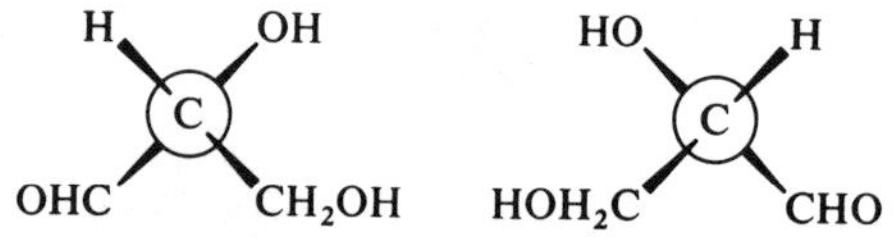

D-(+)-Glyceraldehyde   L-(−)-Glyceraldehyde

Fig. 5-11   The two enantiomeric forms of glyceraldehyde. The signs in brackets indicate the direction in which the plane of polarization of light is turned; + is clockwise, − is anticlockwise.

known as D-(+)-glyceraldehyde. The + sign tells us that the rotation of the plane of polarized light is clockwise, and the D designates this particular structure. Once the absolute configuration of D-(+)-glyceraldehyde had been determined it became possible to assign absolute configurations to other molecules, by preparing them from glyceraldehyde. For example, it is possible to convert glyceraldehyde into lactic acid; the process involves several stages but in none of these is there any disturbance of the bonds to the asymmetric carbon atom. When this is done with D-(+)-glyceraldehyde as the starting point, the product must also have the same absolute configuration of the groups, and this is indicated by calling the product D-lactic acid. It is of interest to note that D-lactic acid, unlike D-glyceraldehyde, rotates the plane of polarized light in the anticlockwise direction; it is therefore called D-(−)-lactic acid.

We shall see in the next chapter that optical enantiomorphs play a very important role in living systems, in that the various metabolic processes are very sensitive to the configurations of the molecules taken in as food.

Polymers

A great many of the materials with which one comes into contact in everyday life are *polymers*; examples are rubber, plastics, textiles, and many of the constituents of living things, such as cellulose and proteins. A polymer molecule is a large molecule which is made up of many smaller molecules bonded together. The smaller molecules are called *monomers*, and there are various ways in which they can be joined together in polymers.

Polymers are conveniently classified according to the way in which the bonds are formed when the monomers join together. If the monomer molecules are simply added together, the polymers are known as *addition* polymers. If, on the other hand, the reaction between the monomer molecules involves the splitting off of a molecule—usually of water or another small molecule—the process is known as *condensation* polymerization, and the product as a condensation polymer. These two types of polymer, and the polymerization processes by which they are formed, will now be discussed.

Addition Polymerization

As a simple example of addition polymerization, we may consider the formation of polyethylene from ethylene. It is possible to bring about this process by generating free radicals in the presence of ethylene; this is sometimes done by photochemical means, since light of suitable wavelength frequently splits a molecule into free radicals. An example is acetone, which by suitable irradiation is split into carbon monoxide and two methyl radicals:

$$CH_3COCH_3 + \text{photon} \rightarrow CO + 2 —CH_3$$

If this is carried out in the presence of ethylene, methyl radicals may add on to ethylene molecules with the formation of a new free radical:

$$—CH_3 + H_2C{=}CH_2 \rightarrow CH_3—CH_2—CH_2—$$

This process can be regarded as the opening of the π bond in ethylene, and the pairing of the odd electron of the methyl radical with one of the π-bond electrons, the other remaining unpaired. The new radical (an *n*-propyl radical) can, in turn, add on to another ethylene molecule with the formation of a still larger radical:

$$CH_3—CH_2—CH_2— + H_2C{=}CH_2 \rightarrow CH_3—CH_2—CH_2—CH_2—CH_2—$$

This process can continue indefinitely.

$$CH_3—CH_2—CH_2—CH_2—CH_2— + H_2C{=}CH_2$$
$$\rightarrow \quad CH_3—CH_2—CH_2—CH_2—CH_2—CH_2—CH_2—$$
$$CH_3—CH_2—CH_2—CH_2—CH_2—CH_2—CH_2— + H_2C{=}CH_2$$
$$\rightarrow \quad CH_3—CH_2—CH_2—CH_2—CH_2—CH_2—CH_2—CH_2—CH_2—$$

Each one of these reaction steps is a *chain-propagating step*, since a radical undergoes reaction and another one is produced; the over-all process is thus a *chain reaction*. In addition to chain-propagating steps, every chain reaction has an initiation step, which in our example is the production of radicals by light. It also has a *termination* step. Termination of chains occurs when any two radicals combine together, and this can happen in a wide variety of ways; one example is

$$CH_3—CH_2—CH_2— + CH_3—CH_2—CH_2—CH_2—CH_2—$$
$$\rightarrow CH_3—CH_2—CH_2—CH_2—CH_2—CH_2—CH_2—CH_3$$

By varying the conditions under which a polymerization process occurs, it is possible to control the average number of monomer molecules in the polymer produced. For example, if high pressures are used so that the combination reactions are important, the chains will be shorter than at lower pressures; there will always be a considerable range of sizes in any polymer produced.

The same kind of addition polymerization will occur with any substituted ethylene. Examples are tetrafluoroethylene (also known as perfluoroethylene)

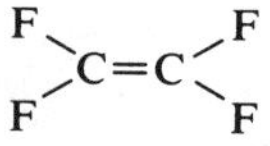

$$\begin{array}{c} F \\ \diagdown \\ F \diagup \end{array} C{=}C \begin{array}{c} \diagup F \\ \\ \diagdown F \end{array}$$

vinyl chloride

$$\begin{array}{c} H \\ \diagdown \\ H \diagup \end{array} C{=}C \begin{array}{c} \diagup Cl \\ \\ \diagdown H \end{array}$$

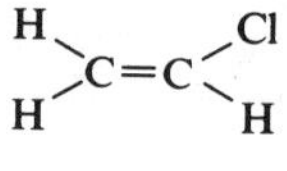

and styrene

$$\begin{array}{c} H \\ \diagdown \\ H \diagup \end{array} C{=}C \begin{array}{c} \diagup H \\ \\ \diagdown \end{array}$$

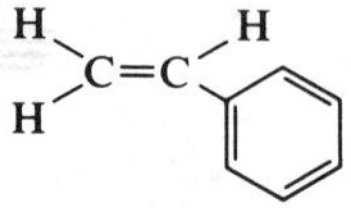

In the former case, the resulting polymer, which is known commercially as Teflon, will have the structure

$$\cdots -CF_2-CF_2-CF_2-CF_2-CF_2-CF_2- \cdots$$

and contains the structural unit

$$-CF_2-CF_2-$$

Polyvinyl chloride, or Koroseal, contains the structural unit

$$-CH_2-CH- \atop \hspace{1.5em} | \atop \hspace{1.5em} Cl$$

which will be repeated many times in the polymer. Similarly, polystyrene contains the structural unit

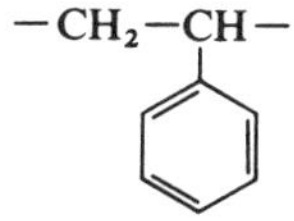

The properties of addition polymers vary widely with the nature of the substituting groups. Polyethylene, for example, is tough and impermeable to water and is usually used in thin films. Polystyrene, on the other hand, is more convenient for use as a moldable plastic (for combs, etc.) and as an insulating plastic foam. Table 5-3 lists a few of the better-known addition polymers and indicates their structure and some of their uses.

The polymers listed in Table 5-3 are all ones in which a single substance has polymerized; they are sometimes referred to as *homopolymers*. If a mixture of two or more substances undergoes polymerization, the result is known as a *copolymer*. Thus if vinyl chloride and vinyl acetate, $H_2C=CHO-CO-CH_3$, polymerize together, the result is a polymer called Tygon, which is used for making flexible tubing. It contains the units

$$-CH_2-CH- \quad \text{and} \quad -CH_2-CH- \atop \hspace{2.5em} | \hspace{7em} | \atop \hspace{2.5em} Cl \hspace{6.5em} O-CO-CH_3$$

but not in a strictly alternating order. Similarly, much modern synthetic rubber is a copolymer of about 25% styrene and 75% butadiene ($CH_2=CH-CH=CH_2$); it contains the units

Table 5-3 Some Commercial Addition Polymers

Name	Monomer	Repeating Unit	Uses
Polyethylene	$H_2C{=}CH_2$ Ethylene	$-CH_2-CH_2-$	Tough, water-impermeable films
Polyperfluoroethylene, Teflon	$F_2C{=}CF_2$ Perfluoroethylene	$-CF_2-CF_2-$	Chemically resistant liners, etc., electrical insulators
Polystyrene, Styron, Lustron	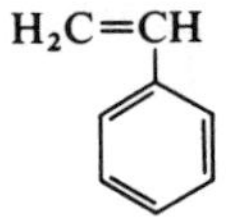 $H_2C{=}CH$ $\bigcirc$ Styrene	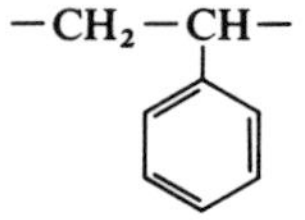 $-CH_2-CH-$ $\bigcirc$	Combs, plastic handles, wrapping material, foams, etc.
Polyacrylonitrile, Orlon, Actilan	$H_2C{=}CH$ $\mid$ CN Acrylonitrile	$-CH_2-CH-$ $\mid$ CN	Fibers
Polyvinyl chloride, Koroseal, Geon	$H_2C{=}CH$ $\mid$ Cl Vinyl chloride	$-CH_2-CH-$ $\mid$ Cl	Raincoats, tank liners, etc.
Polyisoprene	$H_2C{=}C-CH{=}CH_2$ $\mid$ CH_3	$-CH_2-C{=}CH-CH_2-$ $\mid$ CH_3	Synthetic rubber

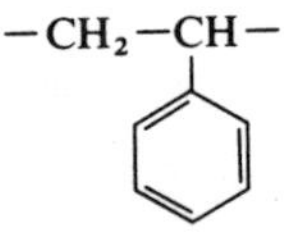

$$-CH_2-CH- \quad \text{and} \quad -CH_2-CH{=}CH-CH_2-$$

The fact that this last structure is obtained is due to the presence of nonlocalized orbitals in butadiene (the same is true in the polymerization of isoprene; cf. Table 5-3).

Various structural arrangements are to be found in addition polymers. Usually the monomers are joined together in a head-to-tail arrangement, that is

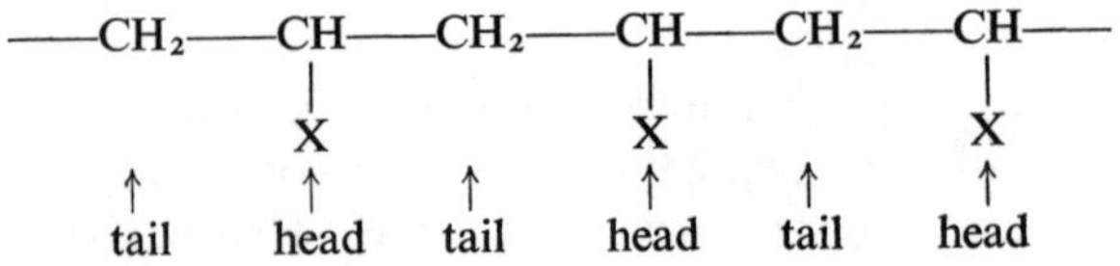

$$-CH_2-\underset{\mid}{CH}-CH_2-\underset{\mid}{CH}-CH_2-\underset{\mid}{CH}-$$

tail   head   tail   head   tail   head

Head-to-head and tail-to-tail arrangements are also found, however.

$$--CH_2---CH---CH---CH_2---CH_2---CH---$$

$$\begin{array}{ccccccc} & & \underset{\uparrow}{X} & \underset{\uparrow}{X} & & & \underset{\uparrow}{X} \\ \underset{tail}{\uparrow} & & \underset{head}{\uparrow} & \underset{head}{\uparrow} & \underset{tail}{\uparrow} & \underset{tail}{\uparrow} & \underset{head}{\uparrow} \end{array}$$

When more than one double bond is present in the monomer, as in divinylbenzene

$$H_2C=CH-\langle\!\bigcirc\!\rangle-CH=CH_2$$

the polymer may form a complicated network and this has a marked effect on the properties. The vulcanization of rubber involves treatment of a polymer with sulfur which forms cross-links between chains:

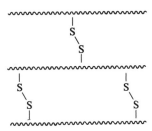

Hard rubber may contain as much as 35 per cent sulfur; it has very little elasticity.

Condensation Polymerization

Condensation polymerization involves reaction between two functional groups, one on each monomer molecule, with the elimination of a small molecule, such as water. For example, the commercial product known as Dacron is a copolymer formed from terephthalic acid

$$HOOC-\langle\!\bigcirc\!\rangle-COOH$$

and ethylene glycol

$$HO-CH_2-CH_2-OH$$

The polymerization process involves esterification reactions between the –COOH groups of the acid and the –OH groups of the glycol.

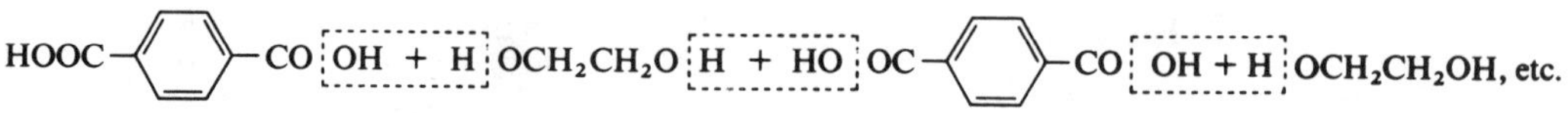

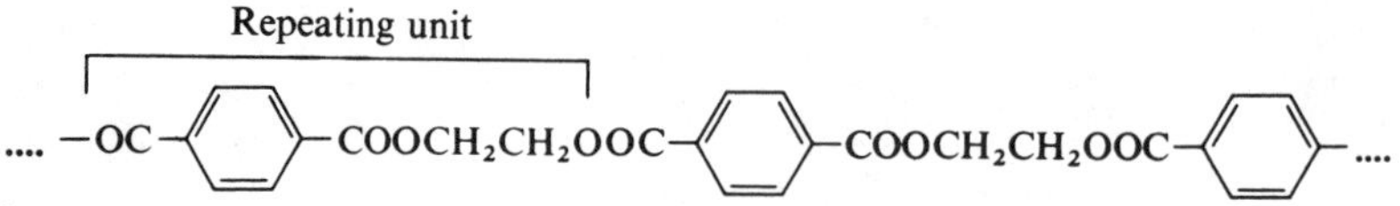

$$HOOC-\langle\!\!\bigcirc\!\!\rangle-CO\,|OH\,+\,H\,|OCH_2CH_2O\,|H\,+\,HO\,|OC-\langle\!\!\bigcirc\!\!\rangle-CO\,|OH\,+\,H\,|OCH_2CH_2OH, \text{etc.}$$

Repeating unit

$$\cdots\,-OC-\langle\!\!\bigcirc\!\!\rangle-COOCH_2CH_2OOC-\langle\!\!\bigcirc\!\!\rangle-COOCH_2CH_2OOC-\langle\!\!\bigcirc\!\!\rangle-\cdots$$

The repeating unit is shown above.

The process of condensation polymerization differs from that of addition polymerization in that all reactions are of the same type, repeated over and over again; we have seen that in addition polymerization there are initiation, propagation, and termination steps, constituting a chain reaction. Apart from esterification reactions, which occur in Dacron formation, there is amide formation, which is involved in the formation of Nylon-6-6:

$$\underset{\text{Hexamethylene diamine}}{H_2NCH_2CH_2CH_2CH_2CH_2CH_2NH_2} + \underset{\text{Adipic acid}}{HOOCCH_2CH_2CH_2CH_2COOH}$$

$$\downarrow -H_2O$$

$$H_2NCH_2CH_2CH_2CH_2CH_2CH_2NHCOCH_2CH_2CH_2CH_2COOH, \text{etc.}$$

The molecules in a condensation polymer are usually more variable in size than those in an addition polymer. Condensation polymerization is, of course, catalyzed by the usual reagents (for example, acids and bases) that catalyze the particular process, such as esterification, that is occurring.

A number of naturally occurring polymers, such as proteins and certain carbohydrates, are considered in the next chapter.

Structure Determinations and Synthesis

Because of the very large number of known organic compounds, the subject of organic chemistry is very complex. A great deal is now known about the reactions of the various functional groups and about the fundamental principles relating to the structures of organic molecules. When, however, a molecule is very large and contains a considerable number of functional groups, the problem of identifying it and determining its structure may be very difficult. This applies particularly to the protein molecules, which contain many thousands of atoms. It was only recently that the structure of any protein molecule was determined, and there still remains a great deal of work to be done in this important field.

A completely satisfactory determination of the structure of an organic compound involves several different procedures. In the first place, the chemist carries out a number of physical and chemical tests on the substance. We have seen that certain functional groups behave in a characteristic way toward chemical reagents, and it is usually fairly easy to determine the more important functional groups present in a molecule. In the same way, the spectra of many of the functional groups are quite characteristic, so that this physical method is also of great value. During recent years, in fact, more and more use has been made of physical methods.

Further information about structure is obtained by breaking the molecule down, using various reagents, and studying the fragments that are formed. Again, both chemical and physical methods can be used for determining the structures of such fragments.

Once a decision is reached about the structure of an organic compound, the next procedure is to synthesize the molecule that one thinks is present and to compare the product with the unknown compound. If they agree in all physical and chemical properties, the structure is confirmed.

Problems

5-1. Arrange the following compounds in order of increasing dipole moment:
$$CH_4, CH_3Cl, CH_2Cl_2, CHCl_3, CCl_4.$$

5-2. Draw structures for the six different isomeric alkenes that have the empirical formula C_5H_{10}. Name each of the compounds.

5-3. Draw structures for the four different alcohols that have the empirical formula C_4H_9OH. Name each of the compounds.

5-4. Write down equations for the following processes:

(a) The addition of a bromine molecule to the double bond in propylene,
(b) The complete oxidation of ethanol, C_2H_5OH,
(c) The reaction of isopropyl alcohol (2-propanol) with hydrogen bromide,
(d) The hydrolysis of ethyl acetate,
(e) The decomposition of isopropyl alcohol on a copper surface,
(f) The oxidation of isopropyl alcohol by dichromate ions in acid solution.

5-5. Write down general equations illustrating the following types of reactions:

(a) The condensation of an organic acid with a molecule of ammonia,
(b) Esterification,
(c) *Cis-trans* isomerization,
(d) Dehydrogenation of an alcohol,
(e) Addition polymerization.

5-6. Write down structural formulas for the following molecules:

(a) 2,4-dimethyl pentane.
(b) methyl ethyl ketone.
(c) 3-methyl-pentene.
(d) 1-butanol.
(e) 3-methyl-2-butanone.
(f) methyl ethyl ether.
(g) tetramethylammonium iodide.
(h) chloroform.

5-7. What are the products when the following hydrocarbons are oxidized with acidic permanganate solution?

(a) 2-butene.
(b) 2-methyl-2-butene.
(c) 3,4-dimethyl-3-hexene.

5-8. Give the name of the compound formed by the addition of HBr to:

(a) isobutene (2-methyl-propylene).
(b) 3-methyl-2-pentene.

5-9. Which of the following molecules are linear (that is, all atoms are in a straight line)?

(a) CO_2.
(b) CS_2.
(c) HCN.
(d) H_2CCH_2.
(e) ClCN.
(f) HOCN.

5-10. Which of the following molecules are planar (that is, all atoms lie in a single plane)?

(a) H_2CCH_2.
(b) H_2CCCl_2.
(c) CH_3CHCH_2.
(d) C_6H_6.
(e) H_2CO.
(f) $COCl_2$.

5-11. Account for the following facts:

(a) CS_2 boils at a higher temperature than CO_2.
(b) CH_4 has a lower boiling point than NH_3, H_2O, and HF.
(c) C_2H_5OH is completely miscible with water, but CH_3OCH_3 is not.

5-12. The heats of formation of C_2H_6, C_2H_4 and C_2H_2 are -20.2, $+12.5$ and $+54.2$ kcal/mole, respectively. Calculate the heats evolved in the following reactions:

(a) $C_2H_2 + 2H_2 \rightarrow C_2H_6$.
(b) $C_2H_2 + H_2 \rightarrow C_2H_4$.
(c) $C_2H_4 + H_2 \rightarrow C_2H_6$.

5-13. Which of the compounds listed below occur in enantiomeric forms?

(a) 1-chlorobutane,
(b) 2-chlorobutane.
(c) 1,1-dichlorobutane.
(d) 1,2-dichlorobutane.
(e) 1,3-dichlorobutane.
(f) 1,4-dichlorobutane.
(g) 2,3-dichlorobutane.

5-14. Which of the following compounds will exhibit *cis-trans* isomerism?
(a) Propylene,
(b) 1-butene,
(c) 2-butene,
(d) Isobutene (2-methyl propylene),
(e) 1-pentene,
(f) 2-pentene.

Suggested Reading relating to the material of this Chapter will be found at the end of Chapter 6.

Chapter 6   Structure and Mechanism in Living Systems

The importance of studying living systems need hardly be emphasized. The control and treatment of disease cannot be carried out effectively in the absence of a detailed knowledge, on a molecular level, of biological structures and of the chemical and physical processes that occur in biological systems. For example, the cure of muscular dystrophy will necessarily be based on a great deal of fundamental knowledge about the structure of muscle and the molecular processes that occur when a muscle contracts and relaxes.

Both inorganic and organic chemistry are deeply involved in studies of living systems. The study of *structure* in living systems is more closely related to organic than to inorganic chemistry, but it is becoming more and more apparent that the *functioning* of biological systems depends very critically on the presence of inorganic compounds.

This chapter is concerned mainly with investigations in the field known as *biological chemistry*, or *biochemistry*. The subject, however, embraces many important aspects of biology and physics as well as chemistry. Naturally, workers in this important area are not concerned with arbitrary subdivisions of knowledge; in order to understand the structures and mechanisms of biological systems, they make use of any intellectual tools that may be useful to them. The subject is still only in its infancy, in that many basic processes, such as the functioning of muscle and nerve, still remain obscure. Attacks are, however, now being made from all sides on matters such as these, and it is to be hoped that very rapid advances will be made in the near future.

Three main classes of chemical substances play a very important role in living systems. These are the lipids, or fatty substances, the carbohydrates, and the proteins. An important group of proteins comprises the enzymes, which are the catalysts that facilitate the occurrence of chemical (and to some extent physical) processes in living systems. Something will now be said about the structures of these various substances and about the reactions they undergo.

Lipids

The lipids are fatty substances which are important structural components of all living systems. One of their functions is to lubricate the tissues. The lipids also occur in the cell walls and play an essential role in controlling the flow of substances into and out of cells. They are also of great importance as fuels—that is, as substances that provide the necessary energy to living systems. They are very effective in this regard, because, when completely oxidized, they provide more than twice as much energy as an equal weight of carbohydrate or protein.

The simplest lipids are esters of the alcohol *glycerol* with a variety of fatty acids. Glycerol is an alcohol that contains three hydroxyl groups, its structure being

$$CH_2OH$$
$$CHOH$$
$$CH_2OH$$

Each of the three OH groups can become esterified with a carboxylic acid as follows:

$$
\begin{array}{ccc}
& & O \\
& & \| \\
CH_2O\!\!-\!\!H \quad\quad HO\!\!-\!\!C\!-\!R & & CH_2OCR \\
& O & & O \\
& \| & & \| \\
CHO \; H \quad\quad HO\!\!-\!\!C\!-\!R' & \longrightarrow & CHOCR' \;\; + \;\; 3H_2O \\
& O & & O \\
& \| & & \| \\
CH_2O\; H \quad\quad HO\!\!-\!\!C\!-\!R'' & & CH_2OCR''
\end{array}
$$

In the naturally occurring fats the acids, known as fatty acids, are long-chain compounds mostly having an even number of carbon atoms. Some examples are

$$myristic\ acid,\quad CH_3(CH_2)_{12}COOH$$
$$palmitic\ acid,\quad CH_3(CH_2)_{14}COOH$$
$$stearic\ acid,\quad CH_3(CH_2)_{16}COOH$$

A few of them are not fully saturated with hydrogen, but have carbon–carbon double bonds in their structures; an example is

$$oleic\ acid,\quad CH_3(CH_2)_7CH{=}CH(CH_2)_7COOH$$

An example of a fat is, therefore

$$
\text{Glycerol residue}
\begin{cases}
& \overset{\displaystyle O}{\overset{\|}{}} \\
& H_2CO-CC_{17}H_{35}\quad (\text{stearic}) \\
& \overset{\displaystyle O}{\overset{\|}{}} \\
& HCO-CC_{15}H_{31}\quad (\text{palmitic}) \\
& \overset{\displaystyle O}{\overset{\|}{}} \\
& H_2COCC_{17}H_{33}\quad (\text{oleic})
\end{cases}
$$

Fats containing more than one double bond are usually liquids at ordinary temperatures, when they are known as *oils*; there is no chemical difference between a fat and an oil, the name used depending on the physical state of the substance at room temperature.

Because a number of different fatty acids occur in fats, and since glycerol has three OH groups, it might be expected that there would be rather a large number of different fats. Actually, however, the fats occur in nature in far fewer variations than might have been expected; apparently, the synthetic processes by which they are formed tend to produce them in relatively few patterns.

In addition to these triglycerides, other distinct classes of compounds are classed as lipids. One important group consists of the *phospholipids*, which are derived from α-glycerophosphoric acid:

$$
\begin{array}{l}
CH_2OH \\
| \\
CHOH \qquad O \\
| \qquad\quad \uparrow \\
CH_2-O-P-OH \\
\qquad\qquad | \\
\qquad\qquad OH
\end{array}
$$

Another important group of lipids comprises the *steroids*, which are derivatives of the aromatic hydrocarbon phenanthrene:

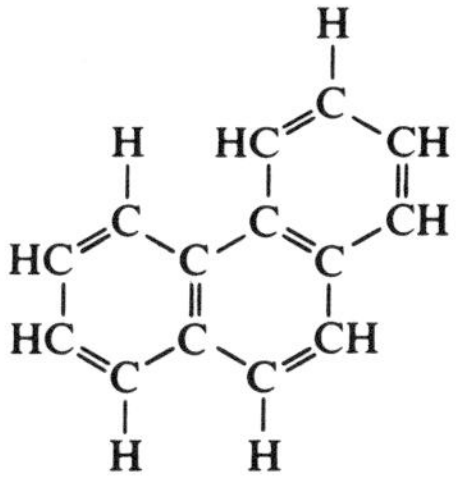

The most important member of this group is *cholesterol*:*

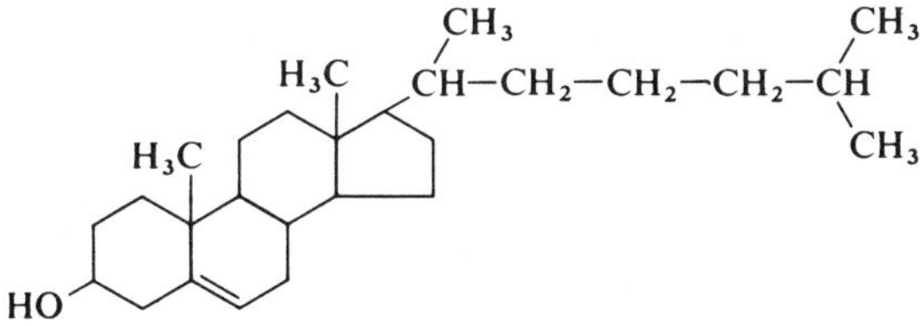

This substance has been studied very extensively in view of its relation to the heart disease atherosclerosis. In this disease, cholesterol is deposited on the inner walls of arteries and restricts the flow of blood.

The lipids are only very slightly soluble in water. This is to be expected, since, in a lipid molecule, most of the chemical bonds are C–C and C–H bonds, which are of the nonpolar variety; the more polar C–O bonds represent only a small fraction of the bonds. We have seen in the last chapter that compounds containing a high proportion of nonpolar bonds tend to be very insoluble in water; they are much more soluble in solvents such as acetone and ether.

Carbohydrates

The carbohydrates, which include sugars, starches, and cellulose, are the most abundant organic compounds in nature. A very considerable variety of them exists, and only a few examples can be given. One of the commonest and the most important carbohydrate is *glucose*. It is convenient to consider first a structure that, for many years, its molecule was believed to have—an idea that has

* For simplicity, the ring carbon atoms in this structure have not been written out; it is to be understood that there is a carbon atom at each corner of the rings and that the appropriate numbers of hydrogen atoms are attached to them.

required modification; this structure is

$$
\begin{array}{c}
\text{H} \\
| \\
\overset{1}{\text{C}}{=}\text{O} \\
| \\
\text{H}-\overset{2}{\text{C}}-\text{OH} \\
| \\
\text{HO}-\overset{3}{\text{C}}-\text{H} \\
| \\
\text{H}-\overset{4}{\text{C}}-\text{OH} \\
| \\
\text{H}-\overset{5}{\text{C}}-\text{OH} \\
| \\
\text{H}_2\overset{6}{\text{C}}-\text{OH}
\end{array}
$$

This molecule is seen to contain a number of alcoholic (–OH) groups. According to this structure, the molecule contains an aldehydic (–CHO) group, and glucose is said to belong to the class of compounds known as *aldoses*; the prefix *ald* indicates that it is an aldehyde and the suffix *ose* that it is a carbohydrate. Glucose can also be called an *aldohexose*, which indicates that it contains six (*hex*) carbon atoms.

If we number the carbon atoms in glucose, giving the number 1 to the aldehydic carbon atom, we see that carbon atoms 2, 3, 4, and 5 are asymmetric carbon atoms; that is to say, the four bonds emanating from them are attached to four different groups. In the structure written above, a particular convention has been used to indicate the stereochemical configurations round the carbon atoms; thus, when we write the –OH group to the right of carbon atom number 2, we imply the following arrangement:

$$
\begin{array}{cc}
\begin{array}{c}
\text{HC}{=}\text{O} \\
\blacktriangle \\
\text{H}\blacktriangleright\text{C}\blacktriangleleft\text{OH} \\
\blacktriangledown \\
\text{C}
\end{array}
&
\begin{array}{c}
\text{CH}_2\text{OH} \\
| \\
\text{CHOH} \quad\quad \text{O} \\
| \quad\quad\quad \uparrow \\
\text{CH}_2-\text{O}-\text{P}-\text{OH} \\
| \\
\text{OH}
\end{array}
\end{array}
$$

We saw in the last chapter that a compound containing one asymmetric carbon atom (such as glyceraldehyde; cf. Figure 5-11) can exist in optically isomeric, or enantiomeric, forms, one of which rotates the plane of polarization to the right, the other to the left. The structure given above for glucose has four asymmetric carbon atoms, and $2 \times 2 \times 2 \times 2 = 16$ forms should, therefore, exist. The substance whose structure is given above is known as D-glucose, because of the relationship of the lower asymmetric carbon atom (C^5) to D-glyceraldehyde. Its mirror image, or optical enantiomer, is called L-glucose:

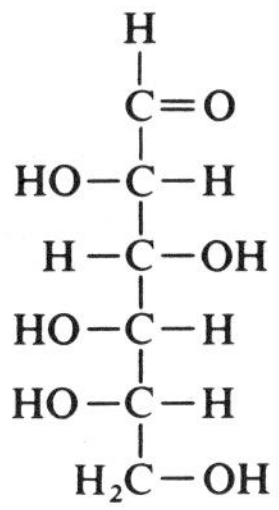

$$
\begin{array}{c}
H \\
| \\
C{=}O \\
| \\
HO{-}C{-}H \\
| \\
H{-}C{-}OH \\
| \\
HO{-}C{-}H \\
| \\
HO{-}C{-}H \\
| \\
H_2C{-}OH
\end{array}
$$

The other 14 members of the group are given different names altogether; examples are

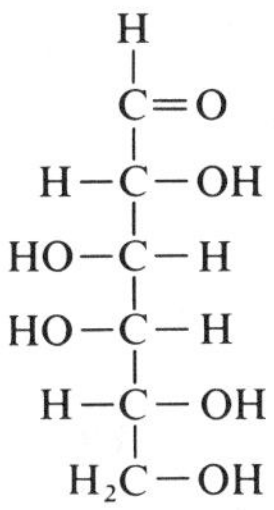

$$
\begin{array}{c}
H \\
| \\
C{=}O \\
| \\
H{-}C{-}OH \\
| \\
HO{-}C{-}H \\
| \\
HO{-}C{-}H \\
| \\
H{-}C{-}OH \\
| \\
H_2C{-}OH
\end{array}
\qquad and \qquad
\begin{array}{c}
H \\
| \\
C{=}O \\
| \\
HO{-}C{-}H \\
| \\
H{-}C{-}OH \\
| \\
H{-}C{-}OH \\
| \\
HO{-}C{-}H \\
| \\
H_2C{-}OH
\end{array}
$$

D-Galactose   L-Galactose

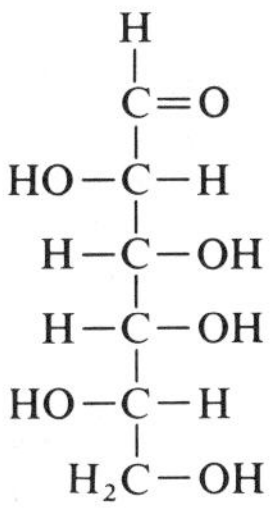

The structures given above for the carbohydrates are old-fashioned. It has been convenient to give them first in order to bring out the aldehydic character of the substances, and also something of their stereochemistry. However, for many years it has been realized that these substances actually exist as ring structures rather than in the open-chain forms given above. The rings can be regarded as being formed from the chains by the transfer of an alcoholic hydrogen atom to the aldehydic oxygen atom and by the formation of a bond between the alcoholic oxygen atom and the aldehydic carbon atom:

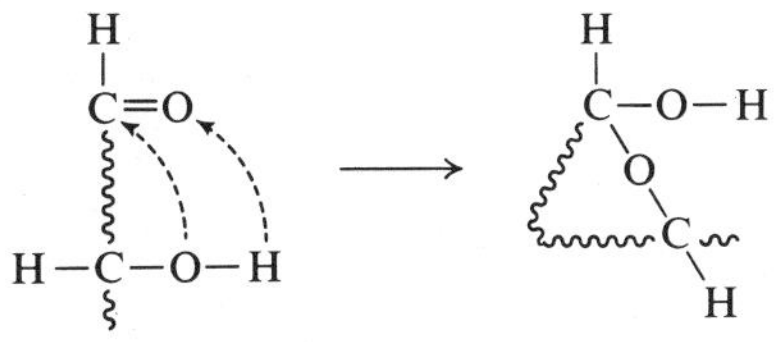

In the case of D-glucose, this process involves the –OH group on carbon atom number 5 and leads to the formation of a six-membered ring:

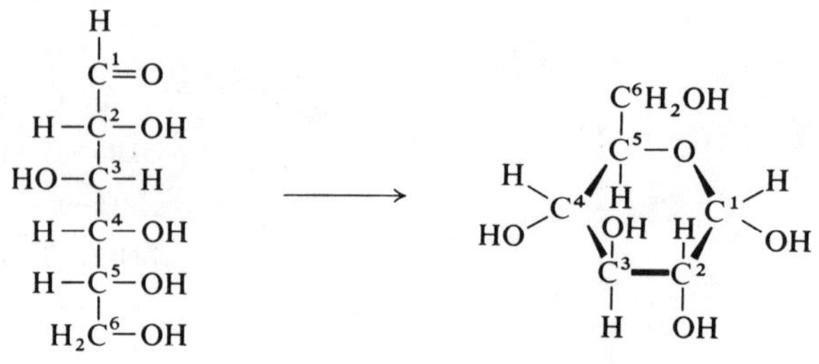

$$\begin{array}{c}
\text{H} \\
| \\
\overset{1}{\text{C}}{=}\text{O} \\
| \\
\text{H}-\overset{2}{\text{C}}-\text{OH} \\
| \\
\text{HO}-\overset{3}{\text{C}}-\text{H} \\
| \\
\text{H}-\overset{4}{\text{C}}-\text{OH} \\
| \\
\text{H}-\overset{5}{\text{C}}-\text{OH} \\
| \\
\text{H}_2\overset{6}{\text{C}}-\text{OH}
\end{array}$$

$\longrightarrow$

α-D-Glucose

When this ring closure occurs, carbon atoms 2, 3, 4, and 5 still remain asymmetric carbon atoms. Now, however, carbon atom number 1 has become an asymmetric atom, which it was not before. It is therefore possible for two rings to be formed; the one shown above, which is known as α-D-glucose, and the one in which the arrangement around carbon atom 1 is

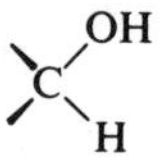

$$\begin{array}{c}
\diagdown \quad \diagup \text{OH} \\
\text{C} \\
\diagup \quad \diagdown \text{H}
\end{array}$$

The latter structure is known as β-D-glucose. In the crystalline form, glucose exists predominantly as α-D-glucose; in solution, an equilibrium is established between the two forms, the β form preponderating.

Besides the aldoses, there is also an important class of carbohydrates known as *ketoses*, in which there is a ketonic, rather than an aldehydic, group; in other words, the $\diagup\diagdown$C$=$O group is not at the end of the molecule. An example is D-fructose, which is a ketohexose (it has six carbon atoms); its open-chain (old-fashioned) and ring forms are as follows:

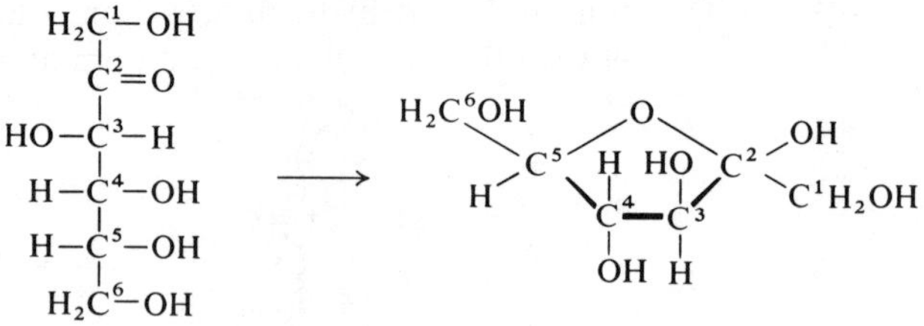

$$\begin{array}{c}
\text{H}_2\overset{1}{\text{C}}-\text{OH} \\
| \\
\overset{2}{\text{C}}{=}\text{O} \\
| \\
\text{HO}-\overset{3}{\text{C}}-\text{H} \\
| \\
\text{H}-\overset{4}{\text{C}}-\text{OH} \\
| \\
\text{H}-\overset{5}{\text{C}}-\text{OH} \\
| \\
\text{H}_2\overset{6}{\text{C}}-\text{OH}
\end{array}$$

$\longrightarrow$

The open-chain structure is again convenient in showing the ketonic character of the molecule. The structure above shows a five-membered ring, in contrast to glucose which is six-membered; actually fructose in the crystalline form exists mainly as a six-membered ring, but the five-membered structure is important in most of its derivatives, including sucrose.

More Complex Carbohydrates

Other opportunities for structural variations among carbohydrates result from the fact that two or more of the smaller molecules such as the hexoses (referred to as *monosaccharides*) may combine together by a condensation reaction in which a molecule of water is split out between two hydroxyl groups:

For example, the sugar maltose, which is known as a *disaccharide*, can be regarded as resulting from the condensation of two glucose molecules:

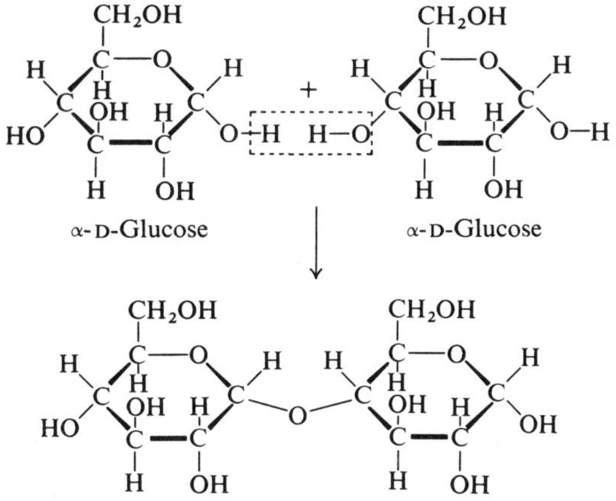

Maltose

Similarly, ordinary cane sugar, known scientifically as sucrose, can be regarded as being formed by the condensation of a molecule of glucose with one of fructose:

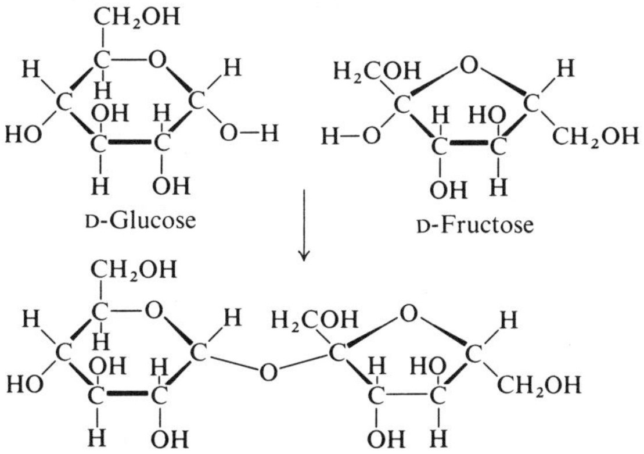

Sucrose

A number of condensation polymers of the smaller carbohydrates are also of great biological importance. Starch, which is present extensively in plants, is a polymer of α-D-glucose, containing structures of the following type:*

CH_2OH CH_2OH CH_2OH CH_2OH

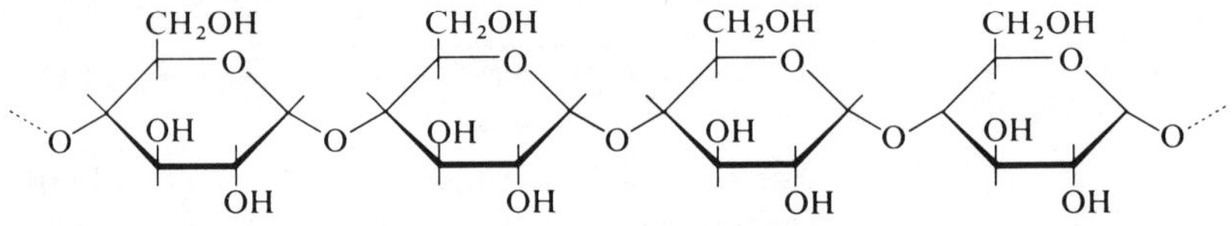

The orientation of the bonds at the oxygen atoms connecting the glucose units is such as to give the molecule a helical (spiral) structure. In addition to this feature, the starch molecule has a considerable amount of branching, structures of the following type being found:

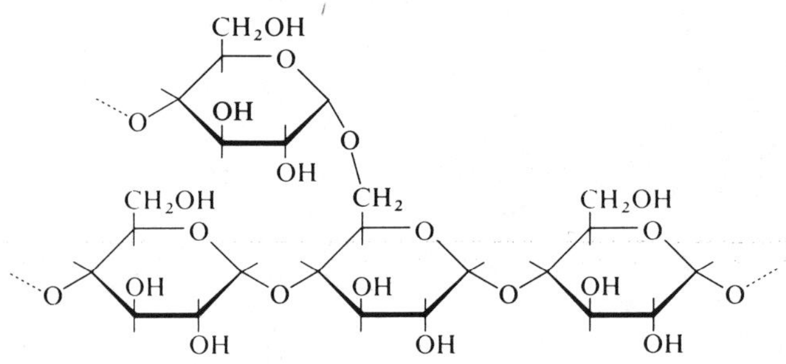

CH_2OH

CH_2OH CH_2 CH_2OH

Glycogen, or animal starch, is very similar to starch, glucose residues again being condensed together in the same manner as in maltose. There is even more branching in glycogen than in starch; Figure 6-1 gives a schematic representation of the glycogen molecule.

In cellulose, on the other hand, the glucose molecules are in the β configuration:

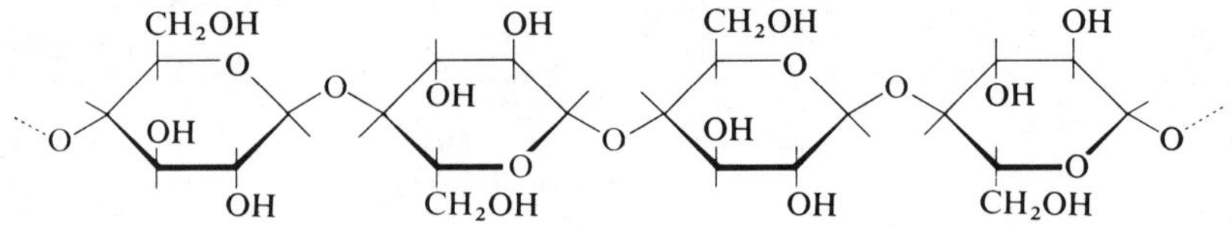

CH_2OH OH CH_2OH OH

The polymer is now linear, as is appropriate for the fibrous materials in plants.

* For simplicity, an abbreviation notation is used for the ring stuctures.

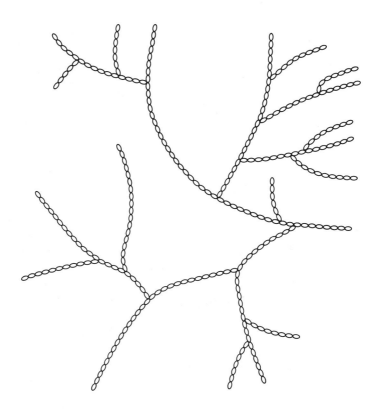

Fig. 6-1 Schematic representation of the structure of a glycogen molecule. Each ellipse represents a glucose residue. Note that there is a considerable degree of branching of the chains.

Proteins

The proteins are of biological importance for two main reasons: they are the structural elements of the cells, and some of them are catalysts for the chemical reactions occurring in the living system.

The components of the proteins are the amino acids, of which there are about 20 important ones. The amino acids possess both an amino group and a carboxylic acid group attached to the same carbon atom:

$$\underset{H}{\overset{H}{}}N-\underset{\underset{H}{|}}{\overset{\overset{R}{|}}{C}}-C\overset{\displaystyle O}{\underset{\displaystyle OH}{}}$$

This carbon atom is attached also to a hydrogen atom and to a group R, which is different for each amino acid; examples are

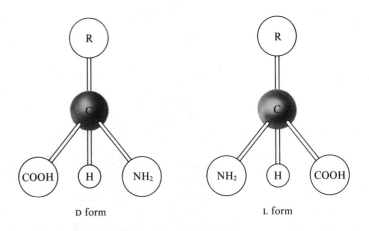

Glycine
(R = H)

Valine
(R = CH(CH₃)₂)

Histidine

All of the amino acids except glycine contain an asymmetric carbon atom, which is connected to the four different groups H, R, NH$_2$, and COOH. They therefore exist in two optically active mirror-image forms; valine, for example, occurs as D-valine and L-valine, which rotate the plane of polarized light to the same extent but in a different direction. Their configurations are shown in Figure 6-2.

D form   L form

Fig. 6-2 The two optically active forms of an amino acid. If R is (CH₃)₂CH—, the molecules are the D and L forms of valine.

The amino acids occurring in nature are nearly all of the L variety; a few microorganisms contain the D-amino acids, but the proteins that occur in the tissues of animals contain exclusively the L forms.

The two amino-acid molecules can be condensed together to form a molecule known as a dipeptide; thus, in the case of glycine the product is known as diglycine, and we see that it still contains an amino group and a carboxylic acid group; it can therefore condense with additional molecules of an amino acid:

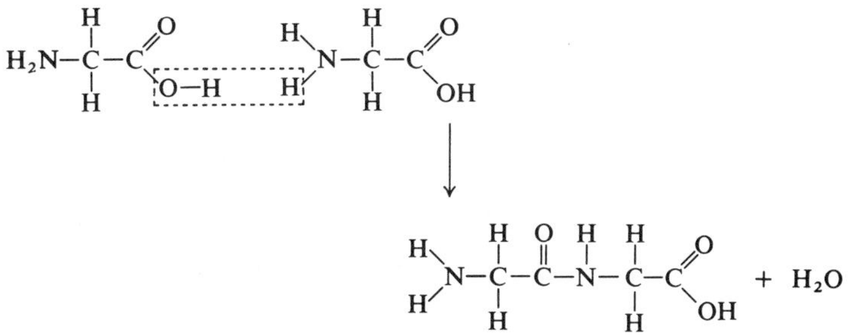

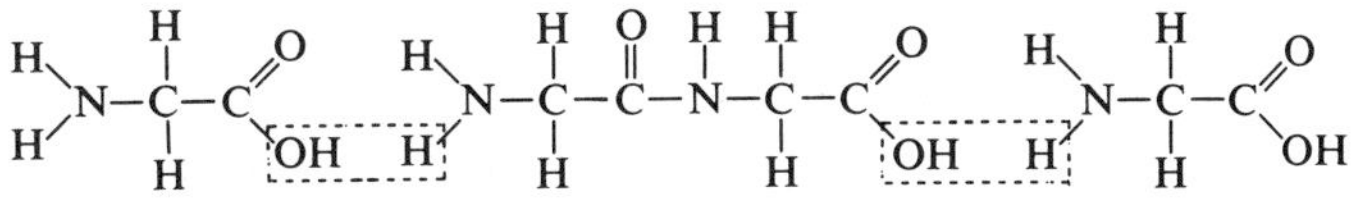

A very large molecule can be produced in this way, and it will be evident that this type of condensation polymerization is possible, because the amino acids contain two functional groups capable of undergoing condensation reactions.

The $-C\!\!\stackrel{O}{=}\!\!N\!\!<^H$ linkage that occurs between each of the amino-acid residues in the proteins is known as a *peptide* linkage. The naturally occurring proteins are made up of about 20 *different* amino .acids, and there may be many hundreds of amino-acid residues in each protein molecule, the 20 different acids being used several times over.

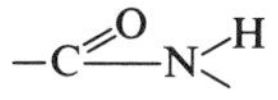

The Sequence of Amino Acids in Proteins

Living systems consist of many different proteins; some of them are enzymes that catalyze chemical reactions; others are structural units in skin or hair; still others are hormones, which perform a regulatory function. Each individual protein has a specific role to play in the living organism; indeed *specificity* is one of the most important characteristics of the proteins.

During recent years it has become increasingly clear that specificity is imparted not only by the number and nature of the amino acid, in the protein molecule, but by the sequence in which they occurs and by the conformation of the protein molecule. Some protein molecules, such as those in muscle and hair, exist as a more or less linear polymer,* whereas the molecules of hemoglobin are wound up somewhat like a ball of wool. These different shapes are determined by the nature of the amino acids and their sequence, all of these factors having a profound bearing on the biological behavior.

The problem of determining the sequence of amino acids in a protein is naturally very difficult, in view of the very large number of the units present in the molecules. One of the smallest protein molecules is that of insulin, which contains 51 amino acids and has a molecular weight of a little under 6000.† The establishment of the amino-acid sequence in a protein molecule was first achieved for insulin in 1955 by the British biochemist Frederick Sanger (b. 1918; Nobel prize for chemistry, 1958). The method he employed was to cause some easily identifiable group to react with one part of the molecule; the protein was then broken down by hydrolysis, and an investigation was made of the amino acid to which the group had become attached. In ways such as this, and by breaking the protein down systematically and in stages, it proved possible, by much painstaking work, for the entire sequence of amino acids to be determined.

The sequence determined by Sanger for insulin is shown in Figure 6-3. It is to be seen that there are really two chains of amino acids, connected by two sulfur–sulfur linkages. In addition, there is a third sulfur–sulfur linkage forming a bridge between two parts of one of the chains. These sulfur–sulfur bridges play a very important role in protein structure. They involve the amino acid cystine, which is a double amino acid of structure

$$\begin{array}{ccc} CH_2-S-S-CH_2 \\ | & | \\ H_2N-C-COOH \quad H_2N-C-COOH \\ | & | \\ H & H \end{array}$$

When these sulfur–sulfur linkages exist, groups that are far apart on the amino acid chain are brought into close spatial proximity. This has a profound effect on the whole conformation, and on the biological activity.

Since Sanger's pioneering work on insulin, the amino-acid sequence has been worked out for a number of larger molecules, such as myoglobin (MW 17,000), ribonuclease (MW 12,600), lysozyme

---

* Actually, as we shall see, they have a spiral or helical structure.

† Insulin usually exists in solution as a dimer, of molecular weight about 12,000.

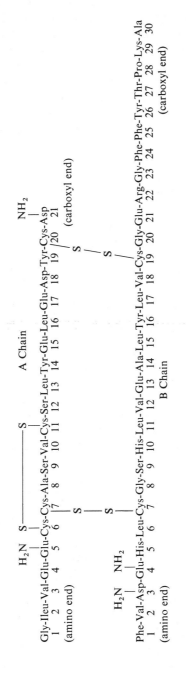

Fig. 6-3 The amino-acid sequence in insulin. The amino acids are given in abbreviated form (e.g. Gly = glycine, Val = valine).

(MW 14,000), and chymotrypsin (MW 25,000). At one time it was suspected that the amino acids in proteins were arranged in some regular and repeating pattern. Now that the sequence has been determined in a number of cases, however, it has become apparent that there is no evidence for such a conclusion. It has also become evident that the sequence is the same for all samples of protein obtained from a given source. Thus, all hemoglobin molecules obtained from normal human beings appear to be identical in amino-acid sequence. Hemoglobin from horse blood, however, shows small differences from that obtained from humans; again, all horse samples appear to be identical.

Protein Conformations   The properties of a protein cannot be understood entirely on the basis of the sequence of amino acids; they also depend very critically on the three-dimensional structure of the molecule. This three-dimensional structure, or molecular conformation, determines the way in which the various side groups on the molecule are brought into close proximity with one another, and this has an important effect on chemical and physical properties. In particular, if the protein is an enzyme, the relative positions of certain groups have a very important effect on the catalytic action.

Certain physical methods have been used for many years for gaining a very general idea of the over-all shapes of protein molecules. These include the measurements of the viscosities of solutions, and of their light scattering. These properties for the molecules that are long and thin are very different from what they are for molecules that have a more or less spherical form. By the use of such physical methods, proteins have been grouped into two main classes, the *fibrous* proteins, in which the molecules are fairly extended, and the *globular* proteins, which are roughly spherical in shape.

Very much more detailed information about protein structure is provided by the technique of X-ray crystallography. The reason that X rays are the most suitable for work of this kind is that the detail with which an object can be observed—that is, the resolving power of an instrument—depends in a fundamental way on the wavelength of the radiation employed; as a rough rule, no two objects can be seen separately if they are closer together than one-half the wave length of the radiation used. The lengths of chemical bonds are between 1 and 2 Ångström units ($1–2 \times 10^{-8}$ cm), so that one must use wavelengths not much longer than this; consequently, X rays must be used. The employment of X rays, however, introduces new difficulties, because no satisfactory way has yet been found to make lenses and mirrors that will focus X rays. The technique employed is to record and study the diffraction pattern produced when X rays strike the material under study. The analysis of an X-ray diffraction pattern is considerably difficult for a molecule as large as a protein, because of the very large number of interatomic distances that are involved. In 1953, the British molecular biologist Max Ferdinand Perutz (b. 1914; Nobel prize for chemistry, 1962) made a very important contribution to the analysis of X-ray patterns by his method of "isomorphous replacement"; this method depends upon the preparation and study of protein crystals into which heavy atoms, such as atoms of uranium, have been introduced without otherwise altering the crystal structure. Since that time a considerable number of protein structures have been worked out.

It is the electrons within the molecules that scatter the X rays, so that the image calculated from the diffraction pattern reveals the distribution of electrons within the molecule. The usual procedure is to calculate, with high-speed computers, the electron density at a regular array of points and to make the image visible by drawing contour lines through points of equal electron density. These contour maps can be drawn on clear plastic sheets, and a three-dimensional image can then be obtained by stacking the maps one above the other. The amount of detail that can be seen depends upon the resolving power of the effective microscope, and, if this is sufficiently good, the atoms appear as individual peaks in the image map. At lower resolutions, groups of unresolved atoms appear, and these can frequently be recognized by their characteristic shapes.

Figure 6-4 shows, in schematic form, the kind of structure that has been found to exist in the insulin molecule, the amino-acid sequence for which was given in Figure 6-3. Each of the two amino-acid chains, known as the A and B chains, occurs as a special type of helix, about which more will be said later. The B chain is entirely a right-handed helix, as shown in the figure. The A chain, however, is partly right-handed and partly left-handed, the break occurring at amino acid 9.

X-ray structures have also been determined for a number of larger proteins, such as myoglobin (MW 17,000), hemoglobin (MW 65,000), lysozyme (MW 14,000), and chymotrypsin (MW 25,000). In myoglobin and hemoglobin there is found to be a considerable amount of helical structure; in myoglobin, for example, about 75 per cent of the protein chain is in this form. In lysozyme and chymotrypsin, on the other hand, there is considerably less helical structure. Figure 6-5

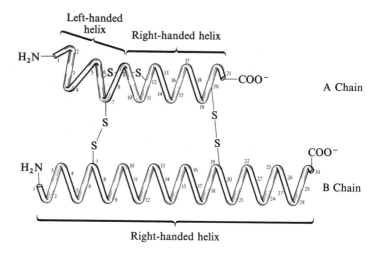

Fig. 6-4 Schematic representation (not to scale) of the type of structure found in the insulin molecule. The amino acids are indicated by numbers.

shows the conformation of the main chain in the chymotrypsin molecule, as determined by the British X-ray crystallographer David M. Blow; some helical structure is to be noted at the left of the diagram, at the end of the C chain.

Before any of this detailed X-ray structural work on proteins had been done, a number of important suggestions had been made about protein conformations, and many of these suggestions proved to be of great value in the further development of the subject. One suggestion, made many years ago by the British physical chemist Eric K. Rideal (b. 1890) and the American physical chemist Irving Langmuir (1881–1957; Nobel prize for chemistry, 1932), is that a protein molecule is "an oil drop with a polar coat." We have already seen that nonpolar groups, such as alkyl groups, tend to stick together in an aqueous environment, because when they do so there are more hydrogen bonds between the water molecules; these apparent attractions between nonpolar groups are now usually known as hydrophobic bonds. Some of the side groups on the amino acids that form the polypeptide chains are nonpolar groups, while others are polar groups such as $-OH$, $-COO^-$, and $-NH_3^+$, which tend to form hydrogen bonds with water. The essence of the suggestion of Rideal and Langmuir is that the polypeptide chains in proteins will become folded in such a way that the nonpolar groups will come into contact with each other as much as possible in the interior of the molecule, and the polar groups will be as far as possible

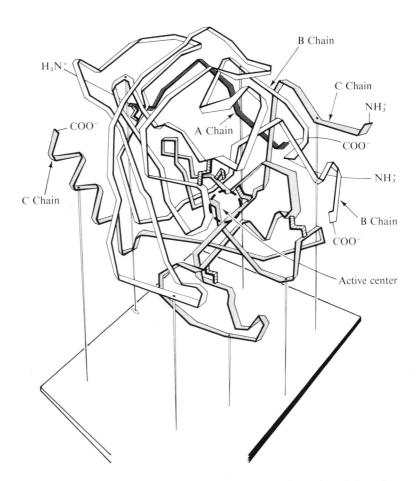

Fig. 6-5 A schematic drawing showing the general conformation of the poly-peptide chains in chymotrypsin. There are three polypeptide chains, A, B, and C, held together by S–S linkages, by hydrogen bonds, and by hydrophobic bonds. The dotted circle shows the active center, that is, the portion of the molecule that is mainly concerned with the catalytic action.

on the exterior where they can form hydrogen bonds with the surrounding water molecules.

It is a fact that the globular proteins, such as chymotrypsin and myoglobin, have, as a rule, a larger proportion of nonpolar groups than the fibrous proteins. The fact that proteins having a larger proportion of nonpolar groups do tend to assume a globular form is almost certainly due to the formation of numerous hydrophobic bonds in the interior of the molecules.

On the other hand, the proteins of wool, hair, and muscle are fibrous proteins, and these show a considerable amount of helical structure. A very important suggestion relating to helical structures was made in 1951 by the American chemists Linus Pauling (b. 1901; Nobel prize for chemistry, 1954; Nobel prize for peace, 1963) and Robert Brainard Corey (b. 1897). They pointed out that certain helical structures formed by polypetide chains allow a considerable amount of hydrogen bonding between the carboxyl group on one part of the chain and the amino group on another:

Pauling and Corey considered in detail the known bond lengths and angles in the flexible chains and concluded that two different helices provide the maximum numbers of hydrogen bonds. The X-ray work has, in fact, shown that one of these helices, the so-called α helix, is quite common in protein structures, particularly in the fibrous proteins. In this arrangement, each N–H group is hydrogen bonded to the third C=O group beyond it along the helix, the result being that there are about 3.6 amino-acid groups per turn of the helix. Such a helix may be regarded as a spiral staircase in which the amino-acid residues form the steps. The height of each step is 1.5 Å. Just as a spiral staircase, like a screw, can be right-handed or left-handed, so can a protein helix. The two cases are illustrated in Figure 6-6. It appears that the right-handed helix occurs more commonly in protein structures. However, we have already noted with insulin (Figure 6-4, p. 250) that a left-handed helix sometimes occurs.

It has been seen that there are three important forces at work in producing protein conformations:

1. the tendency of nonpolar groups to form hydrophobic bonds and to remain in the interior of the molecule;

2. the tendency of polar groups to remain at the exterior of the molecule so that they can form hydrogen bonds with water molecules;

3. the tendency of C=O and N—H groups to form hydrogen bonds, with the formation of a helical structure.

The actual structure of a given protein is determined in a very subtle way by the sometimes conflicting demands of these different effects, and it depends to a considerable extent on the nature and positions of the various amino-acid side groups.

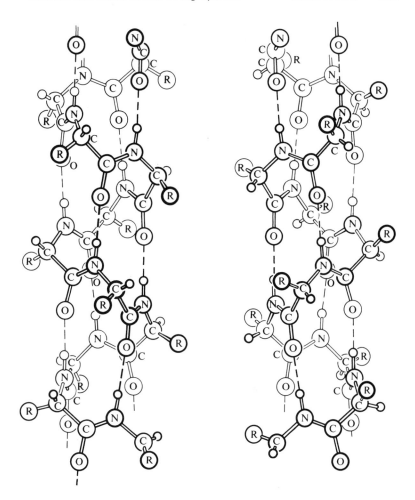

Fig. 6-6 Left- and right-handed α helices. In both cases the amino acids are shown in their L configurations.

Purines, Pyrimidines, and Nucleic Acids

An important aspect of living systems is their ability to reproduce themselves. The compounds responsible for this are the nucleic acids, which tell the living system what kinds of protein to make.

In some ways the nucleic acids are similar in structure to the proteins. They are immense molecules often having molecular weights of several millions. Like the proteins, they are polymers made up of a relatively small number of units replicated many times over. In fact, the variety of constituent units is even less in a nucleic acid than in a protein. The units comprise two closely related sugar molecules, inorganic phosphate groups, and five organic compounds containing nitrogen. The individuality of a nucleic acid results from differences in modes of combination and in changes in the order of the units in the chain.

The two sugar molecules involved in nucleic acid structure are ribose

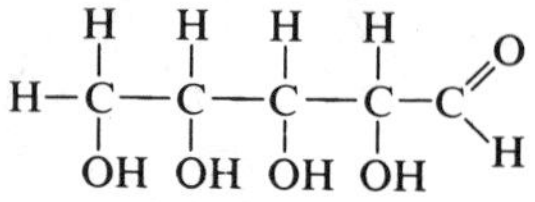

$$H-\overset{\overset{\displaystyle H}{|}}{\underset{\underset{\displaystyle OH}{|}}{C}}-\overset{\overset{\displaystyle H}{|}}{\underset{\underset{\displaystyle OH}{|}}{C}}-\overset{\overset{\displaystyle H}{|}}{\underset{\underset{\displaystyle OH}{|}}{C}}-\overset{\overset{\displaystyle H}{|}}{\underset{\underset{\displaystyle OH}{|}}{C}}-C\overset{\displaystyle O}{\underset{\displaystyle H}{}}$$

and 2-deoxyribose

$$H-\overset{\overset{\displaystyle H}{|}}{\underset{\underset{\displaystyle OH}{|}}{C}}-\overset{\overset{\displaystyle H}{|}}{\underset{\underset{\displaystyle OH}{|}}{C}}-\overset{\overset{\displaystyle H}{|}}{\underset{\underset{\displaystyle OH}{|}}{C}}-\overset{\overset{\displaystyle H}{|}}{\underset{\underset{\displaystyle H}{|}}{C}}-C\overset{\displaystyle O}{\underset{\displaystyle H}{}}$$

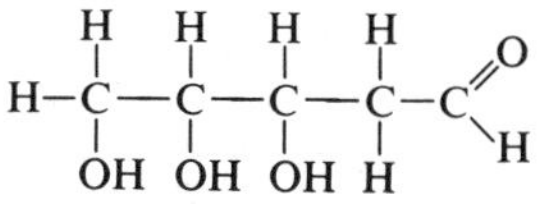

The nucleic acids are of two types, depending on whether they contain ribose or 2-deoxyribose; in the former case, they are described as ribonucleic acids (RNA), in the latter case deoxyribonucleic acids (DNA). The organic compounds containing nitrogen, or nitrogenous bases, are of five types:

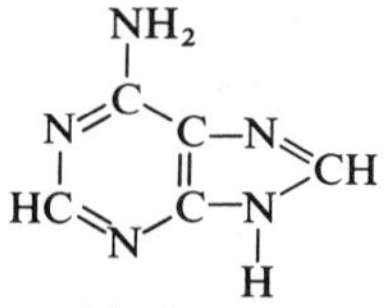

Adenine

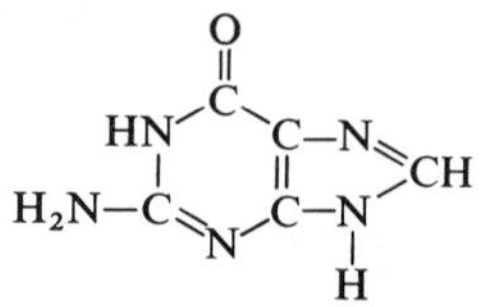

Guanine

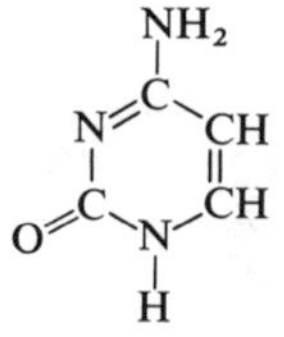

Cytosine

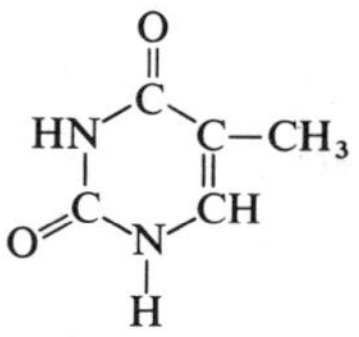

Thymine

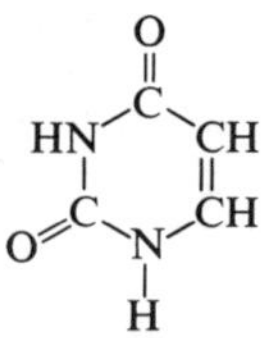

Uracil

The single-ring compounds cytosine, thymine, and uracil are known as *pyrimidines*; the double-ring compounds adenine and guanine are known as *purines*. They belong to the class of *heterocyclic* compounds, having atoms other than carbon atoms in the rings.

RNA contains ribose, phosphate, adenine, guanine, cytosine, and uracil. DNA has a very similar structure except that 2-deoxyribose replaces ribose and thymine replaces uracil. In other words, adenine, guanine, and cytosine are found in combination with either sugar, but uracil is associated only with ribose (in RNA) and thymine is associated only with 2-deoxyribose (in DNA).

A molecule in which one of the organic bases is combined with a sugar is called a *nucleoside*; an example is cytosine riboside:

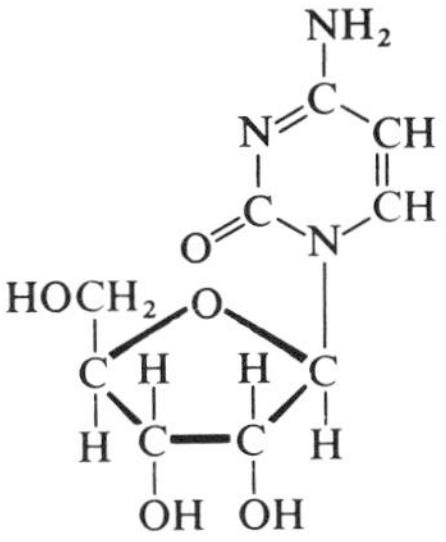

When a phosphate group is attached in addition, the compound is known as a *nucleotide*; an example is cytosine ribotide:

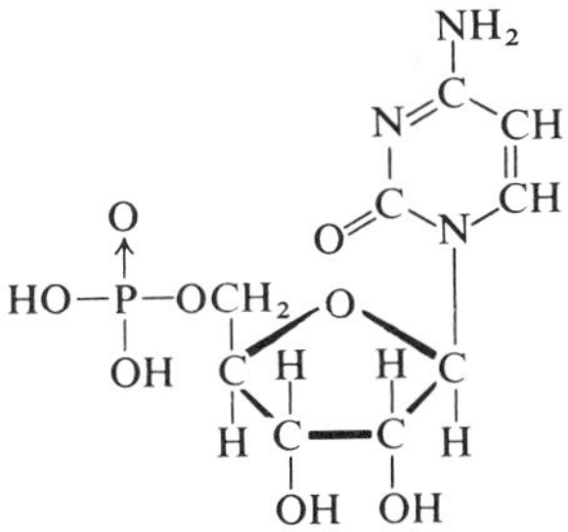

Both RNA and DNA consist of many nucleotides joined together by phosphate bridges between carbon atoms 3 and 5 of adjacent sugar molecules:

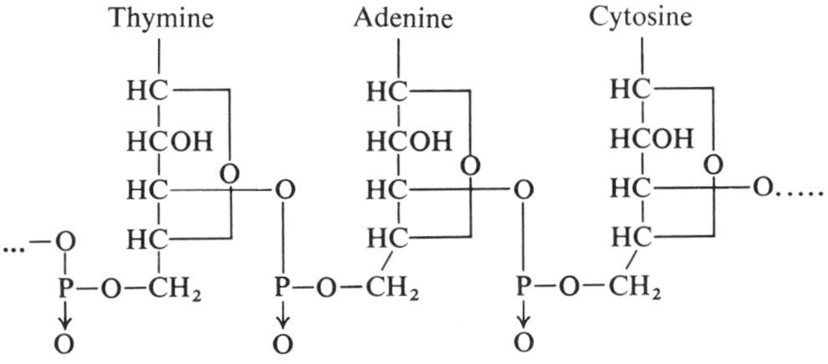

This structure is conveniently represented by a shorthand notation such as

$$\cdots-P\diagup^{T}\diagdown_{P}\diagup^{A}\diagdown_{P}\diagup^{C}\diagdown_{P}-\cdots$$

where P represents the phosphate group, T thymine, A adenine, and C cytosine. Nucleic-acid molecules occurring in nature are composed of many nucleotides in a single extended strand.

Again, the exact three-dimensional shape of the molecules is a matter of great importance. The American molecular biologist James Dewey Watson (b. 1928) and the British molecular biologist Francis Harry Compton Crick (b. 1916)* demonstrated in 1953 that the structure of DNA consists of two strands of nucleotides coiled about one another in helical fashion, as shown in Figure 6-7. The nitrogenous bases are in the center, facing one another, and the phosphate and sugar molecules are outside.

Some Biological Mechanisms

So far we have considered the principal types of chemical compound out of which living structures are built. A second and very important aspect of biochemistry relates to the chemical processes that occur in living systems. These processes may be summarized by the simple statement that living systems take in substances and oxidize them, the energy released in these oxidation processes being utilized in various ways—for the contraction of a muscle, for example. The exact manner in which these oxidation processes occur is exceedingly complicated, and many of the details still remain to be elucidated. In the remainder of this chapter we shall consider some of these biological processes and the enzymes that catalyze them.

Enzymes

The chemical processes that occur in living systems are all catalyzed by enzymes. Without the efficient aid of the enzymes these chemical processes would occur at greatly diminished rates, or not at all.

A considerable number of different enzymes have now been identified, and a number of them have been prepared in pure crystalline form. The first to be purified and crystallized was urease, which catalyzes the hydrolysis of urea into carbon dioxide and water:

$$\overset{\text{O}}{\overset{\|}{\text{H}_2\text{N}-\text{C}-\text{NH}_2}} + \text{H}_2\text{O} \rightarrow \text{CO}_2 + 2\text{NH}_3$$

---

* Watson and Crick shared with the New Zealand–British physicist Maurice Hugh Frederick Wilkins (b. 1916) the 1962 Nobel prize for medicine and physiology, awarded for their work on the DNA structure.

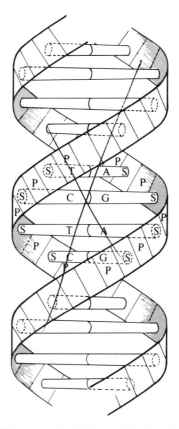

Fig. 6-7 The Watson and Crick model for DNA: S = 2-deoxyribose;
P = phosphate; T = thymine; A = adenine; C = cytosine; and
G = guanine.

It was crystallized in 1926 by the American biochemist James B.
Summer (1887–1955; Nobel prize for chemistry, 1946), who also
showed that the enzyme is a pure protein. Since that time many
other enzymes have been prepared in pure form and have been shown
either to be pure proteins or to be largely protein in nature.

We saw earlier in this chapter that the characteristic feature of a
protein molecule is that it contains amino acid residues, connected
by peptide linkages. The sequence of amino acids has been determined for a few enzymes (trypsin, chymotrypsin, lysozyme, and
ribonuclease, for example), and for some of these (for example,
lysozyme and chymotrypsin) the precise three-dimensional structure
has been established by X-ray analysis (see Figure 6-5, p. 251).
Certain enzymes are pure proteins, whereas others consist of a nonprotein part in addition to the protein. In such cases the protein part

is known as the *apoenzyme*, and the nonprotein part as the *prosthetic group*. Prosthetic groups often undergo oxidation and reduction reactions and in this way facilitate the catalytic action.

In some respects the enzymes are typical catalysts, but they differ from other types of catalysts in two ways. In the first place, they exhibit a high degree of specificity; that is to say, they are not indiscriminate in their action on chemical substances, but act only when various conditions are satisfied. A good example is provided by pepsin, a digestive enzyme occurring in the stomach, whose function is to catalyze the hydrolysis of peptide linkages.

$$
\begin{array}{c}
\overset{O}{\overset{\|}{-C}}\overset{H}{\overset{|}{-N-}} + H_2O \;\rightarrow\; -C\overset{O}{\nwarrow}_{OH} + \overset{H}{\underset{H}{\diagdown N-}}
\end{array}
$$

However, it brings about such a reaction only if certain conditions are satisfied. One of these is that an aromatic group must be present in a certain position relative to the peptide linkage. This is known as *group* specificity. Another requirement, referred to as *stereochemical* specificity, is that the amino acids must be in the L configurations.

Much research work remains to be done before specificity will be understood in detail on a molecular basis. An important factor evidently is that the enzyme and substrate* molecules must be shaped so that they fit together fairly exactly. Many years ago, in 1894, the famous German organic chemist Emil Fischer (1852–1919; Nobel prize for chemistry, 1902) proposed a "lock and key" hypothesis, which has formed the basis of most modern ideas about enzyme specificity. According to this hypothesis, in order for an enzyme to act upon a substrate, it is necessary for the enzyme and substrate molecules to fit together in somewhat the way that a key fits into a lock. Normally a lock can be operated only by a given key; a slight modification to the key, or to the lock, may mean that the key can no longer fit into the lock—or, if it does, it cannot operate it. All types of specificity can be explained by suitable versions of this idea, which is illustrated schematically in Figure 6-8. Group specificity, for example, is explained as the result of interference of projecting parts on the lock or key.

The explanation of stereochemical specificity on this basis is rather interesting. A useful additional analogy here is provided by the fitting of a hand into a glove—a right hand will fit only into a right

* This word is used for the chemical substance on which an enzyme acts.

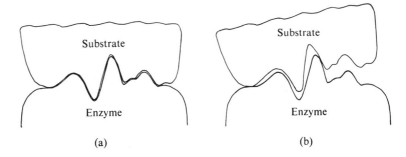

Fig. 6-8 A schematic view of enzyme specificity. In (a) the shapes of the enzyme and substrate molecules are complementary to one another, and the two molecules fit together well. In (b) the substrate molecule is slightly modified, and it cannot come close to the enzyme; reaction, therefore, occurs only to a limited extent, if at all.

glove, a left hand into a left glove. If gloves were designed perfectly symmetrically, a right hand or a left hand would fit equally well into a glove. An ordinary glove has an unsymmetrical character and exists in two forms that are mirror images of one another, like a molecule containing an asymmetric carbon atom. Clearly it is the unsymmetrical character of the glove that allows it to discriminate between right and left hands. It follows that an enzyme that can discriminate between D and L forms of a molecule must have an unsymmetrical character, that is, it must itself exist in D and L forms. This is, of course, no surprising conclusion in view of the fact that the enzyme is a protein composed of amino acids in the L forms.

We noted earlier that the enzymes differ from ordinary catalysts in two ways, one of which is their specificity. The other way is their high efficiency. A number of examples are now known in which the catalytic efficiency of one enzyme molecule has been compared with that of one hydrogen ion, one hydroxide ion, or one molecule of some other catalyst. In all cases, the enzyme is vastly more efficient— in some cases by a factor of 10^{12} or more! Evidently the mechanism by which enzymes exert their action on substrates differs considerably from the mechanisms of reactions catalyzed by ordinary catalysts. At the present time much work is being done on the problem of the exact mechanisms of enzyme action, and much remains to be learned.

During the course of various investigations made on enzyme reactions, it has become apparent that the catalysis is not directly due to the properties of the enzyme as a whole, but depends upon the existence of certain relatively small areas of the enzyme molecules. These small areas, believed to account for the main effects, are referred to as *active centers*, or *active sites*. It is at these active centers that the enzymes combine with the substrates and chemical reaction occurs. These active centers appear to be structures of some complexity, containing a number of different chemical groups arranged in such a manner as to accommodate the substrate molecule. When the enzyme and substrate molecules interact together, chemical bonds are formed, and are subsequently broken, between the groups at the active center and the groups or the enzyme molecule, and it is as a result of these bond formations and breakings that the chemical process occurs.

With some enzymes the evidence indicates that each molecule contains only one active center, of area corresponding to a diameter of only a few Ångströms. This is the case with chymotrypsin, and a variety of structural and kinetic evidence has indicated that the active center lies in the region indicated in Figure 6-5. The rest of the molecule plays a relatively minor role, although the folding of the enzyme undoubtedly has much to do with maintaining the structure of the active center. Enzymes are rather sensitive structures, in that their catalytic abilities may be completely destroyed by relatively minor effects; for example, raising the temperature of an enzyme solution to 40°C very often leads to rapid *deactivation*, or loss of catalytic activity. This is attributed to changes in the three-dimensional structure of the protein molecule, resulting in a change in the relative positions of the groups that are important in the active center.

Digestion

The food we eat consists largely of fats, carbohydrates, and proteins. In most cases, the molecules have to be broken into smaller fragments before they can pass through the walls of the intestine, after which the fragments undergo further chemical change. The process of breaking down the molecules of fats, carbohydrates, and proteins into smaller fragments is known as *digestion;* the subsequent reactions of the fragments are referred to as *metabolism*. We shall now consider some of the basic chemical processes involved in digestion.

The simple fats are esters of glycerol and fatty acids. They are formed from glycerol and acids by the process of esterification, and can be broken down into glycerol and the acids by the reverse process of hydrolysis:

$$CH_2-O{:}H \quad HO{:}C{\overset{O}{\nearrow}}{-}R \qquad\qquad CH_2-OC{\overset{O}{\overset{\|}{}}}R$$

$$\underset{\text{hydrolysis}}{\overset{\text{esterification}}{\rightleftharpoons}}$$

$$CH-O{:}H \quad HO{:}C{\overset{O}{\nearrow}}{-}R' \qquad CHOC{\overset{O}{\overset{\|}{}}}R' \quad + 3H_2O$$

$$CH_2-O{:}H \quad HO{:}C{\overset{O}{\nearrow}}{-}R'' \qquad CH_2OC{\overset{O}{\overset{\|}{}}}R''$$

Hydrolysis can be brought about by boiling the fats with acids or bases, which act as catalysts. It can also be brought about, much more efficiently and at room temperatures, by certain enzymes known as *lipases*. These enzymes are present in the digestive system, particularly in the small intestine. The products of reaction, glycerol and the fatty acids, are able to pass through the walls of the intestine and subsequently undergo metabolism.

The carbohydrates are of various kinds. There are the monosaccharides, such as glucose and fructose, whose structures are shown on p. 240. Then there are disaccharides, like maltose (p. 241), which are formed from two monosaccharide molecules by a condensation reaction which can be represented schematically as

$$R-O\dotplus H \; + \; H-O\dotplus R' \; \underset{\text{hydrolysis}}{\overset{\text{condensation}}{\rightleftharpoons}} \; R-O-R' \; + \; H_2O$$

The reverse of this condensation process, the hydrolysis, is what occurs in digestion, under the action of special enzymes known as carbohydrases.

Starch is a carbohydrate which is made up of a very large number, usually over a thousand, of hexose molecules, which are condensed together in the same manner as in the disaccharides. The hydrolytic breakdown of starch into hexose molecules is brought about by enzymes that can be referred to as carbohydrases, although they belong to the class of *amylases*. Saliva, in fact, contains a certain amount of amylase (known as salivary amylase), so that some starch hydrolysis takes place in the mouth. The process is continued by other forms of amylase occurring in the small intestine.

We have seen that protein molecules are made up of long chains of amino-acid residues, connected by peptide linkages. Although these peptide linkages are hydrolyzed by acids and bases, the process is accomplished very much more efficiently by enzymes:

$$\overset{O}{\overset{\|}{-C}}-\overset{H}{\overset{|}{N}}- \; + H_2O \; \rightarrow \; \overset{O}{\overset{\|}{-C}}-OH + H_2N-$$

If all of the peptide linkages in a protein molecule are broken, the protein is split entirely into its amino acids, and this is what ultimately occurs when a protein is digested. Several enzymes present in the digestive system can hydrolyze proteins, and these are known as *proteolytic enzymes*, or *proteases*. One of the characteristics of these enzymes is that they show a rather high degree of group specificity. They all hydrolyze the peptide linkage, but they have different requirements with regard to groups that must or must not be present in the vicinity of the linkage to be hydrolyzed.

The first enzyme encountered by a protein as it passes through the digestive system is pepsin, which is present in the stomach. More exactly, the stomach stores a precursor, pepsinogen, which undergoes a slight chemical change and is converted into pepsin when food enters the stomach. Pepsin is a rather remarkable enzyme in that it can survive—indeed it is most active—in a solution of very high acidity; the pH of the stomach juices is about 2, which is much too acid for other enzymes to survive intact in it; they would undergo deactivation. Pepsin catalyzes the hydrolytic breakdown of protein molecules in the stomach, but can successfully attack only those linkages for which certain specificity requirements are satisfied (as noted earlier, one of these is that there must be an aromatic group in a suitable position). As a result, only a small fraction of the peptide linkages are broken; the molecule is now in several much smaller fragments, known as *peptides*.

These fragments then pass into the small intestine, where they encounter other proteolytic enzymes, such as trypsin, chymotrypsin, carboxypeptidase, and aminopeptidase. These enzymes have different specificity requirements from pepsin, and between them they are able to break all of the remaining peptide linkages, so that the protein is completely broken down into its constituent amino acids. For example, the enzymes carboxypeptidase and aminopeptidase function by lopping off amino acids that are at the ends of the peptide chain— in the former case at the –COOH end of the chain, in the latter case at the –NH$_2$ end.

Metabolism

The products of digestion, such as glycerol, the monosaccharides, and the amino acids, are able to pass through the walls of the small intestine and into the blood stream. There they are carried to the cells and tissues of the body, where they encounter new enzymes. These enzymes bring about further chemical processes which are of two main classes. First, there are synthetic processes, in which the fragments produced in the digestive processes are built up into larger molecules; the amino acids, for example, may be turned into proteins again. Second, there are oxidative processes, in which the fragments are oxidized ultimately into carbon dioxide, water, and nitrogen, with the release of energy. These oxidations are carried out by the enzymes in a controlled way, so that the energy released is not wasted as heat but is stored chemically and ultimately is utilized for the performance of mechanical work.

The details of the chemical reactions occurring in metabolism are far beyond the scope of this book; here we can only consider in broad outline what occurs. As an example, we shall take the case of a glucose molecule, $C_6H_{12}O_6$. Two types of reactions may take place with this molecule. In the first place, it may combine with a large number of other glucose molecules to form a polymer, glycogen, which somewhat resembles starch in structure and properties; its structure is shown schematically in Figure 6-1. Glycogen is the form in which carbohydrate is stored in the body, and it can be broken down (hydrolyzed) into glucose molecules whenever glucose is needed. The conversion of glucose into glycogen, and the reverse hydrolysis of glycogen into glucose, occur in a very complicated fashion; a number of different elementary processes, and a corresponding number of different enzymes, are involved.

Second, glucose may be oxidized, with the liberation of energy which becomes available for the performance of mechanical work. The complete oxidation of glucose can be written formally as

$$C_6H_{12}O_6 + 6O_2 \quad \rightarrow \quad 6CO_2 + 6H_2O + 690 \text{ kcal/mole}$$

If one mole of glucose is burned in a calorimeter, this is the reaction that occurs, and 690 kcal of energy are liberated as heat. In a calorimeter this heat is simply wasted; it heats up the apparatus, but no mechanical work is done. It would be possible to utilize most of the energy liberated in the glucose oxidation by causing the reaction to occur in a suitable engine, in which case the hot gases produced would perform work by moving a piston. Nothing of this kind, of course, occurs in the living system. In fact, the oxidation of glucose to carbon dioxide and water in the living system occurs by a very large number of steps, and nearly a hundred different enzymes have already been identified as being involved in these processes. It follows from Hess's law that the occurrence of the reaction in steps makes no difference to the over-all energy output.

The energy produced in these processes is not liberated as heat but is stored in the form of a remarkable substance known as adenosine triphosphate, or ATP. Its complete structure is

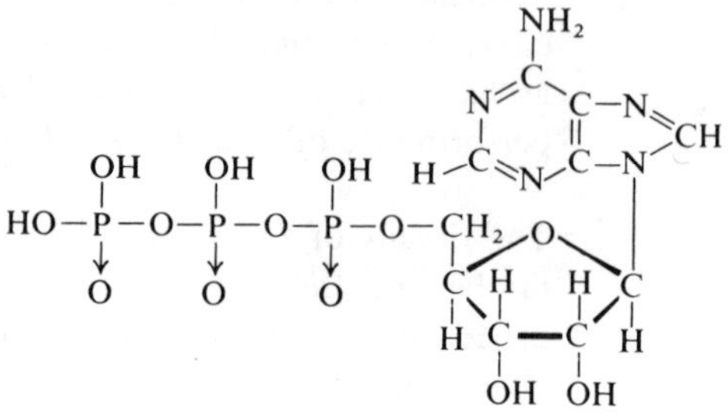

which may be conveniently abbreviated to

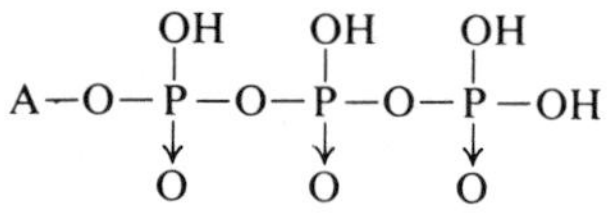

ATP is easily hydrolyzed into adenosine diphosphate (ADP) and phosphoric acid as follows:

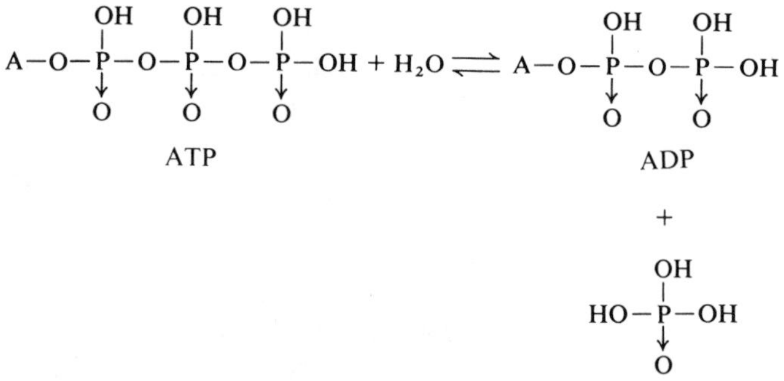

This reaction is somewhat unusual in that when it occurs somewhat more energy is released than when other similar compounds are hydrolyzed. We can therefore say that energy is *stored* in ATP and becomes available for use when the ATP is hydrolyzed. Under suitable conditions these extra calories can be used to synthesize cellular constituents, such as protein molecules, and can be used to effect muscular work, nerve transmission, or other processes in the body that require the expenditure of energy. A useful analogy is to regard the intact ATP molecule as a coiled spring, held in its coiled configuration; when it is hydrolyzed, the spring is released and the stored energy becomes available.

Muscular Contraction   One of the ways that energy is utilized in the living system is in the contraction of a muscle. The contraction of a muscle fiber is actuated by cell structures called myofibrils, which run parallel to the axis of the fiber. The structure of myofibrils was determined in 1953 by the British biophysicist Hugh E. Huxley (b. 1924), and its cross-section presents roughly the appearance shown in Figure 6-9. The myofibril appears to be largely made up of two kinds of thread, fairly closely packed together, the distance between the thicker threads being about 440 Å. These thicker threads represent a protein called myosin,

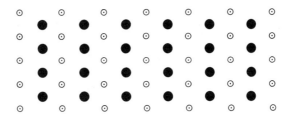

Fig. 6-9   The cross section of a myofibril structure.

the thinner ones a protein called actin. These proteins can be extracted from the muscle fiber and purified, and their characteristics have been studied in considerable detail. Indeed in 1939, long before the fine structure of the myofibril was analyzed, the Russian biochemist Vladimir Aleksandrovich Engelhardt (b. 1894) discovered that mysin is actually an enzyme which catalyzes the hydrolysis of ATP into ADP plus phosphoric acid; myosin is, therefore, often called ATPase. Actin does not possess this property.

Studies on muscle have shown that when the process of contraction occurs, the ATP present is hydrolyzed into ADP and phosphoric acid and that the energy released is in some way used to cause the contraction. The ADP produced in this hydrolysis is at once reconverted into ATP by other energy-rich compounds produced as a result of metabolism; the process of contraction can, therefore, continue.

A considerable amount of evidence, developed mainly by the British physiologist Andrew F. Huxley (b. 1917; Nobel prize for medicine, 1963), has suggested that contraction of the myofibril is due to the actin and myosin threads sliding relatively to one another. It has been found that myosin and actin combine in the form of a complex when Mg^{2+} ions are present and this complex is broken up by ATP, with liberation of actin, and reformed when ATP is hydrolyzed; these processes can be represented schematically as

$$\text{ATP} \rightarrow \left\{ \begin{array}{l} \text{myosin–Mg}^{2+}\text{–actin} \\ \\ \text{myosin–Mg}^{2+}\text{–ATP} + \text{actin} \end{array} \right\} \rightarrow \begin{array}{l} \text{ADP} + \\ \text{phosphoric} \\ \text{acid} \end{array}$$

It appears, therefore, that tension arises through the making and breaking of cross-linkages which connect the myosin and actin threads. The precise nature of these linkages, and how they are affected by ATP, must await the results of further research.

Photosynthesis

Oxygen is constantly being removed from the atmosphere by chemical processes in which it brings about oxidation. In addition, however, oxygen is continuously produced by reactions that occur in the presence of light and in which carbon dioxide and water are converted into organic substances and oxygen. One of the most important of these organic substances is glucose, $C_6H_{12}O_6$, so that we may write the reaction

$$6CO_2 + 6H_2O \underset{\text{oxidation}}{\overset{\text{photosynthesis}}{\rightleftharpoons}} C_6H_{12}O_6 + 6O_2$$

The reaction from right to left represents the ordinary process of glucose oxidation, which in the living system occurs in a considerable number of stages. The photosynthetic reaction from left to right also occurs in a considerable number of stages and involves many different enzymes.

The extent to which photosynthesis occurs on the earth is very considerable. Each year about 4×10^{11} tons of carbon dioxide are converted into about 3×10^{11} tons of organic material The process occurs in the green plants, including the primitive organisms that float in the sea. When light falls on green plants, the greater part of the energy needed for photosynthesis is absorbed by small particles known as chloroplasts. These are ellipsoidal in shape and contain an assortment of pigments, the most important of which is chlorophyll *a*. It turns out that it is light at the red end of the spectrum which, when absorbed by these pigments, is utilized in photosynthesis.

When a mole of glucose is oxidized, about 690 kcal of energy is produced; thus, in the photosynthetic process, $690/6 = 115$ kcal of energy is required per mole of oxygen formed. A quantum of red light contains the equivalent of about 40 kcal/mole, and three photons would, therefore, be sufficient to convert a molecule of CO_2 and a molecule of H_2O into organic material. It appears that in practice the plant needs about eight to ten photons for the process, so that the efficiency is about 30%.

A considerable amount of effort has been devoted to investigating the details of the chemical processes that occur in photosynthesis. The American chemist Melvin Calvin (b. 1911; Nobel prize for chemistry, 1961), for example, caused photosynthesis to occur with carbon dioxide in which the carbon atom had been "labeled"; the carbon isotope of mass number 14 was used instead of ordinary carbon. In this way it was possible to see what compounds containing labeled carbon were produced. The earliest formed stable compound they could isolate was 3-phosphoglyceric acid:

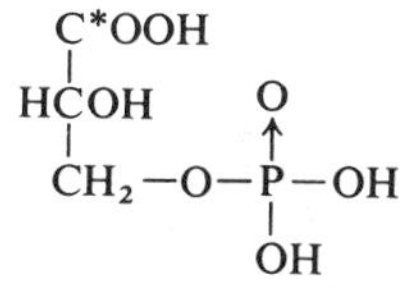

$$\begin{array}{l} \text{C*OOH} \\ | \\ \text{HCOH} \qquad \text{O} \\ | \qquad\qquad \uparrow \\ \text{CH}_2-\text{O}-\text{P}-\text{OH} \\ \qquad\qquad | \\ \qquad\qquad \text{OH} \end{array}$$

The labeled carbon atom is in the position indicated by an asterisk. By investigations of this type it has been possible to identify many of the individual reactions that occur when glucose is produced in photosynthesis. It has also been possible to identify some of the subsequent reactions by which the glucose so formed is converted into other organic compounds.

Problems

6-1. Write down *general* equations representing the following processes:

(a) The hydrolysis of a simple lipid,
(b) The hydrolysis of a peptide linkage,
(c) The hydrolysis of a disaccharide.

6-2. Write down *balanced* equations for the following reactions:

(a) The hydrolysis of α-glycerophosphoric acid,
(b) The condensation of stearic acid with glycerol,
(c) The condensation of two alanine molecules to give the dipeptide,
(d) The complete oxidation of sucrose, $C_{12}H_{22}O_{11}$.

6-3. The *respiratory quotient*, a term used in biochemistry and physiology, is the ratio by volume of exhaled carbon dioxide to oxygen used up during the oxidative metabolism of food. Write balanced equations for the complete oxidation of glucose, ethanol, and glycine, and compare their respiratory quotients.

6-4. Which of the following amino acids are expected to occur in enantiomeric forms?

(a) 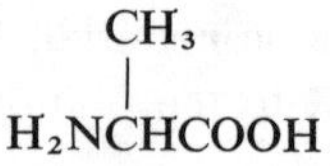 CH₃
     |
     H₂NCHCOOH
     alanine

(b) H₂NCH₂COOH
    glycine

(c)

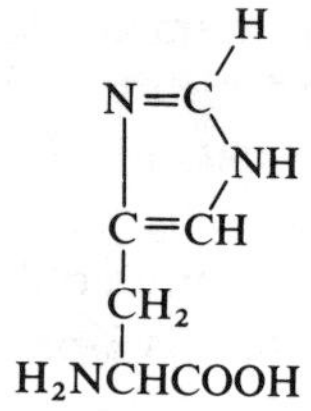

$$\begin{array}{c} \text{H} \\ \diagup \\ \text{N}=\text{C} \\ | \qquad \diagdown \\ | \qquad \text{NH} \\ | \qquad \diagup \\ \text{C}=\text{CH} \\ | \\ \text{CH}_2 \\ | \\ \text{H}_2\text{NCHCOOH} \qquad \text{histidine} \end{array}$$

Suggested Reading

Cheldelin, V. H., and R. W. Newburgh. *The Chemistry of Some Life Processes.* Reinhold, New York, 1964.

Herz, W. *The Shape of Carbon Compounds.* Benjamin, New York, 1963.

Kendrew, J. C. "The Three-Dimensional Structure of a Protein Molecule," *Sci. Am.,* Dec. 1961, p. 96.

Perutz, M. F. "The Hemoglobin Molecule," *Sci. Am.,* Nov. 1964.

Phillips, D. C. "The Three-Dimensional Structure of an Enzyme Molecule," *Sci. Am.,* Nov. 1966, p. 78.

White, E. H. *Chemical Background for the Biological Sciences.* Prentice-Hall, New York, 1964.

Answers to Odd-Numbered Problems

1-1.

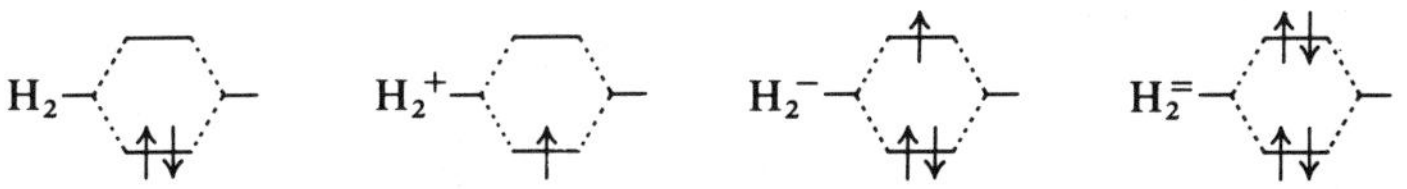

(a) *Bond strengths* will be in the order $H_2 > H_2^+ \sim H_2^- > H_2^{2-}$ because *bond orders* are 1, $\frac{1}{2}$, $\frac{1}{2}$, 0 if one counts up the numbers of bonding electrons and subtracts the number of antibonding electrons and divides the results by 2 to obtain the "bond order." In a more quantitative treatment, it is necessary to take into account the fact that an antibonding electron more than cancels the effect of one bonding electron, and therefore $H_2^+ > H_2^-$.

(b) Bond lengths can be related to bond order, and it is predicted that bond lengths will increase in the order

$$H_2 < H_2^+ < H_2^- < H_2^{2-}.$$

It should be noted that H_2, H_2^+, and H_2^- are all "stable" species, in that there is a net attraction between the two hydrogen atoms, but H_2^{2-} is an unstable species in which the two hydrogen atoms repel each other.

1-3. (a) *Electron donors only:*

$$H_2O, \text{ e.g., } Al^{3+} + 6H_2O \quad \rightarrow \quad Al(H_2O)_6^{3+}.$$
$$F^-, \text{ e.g., } BF_3 + F^- \quad \rightarrow \quad [F_3B \leftarrow F]^-$$

[H_3NBF_3 and BCl_4^- *could*, in principle, be donors, because each chlorine or fluorine atom has nonbonding valence electrons; but, in fact, they are neither donors nor acceptors.]

$$PCl_3, \text{ e.g., } Ni(CO)_4 + 4PCl_3 \quad \rightarrow \quad Ni(PCl_3)_4 + 4CO.$$

(b) *Electron acceptors only:*

$$BCl_3, \text{ e.g., } BCl_3 + Cl^- \quad \rightarrow \quad [Cl_3B \leftarrow Cl]^-$$

$$PCl_5, \text{ e.g., } PCl_5 + Cl^- \quad \rightarrow \quad [Cl_5P \leftarrow Cl]^-$$

[Since BCl_3 and PCl_5 do have nonbonding valence electrons on the chlorine atoms, they could in theory also be donors.]

(c) *Neither electron donors nor acceptors:*
CH_4 : no empty orbitals of low energy, no nonbonding valence electrons. Also H_3NBF_3 and BCl_4^-.

(d) *Both electron donors and acceptors:*
In theory, $BeCl_2$, BCl_3, PCl_3, and PCl_5 are all potential donors and acceptors since each possesses both nonbonding valence electrons (belonging to the chlorine atoms) and low-energy empty orbitals.

$BeCl_2$ usually acts as an acceptor,

$$BeCl_2 + (C_2H_5)_2O \quad \rightarrow \quad Cl_2Be \leftarrow O(C_2H_5)_2$$

but in the polymeric $(BeCl_2)_n$ solid and in dimeric $(BeCl_2)_2$ the molecule is simultaneously acting as a donor and acceptor:

$$Cl-Be \underset{Cl}{\overset{Cl}{\rightleftarrows}} Be-Cl$$

BCl_3 always behaves as an acceptor; however, in the isolated molecule, there is back donation of electrons from chlorine to boron:

$$\overset{Cl}{\underset{Cl}{\diagdown}} B \leftrightharpoons Cl$$

PCl_3, in transition metal complexes such as $Ni(PCl_3)_4$, is also simultaneously a donor and an acceptor,

$$Ni \quad \rightleftharpoons \quad PCl_3$$

but PCl_5 is an acceptor only.

1-5. (i) $\Delta H = +90 - 80 = +10$ kcal/mole.
 (ii) $\Delta H = -174$ kcal/mole (equal to the lattice energy).
 (iii) $\Delta H = +10 - 174 = -164$ kcal/mole.
 (iv) $\Delta H = +19 + 19 - 164 = -126$ kcal/mole.

1-7. Lattice energy $= +160 - 140 - 273 - 290 - 38 - 46$
$\qquad\qquad\quad = -627$ kcal/mole.

Chapter 2

2-1.

$\Delta H_f(H^+(g) \ldots Cl^-(g)) = +52 + 28.5 + 312 - 87 = +305.5$ kcal/mole.
$\Delta H_f(H^+(aq) \ldots Cl^-(aq)) = +305. -5256 - 90 = -40.5$ kcal/mole.

2-3. Apparent oxidation states: $TlCl_3$ $Tl +3$; $TlCl_2$ $Tl +2$; Tl_2Cl_3 $Tl +\frac{3}{2}$; $TlCl$ $Tl +1$; $TlCl_3 \equiv Tl^{3+}3Cl^-$; $TlCl_2 \equiv Tl_2Cl_4 \equiv Tl^{3+}Tl^+4Cl^-$; $Tl_2Cl_3 \equiv Tl_4Cl_6 \equiv 3Tl^+Tl^{3+}6Cl^-$; $TlCl \equiv Tl^+Cl^-$.

2-5. (a) $\qquad Na(s) + H_2O \rightarrow Na^+(aq) + OH^-(aq) + \frac{1}{2}H_2(g)$

or

$$Na(s) + H^+(aq) \rightarrow Na^+(aq) + \frac{1}{2}H_2(g).$$

The *reduction of water* by sodium and the oxidation of sodium by water.

(b) $\qquad B_2H_6(g) + 6H_2O \rightarrow 2B(OH)_3 + 6H_2$

B_2H_6 contains $B -3$ and $B(OH)_3$ contains $B +3$. This reaction could be called the *reduction of water* by diborane and the oxidation of diborane by water or the hydrolysis of diborane by water.

(c) $\qquad F_2(g) + H_2O \rightarrow 2HF(aq) + \frac{1}{2}O_2(g)$

and

$$2F_2(g) + H_2O \rightarrow 2HF(aq) + F_2O(g)$$

Both of these reactions involve the *oxidation of water* by fluorine. (The oxidation state of oxygen changes from -2 in H_2O to 0 in O_2 and to $+2$ in F_2O.)

(d) $\qquad B^{3+} + 3H_2O \rightarrow B(OH)_3(aq) + 3H^+(aq)$

This is *not* an oxidation or reduction reaction (oxidation state of boron stays at $+3$) but is a *hydrolysis* or *acid-base* reaction.

(e) $\quad C^{4+} + 4H_2O \rightarrow [C(OH)_4] + 4H^+ \rightarrow CO_2 + 2H_2O + 4H^+$

The oxidation state of carbon remains constant at $+4$. This is a *hydrolysis* reaction similar to that of B^{3+} above.

(f) $\quad H^- + H_2O \rightarrow H_2(g) + OH^-(aq)$ or $H^- + H^+(aq) \rightarrow H_2(g)$

This is the *reduction* of water by the hydride ion, which is itself oxidized.

(g) $\qquad 2Ag^{2+} + \text{water} \rightarrow 2Ag^{2+}(aq) \rightarrow 2Ag^+(aq) + \frac{1}{2}O_2(g)$

This is the *hydration* of Ag^{2+} followed by the slow oxidation of water by Ag^{2+}.

(h) $\qquad Fe^{3+} + H_2O \rightarrow Fe(H_2O)_6^{3+}$

This is the *hydration* of the ferric ion by water. There is also a small amount of hydrolysis: $Fe(H_2O)_6^{3+} \rightleftharpoons Fe(H_2O)_5OH^{2+} + H^+(aq)$.

2-7. From the given ε^0s, Sn^{2+} is a *powerful reducing agent* and PbO_2 is a *powerful oxidizing agent*. Therefore Sn(IV) is more stable than Sn(II), but Pb(II) is more stable than Pb(IV).

$$Sn^{2+}(g) \rightleftharpoons Sn^{4+}(g) + 2e$$
$$\updownarrow \qquad\qquad \updownarrow$$
$$Sn^{2+}(aq) \rightleftharpoons Sn^{4+}(aq) + 2e$$

The ε^0 is determined by the sizes of

(a) the heats of hydration of Sn^{2+} and Sn^{4+};
(b) the 3rd and 4th ionization potentials of tin.

The Pb(II)/Pb(IV) potential is determined by the same terms as for tin, plus an additional one corresponding to the reaction

$$Pb^{4+}(aq) + 2H_2O \rightarrow PbO_2 + 4H^+(aq)$$

It is, in fact, the difference in ionization potentials of tin and lead that is primarily responsible for the differences in relative stabilities of the $+2$ and $+4$ oxidation states (3rd and 4th ionization potentials: Pb = 1707 kcal/mole; Sn = 1612 kcal/mole).

2-9. Thermodynamically, thallium should react with *both* H_2SO_4 and HCl to give hydrogen and the thallium $+1$ compounds Tl_2SO_4 and TlCl. Tl_2SO_4 is quite soluble in water (49 g per litre) but TlCl is insoluble. TlCl is, therefore, deposited on unreacted Tl metal and protects the metal from further reaction.

2-11. N_2O supports combustion better than air does because:

(1) it is an *endothermic* compound which decomposes on heating

$$N_2O \rightarrow N_2 + \tfrac{1}{2}O_2 \qquad \Delta H = -17 \text{ kcal/mole of } N_2O$$

(2) the products of decomposition are richer in oxygen (30%) than is air (20%).

N_2O does not support combustion as well as does pure oxygen, because the decomposition products of N_2O contains the incombustible diluent nitrogen.

2-13. (a) Evidence supporting statement and against it:

Typical comparisons would be:

(i) Group I

Lithium forms a nitride Li_3H and a carbide Li_2C_2; no other alkali metal does so.

Lithium carbonate and hydroxide decompose fairly readily on heating while the rest of the Group-I metal hydroxides and carbonates do not do so.

The standard oxidation potential of lithium is rather out of line with the values for the rest of the Group-I metals.

Almost all the rest of the chemistry of lithium is in line with that of the other alkali metals.

(ii) Group IV

CX_4 compounds of carbon are very unreactive, while the corresponding compounds of the other Group-IV elements are usually highly reactive. Carbon forms a great many chain compounds, such as the paraffins (CH_3—$(CH_2)_n$—CH_3), and such compounds are generally unreactive. Other Group-IV elements form many fewer chain compounds and the ones that are known are reactive.

Carbon forms the "stable" oxide CO, while Si and Ge do not.

CO_2 is volatile but the other MO_2 oxides are refractory solids.

There are rather few similarities between carbon and the rest of Group IV apart from formal similarities of the formation of compounds of similar formulas and oxidation states—e.g., CH_4 ; SiH_4 ; CO_2 ; SiO_2.

(b) Causes of similarities and differences:

The similarities all arise from the similarities in the valence-shell electronic configurations; for example, all Group-I metals have the configuration [Noble Gas] ns^1. This configuration determines oxidation states in compounds, etc.

The differences between the first member of a group and the rest of the group arise from the following factors:

(i) First-row elements are restricted to maximum coordination number of 4; other members are not.
(ii) First-row elements form much smaller atoms and ions than the rest of the group.
(iii) First-row elements can form $p\pi$-$p\pi$ bonds; heavier elements cannot.
(iv) Second-row and heavier elements can form $d\pi$-$p\pi$ and $d\pi$-$d\pi$ bonds but first-row elements cannot.

[Each example of similarity and difference given under (a) should be explained by a combination of factors listed under (b). It is important to distinguish between thermodynamic and kinetic effects.]

Chapters 3 and 4   4-1. $TiCl_4$: the covalent liquid $TiCl_4$ will first be hydrated,

$$TiCl_4 + water \quad \rightarrow \quad Ti(H_2O)_6^{4+} + 4Cl^-(aq)$$

and, secondly, the $Ti(H_2O)_6^{4+}$ will be hydrolyzed:

$$Ti(H_2O)_6^{4+} \quad \rightarrow \quad TiO(H_2O)_5^{2+} + 2H^+$$

$TiCl_3$: $TiCl_3$ will be hydrated by water:

$$TiCl_3 \rightarrow Ti(H_2O)_6^{3+} + 3Cl^-(aq)$$

The $Ti^{3+}(aq)$ is not a sufficiently powerful reducing agent to reduce water in 1M acid solution, nor is it extensively hydrolyzed. $Ti^{3+}(aq)$ will be slowly oxidized by air to TiO^{2+}.

$TiCl_2$: $TiCl_2$ will first be hydrated,

$$TiCl_2 + water \quad \rightarrow \quad Ti(H_2O)_6^{2+} + 2Cl^-(aq)$$

and then Ti^{2+} will reduce water and will itself be oxidized to $Ti^{3+}(aq)$:

$$Ti^{2+}(aq) + H^+(g) \rightarrow Ti^{3+}(aq) + \tfrac{1}{2}H_2(g)$$

[The ε^0s for the Ti^{2+}/Ti^{3+} and Ti^{3+}/TiO^{2+} couples give one quantitative information on whether species will be oxidized or reduced by water.]
Ti: The value of the standard electrode potential

$$Ti \rightleftharpoons Ti^{2+}(aq) + 2e \qquad \varepsilon^0 = +1.63v$$

would lead one to expect that titanium should dissolve readily in water with the liberation of hydrogen, and with the eventual production of $Ti^{3+}(aq)$

$$Ti + 3H^+(g) \rightarrow Ti^{3+}(aq) + 1\tfrac{1}{2}H_2(g)$$

This is a correct prediction, but in fact the *rate* of this reaction is very low, and titanium metal is resistant to attack by water and most acids.

4-3. V   [Ar] $3d^3 4s^2$
     Nb   [Kr] $4d^4 5s^1$
     Ta   [Xe] $4f^{14} 5d^3 6s^2$

[Note that there is an irregularity in the electronic configurations in this series, indicating the near equality in energy of the configurations nd^3 $(n+1)s^2$ and $nd^4 (n+1)s^1$.] The negligible increase in radius on going from Nb to Ta, even though Ta has 32 extra electrons and its valence electrons are of a higher principal quantum number than those of Nb, is due to the fact that 4f electrons screen 5d and 6s electrons very poorly from the nuclear charge. The effective nuclear charge experienced by the 5d and 6s electrons is much larger than that experienced by the 4d and 5s electrons of Nb. This is just one example of the effect of the "lanthanide contraction."

4-5.

Transition Metal Ions	Electronic Configuration	In Gas Phase: Unpaired Electrons	Octahedral Complexes: Unpaired Electrons
Ti^{2+}	[Ar] $3d^2$	2	2
Ti^{3+}	[Ar] $3d^1$	1	1
Ti^{4+}	[Ar] $3d^0$	0	0
Mn^{2+}	[Ar] $3d^5$	5	1
Mn^{3+}	[Ar] $3d^4$	4	2
Mn^{4+}	[Ar] $3d^3$	3	3
Mn^{5+}	[Ar] $3d^2$	2	2
Mn^{6+}	[Ar] $3d^1$	1	1
Mn^{7+}	[Ar] $3d^0$	0	0
Zn^+	[Ar] $3d^{10} 4s^1$	1	1
Zn^{2+}	[Ar] $3d^{10}$	0	0

4-7.

$[Cr(H_2O)_6]^{3+}3Cl^-$:

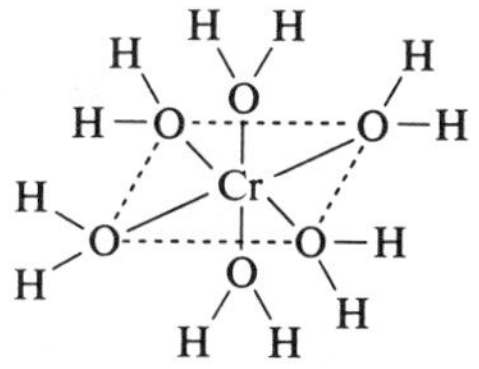

$[Cr(H_2O)_5Cl]^{2+}2Cl^-, H_2O$:

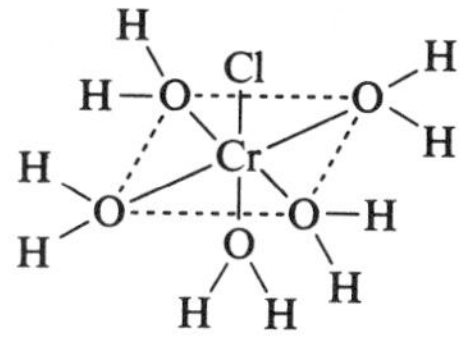

2 isomers of $[Cr(H_2O)_4Cl_2]^+Cl^-, 2H_2O$:

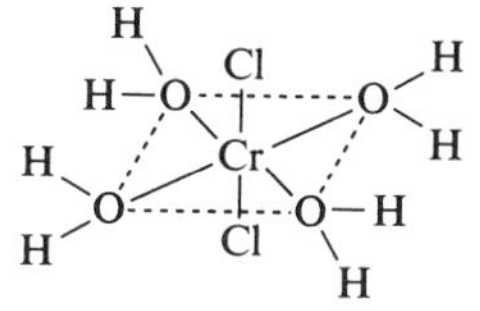

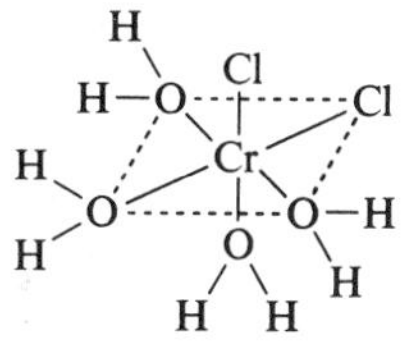

2 isomers of $[Cr(H_2O)_3Cl_3]3H_2O$:

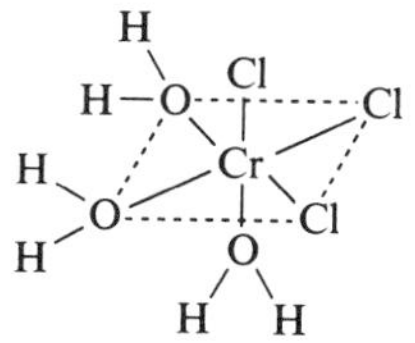

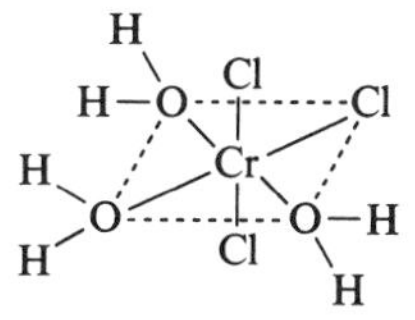

Chapter 5   **5-1.** CH_4 and CCl_4; CH_3Cl and $CHCl_3$; CH_2Cl_2.

5-3.

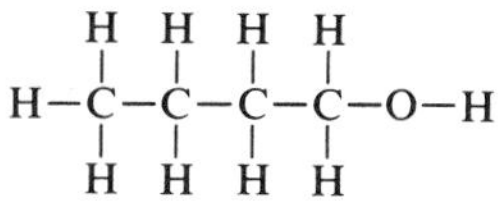

1-butanol

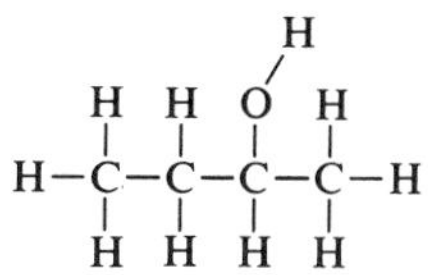

2-butanol

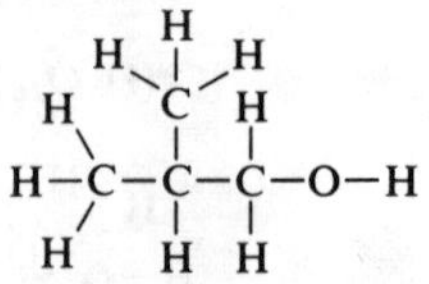

$$\begin{array}{c} H \\ | \\ H-\overset{\displaystyle H}{\underset{\displaystyle H}{C}}-H \\ H-\overset{|}{\underset{|}{C}}-\overset{|}{\underset{|}{C}}-\overset{|}{\underset{|}{C}}-O-H \\ H \quad H \quad H \end{array}$$

2-methyl-1-propanol
(isobutyl alcohol)

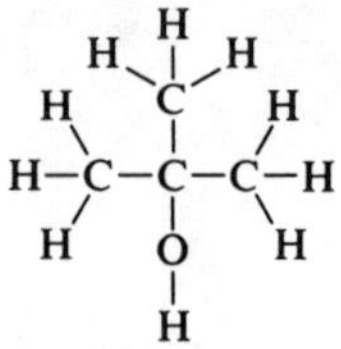

2-methyl-2-propanol
(tertiary-butyl alcohol)

5-5. (a) $RCOOH + NH_3 \rightarrow RCONH_2 + H_2O$

(b) $RCOOH + R'OH \rightarrow RCOOR' + H_2O$

(c)

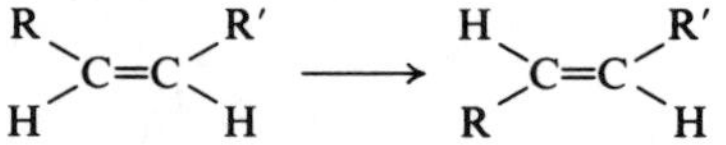

(d) $RCH_2OH \xrightarrow{-2H} RCHO$

(e) 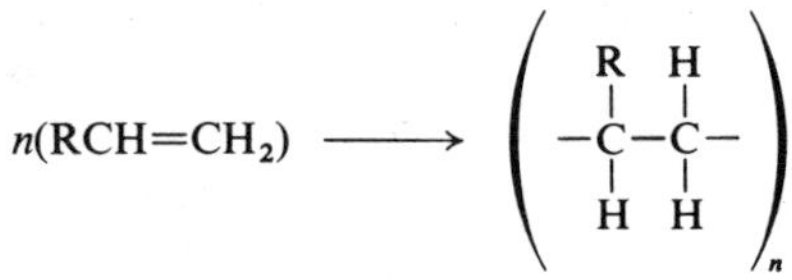 $n(RCH=CH_2) \longrightarrow \left(\begin{array}{c} R \quad H \\ | \quad | \\ -C-C- \\ | \quad | \\ H \quad H \end{array} \right)_n$

5-7. (a) acetic acid

(b) acetic acid and acetone

(c) methyl ethyl ketone

5-9. a, b, c, e.

5-13. 2-chlorobutane, 1,2-dichlorobutane, 1,3-dichlorobutane.

Chapter 6

6-1.

(a) 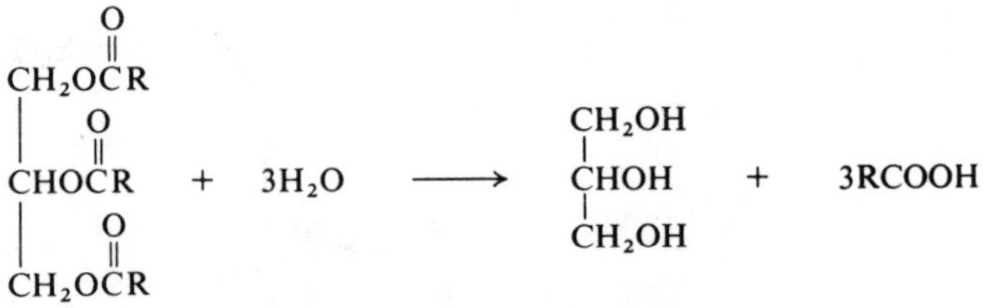 $\begin{array}{l} CH_2O\overset{\displaystyle O}{\overset{\displaystyle \|}{C}}R \\ | \quad O \\ CHO\overset{\displaystyle \|}{C}R \quad + \quad 3H_2O \quad \longrightarrow \\ | \quad O \\ CH_2O\overset{\displaystyle \|}{C}R \end{array} \qquad \begin{array}{l} CH_2OH \\ | \\ CHOH \\ | \\ CH_2OH \end{array} \quad + \quad 3RCOOH$

(b)  $-\overset{\displaystyle O}{\overset{\displaystyle \|}{C}}-N\overset{\displaystyle \diagup}{\underset{\displaystyle H}{}} + H_2O \longrightarrow -COOH + H_2N-$

(c) $R-O-R' + H_2O \longrightarrow ROH + R'OH$

6-3. $C_6H_{12}O_6 + 6O_2 \rightarrow 6CO_2 + 6H_2O$

$C_2H_5OH + 3O_2 \rightarrow 2CO_2 + 3H_2O$

$4H_2NCH_2COOH + 9O_2 \rightarrow 8CO_2 + 10H_2O + 2N_2$

Respiratory quotients are 1, $\frac{2}{3}$, $\frac{8}{9}$, respectively.

Glossary

Acceptor: An electron-acceptor molecule or ion is a species that can form an addition compound (adduct, q.v.) with an electron donor by the formation of a dative (or coordinate) bond (q.v.) For example

$$\underset{\text{acceptor}}{F_3B} + \underset{\text{donor}}{\overset{..}{.}NH_3} \quad \rightarrow \quad \underset{\text{adduct}}{F_3B\overset{..}{.}NH_3}$$

Acceptor molecules possess empty orbitals of low energy. They are also known as *Lewis acids.*

Activation energy: The energy barrier that must be surmounted for a reaction to occur. The rate constant (q.v.) for a reaction, k, is related to the activation energy E by the Arrhenius law, according to which

$$k = Ae^{-E/RT}$$

where A is a constant (the frequency factor), e the base of the natural logarithms, R is the gas constant, and T the temperature in degrees Kelvin. This equation can be written as

$$\ln k = \ln A - \frac{E}{RT}$$

and, therefore, a plot of $\ln k$ against $1/T$ gives a straight line of slope $-E/R$. If the common logarithm, $\log_{10} k$, is plotted, the slope is $-E/2.303R = -E/4.57$, where E is in calories/mole. Activation energies are determined experimentally by use of such plots.

Adduct: The molecule or ion obtained when an electron acceptor combines with an electron donor. Adducts contain dative bonds (q.v.) and are sometimes also known as coordination compounds, or complexes.

Allotropy: The phenomenon of an element occurring in more than one form; each form is termed an *allotrope* of the element. For example, carbon exhibits allotropy by occurring in the two forms diamond and graphite. The two allotropes of oxygen are O_2 (oxygen) and O_3 (ozone).

277

Amphoteric compound: A compound (usually an oxide or hydroxide) that will react with both acidic and basic solutions. Such oxides have both acidic and basic character. Aluminum oxide, Al_2O_3, is an example of an amphoteric oxide:

$$Al_2O_3 + 6H^+ + 9H_2O \;\rightarrow\; 2[Al(H_2O)_6]^{3+}$$

$$Al_2O_3 + 6OH^- + 3H_2O \;\rightarrow\; 2[Al(OH)_6]^{3-}$$

Anion: A negatively charged ion—for example, Cl^-, ClO_4^-, SO_4^{2-}, PO_4^{3-}. During electrolysis, anions travel through a solution to the anode.

Anisotropy: The phenomenon of a material (usually a solid) having differing physical properties in different directions. Graphite is a good example of an anisotropic substance, many of the properties (e.g., ease of cleavage) being different according to whether they are measured in a direction perpendicular to the sheets, or parallel to them.

Anode: The positively-charged electrode in electrolysis.

Antibonding orbital: Electrons in antibonding molecular orbitals cause repulsion to arise between the two atoms forming the orbital. An electron in an antibonding orbital has a *higher* energy than it has when associated with only one atom in an atomic orbital. (See p. 5.)

Bond dissociation energy: The energy required to break a particular bond in a molecule. There are four different bond dissociation energies for methane:

$$D_{CH_3-H}, \quad \text{for the process } CH_4 \;\rightarrow\; CH_3 + H$$

$$D_{CH_2-H}, \quad \text{for the process } CH_3 \;\rightarrow\; CH_2 + H$$

$$D_{CH-H}, \quad \text{for the process } CH_2 \;\rightarrow\; CH + H$$

and

$$D_{C-H}, \quad \text{for the process } CH \;\rightarrow\; C + H$$

The average of these four bond dissociation energies is sometimes referred to as the *bond energy* or *bond strength* of the C–H bonds in methane. Bond dissociation energies are difficult quantities to measure experimentally, but bond energies can be more readily obtained—for example, from heat of combustion determinations.

Bond energy or strength: See above. The bond strength is an additive quantity that is assigned to bonds in such a way as to lead to correct thermochemical relationships. It gives an indication of the strength of the bond as it exists in the molecule.

Bond order: A measure of the multiplicity of a chemical bond. A pure covalent single bond has an order of *unity*, a pure covalent double bond, an order of *two*, and so on. Bonds of intermediate order are also found; thus in benzene, because of resonance (q.v.), the order of each carbon–carbon bond is 3/2, each bond being a hybrid of a single and a double bond.

Bonding orbital: An electron in a bonding molecular orbital causes attractive forces to operate between the two atoms forming the orbital. An electron in a bonding orbital has a *lower* energy than it had when it was associated with only one atom in an atomic orbital.

Born–Haber cycle: A particular thermochemical cycle (q.v.) which is concerned with analyzing the heats of formation of ionic solids from the elements in their standard states. (See p. 21.)

Catalysis: The phenomenon in which a substance, known as a catalyst, brings about a change in the rate of a chemical reaction without itself being used up during the course of the reaction. Another definition of a *catalyst* is that it is both a reactant and a product of a reaction; this definition makes it clear that the catalyst actually enters into reaction even though it is not used up.

Catalysts change the rate but not the equilibrium constant of a reaction. Since they are not used up in the reaction, they cannot supply energy to it and, therefore, cannot displace the equilibrium. When the catalyst and reaction system are present in the same phase (q.v.), the phenomenon is termed *homogeneous catalysis*. When the catalyst is not in the same phase as the reaction mixture, the term *heterogeneous catalysis* is used; in this case, the catalyst is frequently a solid and the reaction system is liquid or gaseous. Examples are:

Homogeneous catalysis: The rate of decomposition of hydrogen peroxide

$$2H_2O_2 \rightarrow 2H_2O + O_2$$

is greatly increased by the addition of an Fe^{2+} or Fe^{3+} solution to the reaction.

Addition of a solution of the enzyme *catalase* also brings about catalysis.

Heterogeneous catalysis: Addition to a hydrogen peroxide solution of various solids, such as manganese dioxide, MnO_2, and platinum metal also catalyzes the decomposition. Metals such as platinum, especially when finely divided so that the surface area is large, also have a strong catalytic effect on the reaction between hydrogen and oxygen:

$$2H_2 + O_2 \rightarrow 2H_2O$$

This reaction is exceedingly slow at room temperature but may be caused to occur explosively by the addition of finely-divided metals.

The terms catalysis and catalyst usually refer to situations in which the rate is *increased* by addition of the substance. However, the term *negative catalysis* is sometimes applied when a substance *decreases* the rate. It is preferable to speak in these cases of *inhibition*, and of the added substance as an *inhibitor*. The mechanisms of inhibition and of ordinary catalysis are quite different. A catalyst speeds up a reaction by introducing an entirely new reaction path, which usually involves a lower activation energy (q.v.). However, a substance cannot decrease the rate by introducing a less favorable reaction path, since the reaction will continue to occur by the old route. Instead, inhibitors act either by interfering with the action of catalysts or by removing intermediates, such as free radicals, which are involved in the reaction mechanism.

Cathode: The negatively charged electrode in electrolysis.

Cation: A positively charged ion, so called because it moves to the cathode during electrolysis.

Cation-exchange resin: An insoluble polymeric material that usually carries carboxylic or sulfonic acid groups and is able to absorb cations from solutions:

The proton of the $-SO_3^- H^+$ (sulfonic acid) group can be displaced by any other cation. For instance, if a solution of sodium chloride is poured through a cation-exchange resin in the protonated form, the sodium ions will be absorbed on to the resin and hydrogen ions will be displaced into solution. If a solution containing Zn^{2+} cations is then passed through the resin, the Zn^{2+} cations will each displace two protons or two sodium ions:

(Which ions will be displaced depends on their relative abundance and how tightly they are absorbed on to the resin.)

Configuration: This term is used in chemistry in two different senses:

1. *Electronic configuration* refers to the distribution of the electrons in an atom or ion between the various atomic orbitals. For example, the electronic configuration of the oxygen atom in its ground state is $1s^2 2s^2 2p^4$.

2. The term *configuration* is also used to refer to different spatial arrangements of atoms in a given molecular structure. Thus *cis* and *trans* forms (see p. 195) are said to be different configurations, and the same is true of D and L forms (see Fig. 5–9, p. 223). Interconversion between configurations involves the breaking of primary bonds; e.g., in the conversion of a *trans* form to a *cis* form, the π bond (q.v.) has to be broken. See also *Conformation* below.

Conformation: This term denotes different spatial arrangements of the atoms in a given molecular structure, the arrangements being interconvertible without any breaking of primary chemical bonds. This definition distinguishes conformations from configurations, since in the latter case interconversion requires the breaking of bonds. Examples of conformations are the "boat" and "chair" forms of cyclohexane (see p. 192).

Coordinate bond: *See* Dative bond.

Coordination complex: This term is synonymous with *adduct*, that is, the addition product formed from an electron donor and an electron acceptor molecule. It is more often used than adduct to describe addition compounds of metal ions (electron acceptors) with electron donors—for example, BF_4^-, $Cu(NH_3)_4^{2+}$.

Coordination number: The number of neighboring atoms or molecules surrounding a particular atom or ion. For example, in $PtCl_4^{2-}$, platinum has a coordination number of 4, while each chlorine atom has a coordination number of 1.

Covalent bond: A bond between two atoms in which each atom contributes one electron to the bond. (In contrast to a dative bond, where one of the two atoms contributes both electrons to the bond.) Covalent bonds can either be nonpolar (e.g., H_2 and Cl_2) or polar (e.g., HCl).

Dative bond: A bond between two atoms in which one atom contributes *two* electrons to the bond. Dative (or coordinate) bonds are necessarily highly polar; for example

$$F_3B \longleftarrow NH_3$$

Diagonal relationship: This expression refers to the chemical similarities sometimes found between one element and another element in the next lower period and one group to the right in the periodic table, for example, between Li and Mg and between B and Si.

Diamagnetism: Certain materials are repelled by more intense magnetic fields and are said to be diamagnetic. Diamagnetic materials contain all their electrons in pairs with their spins opposed.

Dimerization: A process in which two molecules of a compound react together to form one molecule; for example

$$2AlBr_3 \; \rightarrow \; Al_2Br_6, \quad 2NO_2 \; \rightleftharpoons \; N_2O_4$$

Dipole moment: The electric dipole moment of two equal and opposite charges is defined as the product of the charge and the distance separating them:

Dipole moment = qr

The dipole moment is a vector quantity, having direction as well as magnitude. The dipole moment of a molecule represents the over-all asymmetry of the charge distribution.

Dispersion forces: Very weak attractive forces between molecules that arise from interactions between mutually induced dipoles. These dipoles are caused by fluctuations in the electronic distributions of electrons in the molecules. Dispersion forces are sometimes called *van der Waals* forces.

Disproportionation: The reaction of two or more ions or molecules of an element in a given oxidation state with each other to give species in both higher and lower oxidation states; for example

$$2Cu^+ \; \rightarrow \; Cu + Cu^{2+}$$

Donor: An electron donor or Lewis base is a species that can form an adduct with an electron acceptor (q.v.).

Eigenfunction: This term is used synonymously with wave function (q.v.). The energies for the system that result from the solutions of the wave function are called *eigenvalues.*

Electron acceptor: *See* Acceptor.

Electron affinity: The heat evolved when electrons are added to one molecule or mole of the atoms or ions of a particular element in the gas phase; for example

$$F(g) + e \; \rightarrow \; F^-(g) \quad \Delta H = -82 \; kcal/mole$$
$$\text{Electron affinity of fluorine} = +82 \; kcal/mole$$

Electron-deficient molecules: Molecules which do not possess sufficient valence electrons to form ordinary two-electron covalent bonds between neighboring atoms. Such molecules contain some multicenter bonds (q.v.)—for example, B_2H_6.

Electron donor: *See* Donor.

Electronegativity: A quantitative measure of the ability of an atom *in a molecule* to attract electrons to itself. It is connected with the stability of the particular atomic orbitals involved in forming molecular orbitals and is used when one is discussing such properties as the polarity and strength of bonds.

Electrophilic substances: Electron-acceptor molecules or ions which readily attack atoms having pairs of nonbonding valence electrons.

Endothermic compounds: Compounds with *positive* heats of formation (when formed from the elements in their standard states); when these compounds are formed from the elements in their standard states, there is *absorption* of heat from the surroundings. For example, nitric oxide (NO) is an endothermic compound

$$\tfrac{1}{2}N_2(g) + \tfrac{1}{2}O_2(g) \quad \rightarrow \quad NO(g) \quad \Delta H_f = 22 \text{ kcal/mole}$$

Endothermic compounds are thermodynamically unstable with respect to decomposition into the elements.

Endothermic reactions: Reactions that are accompanied by the *absorption* of heat from the surroundings, that is, reactions that have a positive ΔH value.

Energy of activation: *See* Activation energy.

Enthalpy: The heat content of a system. Changes in enthalpy are often measured by determining the heat given out or absorbed during a reaction carried out at constant (atmospheric) pressure.

Entropy: A measure of the degree of randomness of a system. The entropy is a measure of the degree to which the energy of a system is unavailable for the performance of external work.

Exothermic compounds: Compounds that have *negative* heats of formation from the elements in their standard states. Such compounds are thermodynamically stable with respect to decomposition into the elements. For example, ammonia is an exothermic compound

$$\tfrac{1}{2}N_2(g) + \tfrac{3}{2}H_2(g) \quad \rightarrow \quad NH_3(g) + 11 \text{ kcal/mole}$$

$$\Delta H_f = -11 \text{ kcal/mole of } NH_3$$

Exothermic reactions: Reactions that are accompanied by the *evolution* of heat, that is, which have a negative ΔH.

Free energy: Energy available for the performance of external work. One free energy, the Gibbs free energy G, which is relevant to reactions occurring at constant pressure, is related to the enthalpy, H (q.v.), entropy S (q.v.), and the absolute temperature T, as follows:

$$G = H - TS$$

Giant molecules: Solids that consist of single very large molecules, for example, graphite, diamond, and silica. They can be thought of as polymers of much smaller atoms or molecules, such as C or SiO_2.

Ground state: The lowest possible energy state of an atom or molecule.

Half-life: The time taken for the disappearance (in a chemical or physical process) of half the total amount of the substance being considered. The quantity is most commonly used for first-order reactions and radioactive decay processes.

Heat of reaction: The amount of heat ΔH absorbed during a chemical reaction. It is usually measured in a calorimeter and is quoted either in joules or calories and measured at constant pressure or constant volume.

Heat of sublimation: The heat required to convert a mole of solid into gas; for example

$$Na(s) \;\rightarrow\; Na(g) \qquad \Delta H_{sub} = +26 \text{ kcal/mole}$$

$$I_2(s) \;\rightarrow\; I_2(g) \qquad \Delta H_{sub} = +15 \text{ kcal/mole}$$

Hess's law: This law states that the amount of heat absorbed or evolved in a reaction or series of reactions depends only on the initial and final states and not on the intermediate stages. This law is a particular instance of the first law of thermodynamics and is useful in obtaining heats of reaction which cannot be directly determined.

Hybridization and Hybrid orbitals: The procedure of combining atomic orbitals to form new ones for use in forming molecular orbitals is termed hybridization. Hybrid orbitals are linear combinations of atomic orbitals. For example, the combination of one 2s and three 2p atomic orbitals of carbon yields the four equivalent sp^3 hybrid orbitals used to describe the bonding in methane, CH_4.

Hydrogen bond: The rather weak (usually 5–10 kcal/mole) bond sometimes formed between a covalently bonded hydrogen atom and another atom. For example

$$H{-}F \cdots\cdots H{-}F \cdots\cdots H{-}F$$

These bonds are largely due to attraction between dipoles. Because of the small size of the hydrogen atoms, the molecules can come close together, so that hydrogen bonding is stronger than any other kind of dipole-dipole attraction.

Hydrogen bonds are referred to as secondary bonds, in contrast to the primary covalent bonds.

Hygroscopic compounds: Compounds that absorb water vapor from the atmosphere. Examples are phosphorus pentoxide, P_4O_{10}, and calcium chloride, $CaCl_2$.

Inert pair of electrons: A pair of valence electrons that are not used in bonding; examples are found in $\overset{x}{x}SnCl_2$ and $\overset{x}{x}Tl^+$.

Interstitial compounds: Compounds which are often nonstoichiometric (q.v.) and consist of small atoms inserted into (somewhat expanded) holes or interstices in the solid structure of another element or compound. Examples are the hydrides of transition metals, many metallic nitrides, borides and carbides, and "graphitic compounds."

Intramolecular dative π bonding: Dative π-bonding between two or more atoms in the *same* molecule, as in BF_3 (p. 51) and SiF_4 (p. 65).

Ion-exchange resin: An insoluble polymeric material which carries either negatively charged substituent groups (cation-exchange resin) or positively charged substituent groups (anion-exchange resin). An ion-exchange resin can be used to separate ions in aqueous solution. See also *Cation-exchange resin.*

Ionic bond: A bond resulting from the attractive force between oppositely charged ions—for example, Na^+Cl^-; it is electrostatic in character. Ionic bonds are *nondirectional* and impose no restriction on the number of atoms that can be so bonded to the atom under consideration. For example, in crystalline NaCl six Cl^- ions are "bonded" to each Na^+, and vice versa, while crystalline CsCl contains 8 Cl^- ions "bonded" to each Cs^+, and vice versa.

Ionization energy or potential: The energy required to remove an electron completely from an atom, ion, or molecule in the gas phase; for example

$$Na(g) \;\rightarrow\; Na^+(g) + e(g) \quad \Delta H = +118 \text{ kcal/mole}$$

$$\text{Ionization energy} = 118 \text{ kcal/mole}$$

Isoelectronic: Two species are isoelectronic when they contain the same number of electrons. The expression is most often used to describe species which have the same number of electrons and atoms. For example,

$$BH_4^-, \; CH_4, \text{ and } NH_4^+ \text{ are all isoelectronic.}$$

In their ground states these species have the same electronic configurations.

Isotopes: Atoms of the same element (that is, with the same nuclear charge) but of differing nuclear mass. For example, ^1_1H (protium), ^2_1H (deuterium) and ^3_1H (tritium) are all isotopes of hydrogen, and $^{235}_{92}U$ and $^{238}_{92}U$ are two common isotopes of uranium. (The symbol $^{235}_{92}U$, for example, implies that the species has a mass number of 235 and an atomic number of 92.)

Kinetic stability: When a compound has available an exothermic decomposition path but the rate of decomposition is negligibly small, the compound is described as having kinetic stability. An example is nitric oxide (NO):

$$NO(g) \;\rightarrow\; \tfrac{1}{2}N_2(g) + \tfrac{1}{2}O_2(g) \quad \Delta H = -22 \text{ kcal/mole}$$

Nitric oxide has kinetic stability, since the rate of its decomposition into nitrogen and oxygen is immeasurably small under normal conditions. This phenomenon is sometimes called "meta-stability."

Lattice energy or enthalpy: The lattice energy or enthalpy of an ionic solid is the amount of heat evolved when one mole of the solid is produced from the ions in the gas phase; for example,

$$Na^+(g) + Cl^-(g) \;\rightarrow\; NaCl(s) \quad \Delta H = -183 \text{ kcal/mole}$$

The lattice energy or enthalpy of NaCl is $+183$ kcal/mole.

Lewis acids: Electron acceptors (q.v.), e.g. BF_3.

Lewis bases: Electron donors (q.v.), e.g. NH_3.

Ligand: A donor molecule or ion, capable of forming complexes or coordination compounds with metal ions—for example, Cl^-, CO.

Lone pair of electrons: A pair of valence electrons that are not involved in bonding to other atoms—for example, the pair of nonbonding valence electrons of ammonia, NH_3.

Maximum coordination number: The highest number of atoms that can be "bonded" to (or coordinate) another atom. For elements in the first row of the periodic table, this number is 4; for elements in the second row, it is 6. For elements in the rest of the periodic table, there is no restriction, the maximum coordination number being, in practice, between 6 and 12. Examples are

BF_3 Coordination number of boron = 3
BF_4^- Coordination number of boron = 4 (the maximum)
SiF_4 Coordination number of silicon = 4
SiF_5^- Coordination number of silicon = 5
SiF_6^{2-} Coordination number of silicon = 6 (the maximum observed for Si)

The term is also applied to the number of solvent molecules that surround an ion in solution.

Maximum overlapping, principle of: The strength of a covalent bond is related to the amount of overlap of the two atomic orbitals (A.O.) which make up the molecular orbital (M.O.). It was suggested by L. Pauling that the maximum bond strength is achieved when there is a maximum overlap of atomic orbitals. This principle is particularly useful in determining the shapes of molecules.

As two atoms are brought closer together, overlap of their atomic orbitals will increase. However, at some interatomic distance, any increase in overlap caused by a decrease in the interatomic distance will not further strengthen the bond, because internuclear and nonbonding electron repulsive forces will become dominant.

Molecular orbital: An orbital associated with more than one atomic nucleus, unlike an atomic orbital associated with only one atomic nucleus. Molecular orbitals can be bonding, antibonding, or nonbonding in character.

Multicenter bond: A bond formed by electrons in molecular orbitals which are associated with 3 or more atomic nuclei, such as are found in the hydrogen bridges of B_2H_6. Multicenter bonds are to be contrasted with the "normal" two-center bond formed by electrons in molecular orbitals associated with only two atomic nuclei.

Nonlocalized orbital: A molecular orbital associated with three or more atomic nuclei. Electrons in bonding nonlocalized orbitals give rise to multicenter bonds.

Nonstoichiometric compounds: Compounds which, on chemical analysis, do not yield formulas in which the numbers of atoms are in the ratios of small whole numbers. Many nonstoichiometric compounds also have variable compositions which depend on the precise conditions of their preparation. Examples are the hydrides of the transition elements.

Nucleophilic compound: A compound with a pair of nonbonding valence electrons which is able to bond to a molecule or ion which has an empty orbital of low energy. Nucleophilic compounds are electron-donor molecules (Lewis bases).

Octahedral compound: A compound in which six atoms or groups are arranged around a central atom in the form of a regular octahedron:

The term is also used to describe compounds which depart slightly from this exact shape.

Odd molecules: Molecules which contain an odd number of electrons—for example, NO, NO_2, ClO_2.

Orbital: A one-electron wave function (q.v.).

Order of reaction: *See* Rate constant.

Oxidation: A process which can be represented as the removal of an electron from a species; for example

$$Fe^{2+} \rightarrow Fe^{3+} + e$$

$$C_2H_5OH \rightarrow CH_3CHO + 2H^+ + 2e$$

An atom whose oxidation number (q.v.) is increased in a chemical reaction is also said to be oxidized; thus in the process

$$CH_4 + 2O_2 \quad \rightarrow \quad CO_2 + 2H_2O$$

the carbon atom can be said to be oxidized, since its oxidation number changes from -4 to $+4$.

Oxidation number or state: A number, either positive or negative, which is assigned to an atom according to an arbitrary set of rules (see p. 17) and which gives an indication of the degree of oxidation of the atom in the molecule. It is not necessarily a whole number.

Oxidation potential: The voltage assigned to the half-cell reaction

$$M^{n+}(aq) \quad \rightleftharpoons \quad M^{(n+m)+}(aq) + me$$

Oxidation potentials are based on the arbitrary standard of

$$\tfrac{1}{2}H_2(g) \quad \rightleftharpoons \quad H^+(aq) + e \quad \varepsilon^0 = 0.00 \text{ volt.}$$

Paramagnetism: Materials that are attracted toward more intense magnetic fields are said to be paramagnetic. Paramagnetic compounds contain one or more unpaired electrons, and the magnitude of the paramagnetism can be used to determine the number of unpaired electrons.

Phase: The homogeneous parts of a system, having identical properties and separated from dissimilar parts by boundaries, collectively constitute a phase. For example, in an oil-water emulsion, the water constitutes one phase, while the oil particles collectively constitute another.

π-bond: This type of bond is formed when electrons occupy a π-type molecular orbital, which is one whose nodal plane includes the line joining the two atoms. Such orbitals are not cylindrically symmetric about this line, in contrast to σ-type orbitals; for example

p$_\pi$ p$_\pi$ π-type bonding
A.O.   A.O.   M.O.

Polarizability: Electric polarizability is a quantitative measure of how easily the electronic distribution of an atom or molecule is deformed by an external electric field; for example

no applied   applied
electric field   electric field

Polymerization: A chemical process in which small molecules react together to give molecules of large size; for example

$$nCH_2{=}CH_2 \quad \rightarrow \quad -CH_2{-}CH_2{-}CH_2{-}CH_2{-}CH_2{-}CH_2{---}$$
     ethylene   polyethylene

Primary bond: A covalent or ionic bond; to be contrasted with much weaker secondary bonds, such as hydrogen bonds (q.v.).

Promotion: The process in which electrons in low energy states are raised to higher energy states. The higher energy state of an atom usually contains more unpaired electrons than the lower energy state. For example,

$$\text{carbon [He]}2s^2 2p^2 \xrightarrow{\text{promotion}} \text{[He]}2s2p^3$$

$$\text{ground state} \qquad\qquad \text{higher energy state}$$

Pseudo-isoelectronic: Molecules and ions are said to be pseudo-isoelectronic when they contain the same number of valence electrons but not the same number of total electrons. The expression is usually restricted to species containing not only the same number of valence electrons but also the same number of atoms; for example, F^-, Cl^-, Br^-, and I^-; XeO_4, SO_4^{2-}, and PO_4^{3-}.

Rate: The rate of a chemical reaction (which can also be called its speed or velocity) is the rate of disappearance of a reactant or the rate of appearance of a product. If the concentration of a reactant or product is plotted against time, the slope of the curve at any point (with the negative sign dropped if necessary) is the rate at the corresponding time. Rate is usually measured in units of moles liter^{-1} sec^{-1} or moles cc^{-1} sec^{-1}.

It should be noted that the rates of disappearance of reactants and of appearance of products may not all be the same; thus in the reaction

$$N_2 + 3H_2 \;\rightarrow\; 2NH_3$$

the rate of formation of ammonia is twice the rate of disappearance of nitrogen, which is one-third the rate of disappearance of hydrogen.

Rate constant: Sometimes the rate v of a reaction is related to the concentrations of reactants [A], [B], etc., by an equation of the form

$$v = k[A]^\alpha [B]^\beta \ldots$$

where k, α, β, . . . are constants. When this is the case, the constant k is known as the rate constant (or rate coefficient, or specific rate) and α, β, etc. are the *orders* of reaction with respect to A, B, etc. When a more complicated type of equation applies to the rate, it is better not to speak of a rate constant or of orders of reaction.

Reduction: The process of decreasing the oxidation number (q.v.) of an atom in a chemical reaction; for example

$$FeO + H_2 \;\rightarrow\; Fe + H_2O$$

in which the oxidation state of iron is reduced from $+2$ to 0;

$$N_2 + 3H_2 \;\rightarrow\; 2NH_3$$

in which the oxidation state of nitrogen is reduced from 0 to -3. Reduction can be represented formally by the addition of electrons; for example

$$MnO_4^- + 8H^+ + 5e \;\rightarrow\; Mn^{2+} + 4H_2O$$

Resin: An amorphous, polymeric, and insoluble material.

Resonance: In valence-bond theory, a molecule is described in terms of definite ionic or covalent bonds. However, there are many molecules for which this procedure is unsatisfactory. The properties of benzene, for example, cannot be explained in terms of the structure

$$
\begin{array}{c}
\text{H} \\
| \\
\text{C} \\
\diagup \quad \diagdown \\
\text{H—C} \qquad \text{C—H} \\
| \qquad\qquad \parallel \\
\text{H—C} \qquad \text{C—H} \\
\diagdown \quad \diagup \\
\text{C} \\
| \\
\text{H}
\end{array}
$$

which would imply that three of the carbon–carbon bonds are single bonds and three of them double bonds; in fact, the substance does not behave as if it contained double bonds. Its properties can be explained on the hypothesis that the actual molecule is in a *resonance* or *hybrid* state between the two following structures

$$
\begin{array}{c}
\text{H} \\
| \\
\text{H}_\diagdown \ \text{C} \diagup^{\text{H}} \\
\text{C} \parallel \text{C} \\
| \qquad | \\
\text{C} \ \ \text{C} \\
\diagup \quad \diagdown \\
\text{H} \quad \text{C} \quad \text{H} \\
| \\
\text{H}
\end{array}
\qquad \longleftrightarrow \qquad
\begin{array}{c}
\text{H} \\
| \\
\text{H}_\diagdown \ \text{C} \diagup^{\text{H}} \\
\text{C} \parallel \text{C} \\
| \qquad | \\
\text{C} \ \ \text{C} \\
\diagup \quad \diagdown \\
\text{H} \quad \text{C} \quad \text{H} \\
| \\
\text{H}
\end{array}
$$

The substance must not be regarded as a mixture of the two molecules; instead, each molecule is a hybrid, each carbon–carbon bond being half way between a double and a single bond (it has a bond order (q.v.) of 1.5). When such resonance occurs, the energy level of the resulting hybrid structure is substantially below that of the single- and double-bonded structure, which means that the substance is more stable than if it had the simple single- and double-bonded structure. This lowering of energy is known as the *resonance energy.*

Resonance is also found in HCl, which exists in a resonance state involving the structures

$$ \text{H—Cl} \ \leftrightarrow \ \text{H}^+\text{Cl}^- \ \leftrightarrow \ \text{H}^-\text{Cl}^+ $$

$$ \text{(pure covalent)} \qquad \text{(ionic)} \qquad \text{(ionic)} $$

The third form is unimportant because of the high energy required to produce H^- and Cl^+. All nonpolar covalent bonds can be interpreted as resonance states between the purely covalent structure and the possible ionic states. The direction of a dipole can be understood in terms of the relative importance of the ionic states; in the above example, H^+Cl^- is more important than H^-Cl^+, so that the dipole is in the direction

$$
\begin{array}{cc}
\delta+ & \delta- \\
\text{H} & \!\!\!\!\text{—Cl} \\
\multicolumn{2}{c}{\longrightarrow}
\end{array}
$$

It is important to distinguish between resonance and tautomerism (q.v.) which refers to the situation in which there exist two distinct forms of a substance, the two forms being rapidly interconvertible. The symbol $\leftrightarrow$ is used to denote resonance; double arrows $\rightleftharpoons$ are used to indicate interconversion between tautomeric forms.

Sandwich compound: A compound in which one atom is situated between two flat molecules, for example, $Cr(C_6H_6)_2$. (See p. 165.)

Screening: The effect of electrons in an atom or molecule in reducing the nuclear charge experienced by other electrons in that atom or molecule. For example, in a sodium atom from which all the electrons but the 3s electron were removed, the 3s electron would experience a nuclear charge of $+11$. In the uncharged sodium atom, with the electronic configuration $1s^2 2s^2 2p^6 3s^1$, the 1s, 2s, 2p electrons are "screening" the 3s electron from the $+11$ charged nucleus, and as a result the effective nuclear charge experienced by the 3s electron is approximately $+1$ instead of $+11$. Because of their differing spatial distributions, s, p, and d electrons differ in the effectiveness of their screening.

Secondary bond: A bond that is much weaker in strength than a primary covalent or ionic bond. Hydrogen bonds are classed as secondary bonds, as are other bonds arising from dipole–dipole or ion–dipole attraction.

Solvated electrons: Electrons that are not attached to any one atom but are contained in a solvent "cage," associated with a number of solvent molecules. The energy of the electron is reduced by the interaction of solvent molecules (solvation) in the same way that the energy of anions is reduced on solvation. Solvated electrons are produced when sodium is dissolved in liquid ammonia:

$$Na(s) \xrightarrow{\text{liquid ammonia}} Na^+(solv) + e(solv)$$

Square-planar molecules: Molecules which contain at least five atoms all in one plane and in which four atoms surround the central atom at the corners of a square; for example

Standard free-energy change: For a chemical process represented by the stoichiometric equation

$$aA + bB + \cdots \rightleftharpoons pP + qQ + \cdots$$

the standard free energy change ΔG is the change in free energy (q.v.) when a moles of A react with b moles of B, etc., to from p moles of P, q moles of Q, etc. The standard free-energy change is related to the equilibrium constant K by the equation

$$\Delta G = -RT \ln K$$

Thus, if ΔG is large and positive, K will be a small fraction and there is little tendency for A, B, etc. to react to form P, Q, etc.: if ΔG is negative, K will be large and reaction will occur to a considerable extent.

Free-energy changes are related to changes in enthalpy (q.v.) and entropy (q.v.) by the equation

$$\Delta G = \Delta H - T\Delta S$$

Sublimation: The process in which a solid is converted into gas without passing through a liquid phase. Solid CO_2 and NH_4Cl are examples of solids which, when heated at 1 atm pressure, are converted directly into gas without melting.

Tautomerism: The existence of two distinct forms of a compound, which are rapidly interconvertible. Thus acetone exists in keto and enol forms at equilibrium with each other:

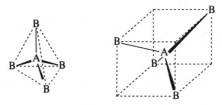

keto form   enol form

In principle, tautomeric forms can be isolated separately, although this may be difficult because of the speed of their interconversion. This possibility of isolation distinguishes the phenomenon from resonance (q.v.) where the forms do not have separate existences and cannot be isolated; they are hypothetical structures, the molecule existing as a hybrid of two or more such structures.

Tetrahedral molecules: Molecules in which a central atom is surrounded by four atoms, each of which is at one of the corners of a regular tetrahedron, with the central atom at its center:

The expression is sometimes also used to describe rather less regular molecules, and also molecules which lack the central atom, for example, P_4:

Thermochemical cycles: Cyclic processes by which a complicated reaction is resolved into a series of less complicated steps (for the purpose of studying its thermochemistry). The Born–Haber cycle (see p. 21) is an example of such a thermochemical cycle.

Thermodynamic stability: The property of a molecule when its decomposition or common reaction paths all have *positive* free energies. Such a molecule will not decompose nor react for thermodynamic reasons (contrast kinetic stability, q.v.).

Three-center bonds: A particular instance of multicenter bonding in which two electrons occupy a molecular orbital that is associated with *three* atomic nuclei; for example

B〔H〕B   in B_2H_6

Valence electrons: The electrons of an atom which, in principle, are capable of participating in bonding. They are to be found in atomic orbitals that lie outside a noble-gas electronic configuration; for example

Li [He]2s^1 1 valence electron

C   [He]2s^{2}2p^2 4 valence electrons

F   [He]2s^{2}2p^5 7 valence electrons

Na [Ne]3s^1 1 valence electron

van der Waals forces: Very weak attractive forces between molecules and ions which arise from interactions between mutually induced dipoles. They are sometimes called *dispersion forces.*

Wave function: A mathematical function which is a solution of the electronic wave equation for an atom or molecule. The square of the value of the function in any small element of space times the volume of the element of space is a measure of the probability of finding an electron in that region.

Index

References to the Glossary are shown in italics.